UNCOMMON CARGO

UNCOMMON CARGO

SACRIFICE. SURVIVAL. HOPE.

Jason Nulton
Eva Nguyen Whitfield

Deeds Publishing | Athens

Published by Deeds Publishing in Athens, GA
www.deedspublishing.com

Printed in The United States of America

Cover and interior design by Deeds Publishing

ISBN 978-1-961505-09-4

Books are available in quantity for promotional or premium use. For information, email info@deedspublishing.com.

First Edition, 2023

10 9 8 7 6 5 4 3 2 1

For Chau

Acknowledgements

EVA NGUYEN WHITFIELD

It's hard to believe that this incredible journey began in 2014 with a casual question, "Does your father live in this area?"

For some reason, I decided to answer this seemingly simple question from Jason Nulton with honesty and more detail than I usually provide. Jason was a family friend from our sons' Boy Scout Troop, so I shared the story of that fateful day when Saigon fell in 1975. His immediate response was, "You need to share this story."

I was surprised but energized by his interest and encouragement. His drive, support, and positivity were infectious, and this book would not be possible without him. He was the perfect writer, and the only one who could have earned my family's trust, which made it easier to truly open up. It was difficult at times, but also therapeutic, and it brought us even closer together as we shared stories we'd never told each other before.

I feel truly blessed to have such a strong and loving family. My mother, Mai is one of the most resilient people I know. She has never "felt sorry" for herself, and instead has always looked forward, not backwards. Despite the sudden and tremendous loss of her husband—my father, Chau—she did not let the grief defeat her. Instead, she focused on making our lives better in a new country, even though all we started with were the clothes on our backs and each other. Fortunately, she didn't have to do it alone. It truly takes a village, and her parents and siblings helped to raise my wonderful brother, Trung, and me. He has always been in my corner, and I'm so thankful for the joy he and his adorable kids, Sofie and Devin, bring into our lives.

My amazing Aunt Nga and three uncles, Sonny, Dzung, and Tuan, provided a solid foundation for my childhood. Aunt Nga was my favorite storyteller growing up, and I used to love when she would read to me. She was a calm and soothing presence. My uncles have always been like older brothers whom I admired and looked out for me. In fact, we lived together until I was a teenager, so they were an ever-present part of my daily life. They were central to my happiness, well-being, and sense of belonging. I cherish the fond memories of going to the movies, taking road trips, hitting video arcades, and packing up for college.

The real rocks of our family, however, were my cherished grandparents, Hong and Dat. They raised a family that *never* gave up and could always find strength in each other. They were well into their 50s when Saigon fell, and it wasn't easy losing their country, social status, and livelihood. My late grandfather was the one that built us a swing in our back yard, and who removed plenty of splinters acquired during my tomboy days. I fondly remember him telling me how my father, Chau, was like a son to him. However, it was my late grandmother, Dat, who took care of the entire family and was the constant in all our lives. She was very much the glue that held us together. Never once did I hear her complain. All that mattered to her was that she was present for her kids and grandchildren, and she showered us with her love and devotion.

My remarkable aunt, Cuc Nguyen, and her husband, Xuan Le have been a constant source of strength and unity for my entire family and me. Aunt Cuc is the eldest of eight children. My grandparents leaned on her and Uncle Xuan to help with our large household in Saigon, and when they finally escaped to the US. They are the most selfless, giving, and caring pillars of our family who have hosted countless family meals and celebrations to ensure we remain close. It's hard to imagine life without them.

Additionally, I am thankful for my aunts, Diep, and Khanh, who bring so much joy and warmth into my life. Aunt Diep has a generous, loving nature and always greeted my brother and me with big hugs. We couldn't wait for she and her family to visit us from Houston. Aunt Khanh was the "big sister" who made sure we were well-fed and well-groomed. She worked tirelessly to keep the house as clean as possible - a difficult prospect with 12 people living under the same roof! She lights up any room with her positivity and fun-loving energy.

Without the support of my husband, Scott, this book would never have reached an audience. He has always encouraged my family and me to document our stories before they were lost, even before Jason and I started this project. He's my cheerleader, and he has the biggest heart. Our sons, Jake and Chase, are my priceless joys. They are great travel buddies, conversationalists, and explorers of life who remind me of what's important.

Finally, I want to dedicate this book to the loving memory of my father, Chau. I didn't fully grasp the impact of his absence until I was older. But I know he did everything in his power to ensure that his wife, kids, and extended family could escape Saigon. Ultimately, it was his sacrifice that secured our survival that day so we could live to see a brighter future. I wish that I could have known him, but my hope is that by sharing this story with you, in some way we honor him and keep his memory alive.

Last, I want to express a *heartfelt* thanks to this great country. There's no other like it. When my family was in our most desperate time of need, the United States of America and its citizens welcomed us as refugees and helped us rebuild our lives. We're eternally grateful.

— Eva Nguyen Whitfield
Burke, VA
November 2023

JASON NULTON

The story of the Nguyen family is a real one, and the members of that family—real people—have become legendary in my mind. In the United States, we venerate and honor our veterans as heroes for the cause of freedom, who sacrifice in the name of the flag, the Constitution, and our way of life. This is, of course, a very noble thing—but Chau Nguyen transcended that type of honor. It was through fighting for the failing country that he loved, then dying for the freedom of others, that he became a veteran of something higher than a flag or a constitution. It was *for his family* and for hundreds of others he saved, and he did it in near impossible circumstances that most Americans can't even imagine. This is the mark of a true hero. There is no more honorable cause than love and family, and my biggest regret is that I'll never get to shake his hand and express my respect for what he so virtuously died for. If not for Chau, his family, and indeed many others, may never have survived the collapse of South Vietnam. But instead—because of him—they have survived and thrived.

My thanks have to begin with the Nguyens. They are a truly *amazing* family. Eva and Scott Whitfield, Eva's mother Mai and Aunt Nga, Uncles Tuan, Dzung, and Sonny and their families allowed me the honor of documenting and novelizing their dramatic story of escape. We met on a number of occasions for interviews so we could capture and record their memories, and each time they were so gracious to me and gave me access to anything I needed, and *more*—photos, letters, scrapbooks, etc. that greatly enriched this volume in order to bring it to readers. For *all* of this, I am profoundly grateful, honored, and deeply humbled.

On my side of things, there are several people who were constants in my life during the high highs and low lows of the several years it took to prepare this work, not the least of which is my wife Kim. When I needed her most, she appeared out of nowhere like a miracle and became a rock for me in the truest sense of the word. Without her support and sincerest of love, there's no way this effort would ever have reached completion. I am forever grateful and in her debt for what she so has selflessly done for me and continues to do.

My two wonderful kids, Wyatt and Amelia, are friends with Scott and Eva's sons, and through the writing process, they were also exposed to the family's story. I remember showing my son the first chapter of the book when I first completed it. Even at a young age, he was riveted and in total disbelief that this could have happened for real to actual people that he knew. It really validated the work for me, and established exactly why this story must be brought to audiences (especially young ones). My kids are my greatest blessings. They have been constants, sources of love, humor, and support and I count myself so lucky that they are in my life.

My family—in particular my mom and dad, Lynn and Dave, and my sisters Jennifer and Julia—provided me a lot of encouragement as I muscled through the research, writing, editing, and rewriting. My parents have always been avid readers and their ideas, feedback, and encouragement were honest and constructive and truly helped make this book better. John and Pat Cunningham and Jason and Chrissy Hall—Kim's outstanding family—have also been central and unwavering sources of encouragement to me in the completion of all of this. The most important support comes from family, and I am thankful and humbled by what mine have provided to me.

I would be remiss if I didn't thank some of my friends and colleagues who created an environment for me to thrive in and complete this project. They are Dr. Dan Blair, who as a boss, mentor, and friend, left an indelible mark on me. Other than my own father, there's never been a man who has made such a significant impact on my life. He encouraged and grew me spiritually and gave me a place where I was free to lead and create. For that I am eternally grateful, and I miss him.

My colleagues, Dr. Alexandra Perry, Dr. Amy Elliott, and Kristi Cowdery have provided the most supportive professional environment I've had since before retiring from the Air Force. They have made me a better version of me, and their resolute support and encouragement, as well as humor and realness, have been a true blessing to me. Tina Soloman is an amazing friend who, as a gifted artist and writer herself, provided me constructive criticism, edits, and even a few (artistic) smacks upside the head that were major contributors to this effort. I am so thankful to her for her honesty and vision, which she has been gifted with in measures few others are able to boast.

Others that encouraged me are my former Air Force First Sergeant Jeff Garner, who's encouragement and hilariously sarcastic humor has been a wonderful release for me, and my old Air Force buddy Chuck Grossart—a published author himself—gave me incredibly valuable professional guidance that led Eva and I through the character development and publishing processes. In addition, Ben LeRoy was an invaluable resource during the editing process. Not only did he do a masterful, professional edit of the entire manuscript, he also provided me some solid and honest mentoring about the literary world and publishing industry, for which I am very grateful.

I also want to say thank you to my students! When I left the Air Force in 2015, I wasn't sure I'd ever work with younger generations again, but I stumbled (clumsily, I might add) into higher ed and it put me in front of such people once again. Getting up in front of them every day to teach, discuss, mentor, and laugh has been an intensely rewarding experience that I would not trade for anything.

My deepest thanks also to authors and historians Martin King and Mike Collins. I worked with these guys on *To War with the Fourth* (my first foray into the literary world), and with Martin on a number of other projects over the years. Collaborating with these gentlemen made me smarter, and their inclusion of me in their efforts is what inspired me to take on this one. If not for them, the story of the Nguyens would never have made it to audiences, and I am grateful for their friendship.

Last, I want to humbly thank God, for His grace, and for so many undeserved blessings.

— *Jason Nulton*
Parkersburg, WV
November 2023

1

"It has to be now, Mai."

Mai Nguyen could hear her husband, Chau, take a shaky, nervous breath over the phone. After the violence of what he must have endured the night before, she knew he'd be chewing his bottom lip to a shredded, bloody pulp.

"The shelling has stopped for now and if we do not move, we will not get out."

There was a pregnant pause as Mai tried to fully digest Chau's words. Would it be for real this time?

"We will be ready," she finally answered, stiffening her spine and trying to sound strong.

Her heart skipped, and her stomach filled with a queasy sense of dread that she desperately tried to avoid showing. After the failed attempt to get out of Vietnam the night before, she was sure they wouldn't be in Saigon much longer. If not for the communist attacks that had started on Tan Son Nhut Air Base, which shared a runway with the city's airport, she and her family might have already been gone. Instead, northern forces had broken through the aerodrome's outer defenses as they closed in on the city, and the opportunity was lost.

The distant and sporadic sounds of shell bursts thumped across the muggy tropical air, and as Mai's nose detected the trace odor of cordite drift into the house, a lump steadily rose in her throat. Countless questions swarmed in her mind.

"I will be there in thirty minutes," Chau said, his voice composed, but intense on the other end of the phone line. "We will not have much time. Be as calm as possible for the children. Things will be bad on the streets."

There was a quiet pause, and Mai almost thought the line went dead.

"Mai," he said, his tone softening. "I love you."

"Chau..."

But there was only a clicking sound, and then silence.

Mai rested the phone on its cradle, then stood stoically for a moment, reflecting on how much she adored her husband, Lieutenant Colonel Chau Tan Nguyen. For years, he'd been a South Vietnamese Air Force C-130 instructor pilot who was all-business with his students. Sometimes he'd come home from training missions and Mai found it difficult to help him to unwind and come out of "work mode." Sixteen years his junior, she'd planned a small family get-together for his fortieth birthday to help him relax but was disappointed when it was pre-empted by what was becoming a grave situation in South Vietnam. That was less than two months ago. Ever since, Chau had been spending longer and longer days at the base, and on the nights he didn't return home at all, worry and fear consumed her. This time, it had been nearly thirty-six hours since she'd seen him.

Scenes from the previous weeks crowded her mind. Chau had hatched a strategy to commandeer a broken C-130, pack it with the family, extended family, and as many other people as he could, then fly them all out of the country. She knew he was doing what he could to save lives, working without a break to make sure hundreds of their fellow South Vietnamese citizens were able to escape the chaos that had embroiled the country.

Mai let out a slow breath and counted to ten. Knowing she had to move swiftly, she was relieved it wouldn't take much time to get everything together. With the help of her mother, father, and younger brothers who also lived in the home, she had already prepared for their quick getaway. They had checked and re-checked their baggage what seemed like hundreds of times. Everyone was packed and traveling light: powdered baby formula for their eighteen-month old son Trung, ramen noodles and other small food items, some clothing for their three-year old daughter Truc, and the garments on their backs. Mai's three younger brothers, thirteen-year-old Son, eleven-year-old Dzung, and nine-year-old Tuan had also filled several pillowcases with many of the essentials. Several days before, Chau had stuffed every zipper-pocket of his worn, sage green flight suit with the family's valuables — small gold bars, American dollars, and the most precious pieces of Mai's jewelry.

The Nguyen home, which Mai's father, Hong, had built himself, was the largest in their neighborhood and at two miles from the base, it was an easy commute for Chau. Hugging the outskirts of Saigon's noisy and chaotic sprawl, it loomed large over the surrounding homes, most of which only had a single floor and a handful of small rooms. At three stories tall, the family had divided almost half of the structure into a small apartment, which now stood empty. It had been rented out to

Americans working in Saigon for the last several years (whom they'd long suspected were part of the CIA or some other covert US entity), but earlier in the month was vacated by the young West Virginia man who lived there with his Vietnamese wife and her family.

After the previous night's abortive attempt to leave, a cacophony of fire and explosions had grown dramatically as enemy attacks on the base increased. At several points Mai had climbed to the house's flat roof, and every time it proved to be a dreadful mistake. She was horrified to see her husband's military post being relentlessly pounded with communist artillery, mortars, and rockets. Flashes from the detonating munitions and the yellow-orange glow of burning structures and aircraft lit the sky above like a hellish campfire. Paralyzed with anxiety over her husband's safety, she barely slept.

South Vietnam's Air Force had been slowly falling apart since American aid had dried up. Air defenses were weak. A large number of military officers had defected northward, fearing death for themselves and their families if they continued fighting.

That morning, Mai had arisen early from several disquieting hours of sleeplessness to the sound of chest-thumping concussions as she separated her bed from its mosquito net. The reverberations of small arms and heavy machine guns filled the air, punctuated by the staccato thud of mortar impacts that destroyed structures and planes on the airfield. Chau's side of their thin mattress had remained cold all night long. *Please come home, Chau,* she thought to herself in the wee hours of the morning, almost as if it were a prayer. *Please come get us.*

Tears constantly filled her eyes as the agonizing hours passed waiting for any sign that her husband was still alive after the night of persistent, brutal bombardment. But word hadn't come.

Mai began to feel an odd uneasiness when her husband began spending excessive hours at work just after his birthday, but she was one of only a few Saigon residents who felt it at the time. Up until very recently, she placed a lot of faith in the state media, but she was now convinced they'd been over-promising that little was amiss in South Vietnam. Her fears had grown when her older sister Nga, studying in Australia, sent a concerned letter home earlier in the month. With unfettered access to western news reports, Nga shared details about violence and communist advances which encroached ever closer to the family. The day it arrived she was able to get a rare phone call through to the family. Nearly hysterical, she pleaded with her father to leave the country, but he dismissed her concern. That was almost two weeks ago, and Mai couldn't help but feel some frustration that her sister's warnings were initially ignored.

For most, it paid to be friends with someone who knew how to fly—a military helicopter pilot or someone like Chau. Those who didn't tried to get out by sea from port facilities along the congested Saigon River. Still other people were able to find escape routes through the commercial airport. But now on April 29th, there were almost no planes available, and even if there had been, the air base wasn't exactly a safe place to take off from.

It was a relief when Chau's mid-morning phone call finally came, but Mai knew there was almost no time left. They had to be fast.

April 29th, 1975
TAN SON NHUT AIR BASE
2:05 PM

Chau hung up the phone and rubbed his tongue across the shredded skin on the back side of his lower lip. The metallic taste of blood filled his mouth as he looked down at his right hand and noticed a small tremor. Was he really *that* rattled from the attacks of last night and this morning? He'd been in hairy situations before, but it had been a supremely loud and sleepless night. He learned through the shrinking grapevine that several of the few South Vietnamese military members that remained on Tan Son Nhut had found themselves in a building right next to a shell impact, and the concussion had ruptured a few of their eardrums. Other than the blood running from their ears, they were all right. Chau couldn't help but wonder if they had the shakes too.

His stomach churned, reminding him he hadn't eaten in hours. His flak vest, which he'd donned the night before and never removed, had caused him to sweat through his flight suit, and he could hardly stand the way he smelled.

Earlier in the day, the sounds of shelling had given way to the rattle of Chinese-made AK-47s answering the slow clunk of his own forces' M-60 machine guns. Gunshots echoed through the lush air and bounced off man-made structures that stood on the city's outskirts surrounding the airfield. Because the efforts to get his family to safety the night before had fallen flat when the attack began, Chau was forced to hunker down with his crew and a large contingent of citizens in a small nose dock hangar. The building had filled with dust and flying concrete and nobody slept as the air and artillery barrage continued unabated all night.

Smoke from destroyed military aircraft seeped into the building and burned the back of his throat. Every swallow felt like trying to choke down a dry sock, and no amount of moisture seemed to keep his mouth wet. He was sure the crowd of well over three hundred hopeful passengers who littered the hard-concrete floor were feeling the same as he was. They'd been trickling in over the last several days. Most of them (thankfully, Chau thought) currently in a numb daze after the violence they'd been through. A yellowish-brown haze laid thick like a blanket on the building's fetid air, and the rotten odors of jet fuel, smoldering rubber, and melted plastic filled his nostrils. The number of troops around had been shrinking significantly in recent days—during the past week, aircraft of every kind were constantly taking flight as both soldiers and civilians were hurled skyward on anything available, bound for Thailand and other nearby safe havens. What had started as orderly departures had devolved into a manmade chaos as the North Vietnamese threat grew. Chau and his cohorts were some of the few military personnel left.

Chau felt duty-bound to make sure his men and as many civilians as he could find were able to get away, and he'd decided to be one of the last to go. An old US Army jeep he'd used intermittently as a private vehicle for the last few years was parked nearby, and he hoped it would be enough to get himself off the airfield property, into town, and return with his family to try and make a successful flight out. His C-130, the last one on the ramp, was stowed away in the small hangar in the hope of maintaining as low a profile as possible—it was (he thought) one of the most secure places there was, assuming a stray rocket or incoming shell didn't take it out. Chau had shrewdly tried to keep the four-propellered aircraft's existence and location as quiet as possible, ensuring the plane looked as un-airworthy as it could—it had to be available ... for his family and anyone else who could get there and cram in.

To be technical, the 1950s-model American-made plane really *was* only partially operable; the portside personnel hatch was missing, so it wasn't much of a stretch to pass it off as non-flyable. Mechanics had been waiting for a replacement door to arrive but since foreign military aid had slowed to a trickle over the months and years since American troops had left, parts and other support were limited. Chau was an experienced pilot however, and even if it wasn't perfect, he knew the plane was functional enough to get airborne.

The nose dock's immense doors were barely cracked open and the only part of the plane that could be seen from the outside was the tail, protruding from the doors' 'hole,' which was constructed for just that purpose. Originally built by American engineers during the war, it had held up well and Chau counted himself extremely fortunate that the facility was only slightly damaged by shrapnel and strafing. A couple days before, he'd ensured the plane's wing and auxiliary tanks were filled, and his nimble airplane was now as ready to fly as it was going to get.

Time to go.

Chau grabbed the Jeep's keys and quickly left the building. He knew Tan Son Nhut was in pretty bad shape, but what he saw as he emerged into the heat of the day stunned him. Unable to dismiss his shock at the scene, he tried to swallow and couldn't. It looked like old photos he'd seen of the Japanese attacks on Pearl Harbor some thirty-odd years before. Fighter aircraft and small cargo planes were reduced to smoking heaps of twisted metal on the ramp, their ripped frames and skins turned ashy white as black smoke gushed into the sky. All that remained intact were awkwardly-positioned nose and cockpit sections, some with their rear portions completely gone, laying cockeyed with their severed ends lying on the apron's surface. One was blown in half, with a wing vaulted skyward by an un-damaged landing strut, and another just a charred ruin sprawled across the ground in grotesquely distorted pieces.

Chunks of concrete block, rebar, and roof fragments lay everywhere, and stretches of cement were charred with the black wisps of fires that had since burned out. In many places, only smoking ruins and the skeletal remnants of once solid structures were left where American-built wood framed barracks and work centers had once stood. In those that were still intact, broken glass and ruined windows were the rule, not the exception, littering the ground with the shattered vestiges of their former selves, surrounded by splintered palm trees.

Chau had to function, so he buried every disturbing image and odor into the deepest recesses of his brain, then made his way for the Jeep through perversely-shaped bits of debris strewn across the pock-marked ramp surface.

Would there be enough flat runway to get into the air? he wondered.

He was glad he'd parked his vehicle behind the loading dock area of a low-roofed forward supply facility—the solid, masonry structure could hopefully absorb a large shell impact and protect the Jeep from all but a direct hit. As he jumped into the driver's seat, he once again became acutely aware of his completely drenched flight suit underneath his thick flak jacket. Sweat dripped down his temple from under his steel helmet, and he briefly took it off to wipe his brow. He longed for a bath, or even a quick dip in the water tank on the roof of his family's home—the one that Mai's younger brothers often climbed into to cool off on hot days, much to the chagrin of his father-in-law.

He turned the ignition and the Jeep coughed to life. Tan Son Nhut had been more-or-less closed to the outside world in recent days, and he was certain the gate area would be mobbed with desperate people trying to find their way towards anything with wings. It could be ugly. He reached into his brown leather hip holster, removed his Colt pistol, and clicked the safety off. Chau couldn't help but stare at it for a moment before returning it to his side. He hated carrying the thing, and hated even more that if things got really bad, he might have to shoot one of his own countrymen to ensure the safety of his wife and kids. He'd never fired his gun in anger, and it was the last thing he wanted to do, but he knew he would if he had to. Family came first.

Chau approached the gate through the base's destroyed throughways and buildings, still absorbing the profound destruction that surrounded him. There were a few people milling around and a handful of cars and fire department vehicles moving here and there, but overall, there wasn't a lot of activity. Near the base's pockmarked air traffic control tower, he could hear automatic weapons fire coming from the direction of the installation's main gate, causing him to quickly perk up his ears, but it was hard to tell if it was enemy fire or sentries trying to control a crowd. Either way, he had to keep moving—there was no telling when communist shelling would resume. The Jeep rumbled under his thighs as he sped up and threw it into a higher gear. As the wheels bounced over small bits of concrete and ruined building materials, he hoped the road that led to the gate would be clear. He pressed the gas pedal to the floor, and the small, hoary engine shook as it moved Chau towards the loves of his life. His co-pilot, Major Vinh Do, always told him

American Jeeps sounded like a bunch of mad rats scampering through a drainpipe.

Chau passed a damaged building in front of one of the base's two large, white golf ball-like radar stations and steered around debris that lay in the street. It was as if he was the last man on earth. As he passed a long stretch of buildings, he realized he couldn't tell whether they'd been damaged in the last night's attacks, or if they had been falling apart before. When the Americans left in 1973, they abandoned the facilities they used, and the South Vietnamese Air Force, either not needing them or absent the money to maintain them, let them rot.

The sign for the boarded-up "Base Exchange" was still visible as he rounded a corner, and on the approach to the gate, several guards stood nervously inside the perimeter fence with their rifles ready. An intractable crowd of people had congregated outside, their sweat-glazed faces painted with mounting desperation. The entrance area was inset from the road outside, flanked by high fencing with spirals of aging gray razor wire at the top. Chau could see people standing on large, concrete jersey barriers aligned in a 'serpentine' layout—they'd been set up in the road that led up to the guard shack to make it more difficult for vehicles to ram the gate or try to break through it.

As he slowed, he could see terrified people young and old with their fingers twisted into the chain-link fence, shaking it as their mouths cried out in desperation. Despite the concertina wire, he wondered if anyone would try and climb over the perimeter fence anyway. With it coiled so densely at the top, he doubted even the most limber human could get over without severe injury.

Chau skidded to a stop, frantically leaning on his horn to get the attention of the security personnel over the din. The ones outside the small guard shack turned toward him, clearly agitated by the chaos, with tensed postures appearing ready to fire their rifles in his direction. Chau threw a hand up to avoid getting impulsively shot by a distressed young guard and motioned for one to come over to him.

"I need to go out!" he exclaimed in a panicked voice, barely audible over the commotion of his engine, combined with the sounds of the desperate crowd outside.

The guard abruptly turned and yelled to his cohorts, then frantically waved his hand to open the chain link.

"I am coming back!" Chau yelled. "When I do you must let me back in."

It was hard to tell if his words had been heard. The young sentry next to the locking mechanism quickly disabled it, fighting the crowds who were struggling to get it open. As he tussled with them from inside the fence, another soldier joined him, ready to hold back the mob, then they anxiously turned back as if to say, *ready?* The guard next to Chau nodded, then lifted his rifle and fired several shots over the civilians, causing them to briefly fall back and disperse. Startled at the sound, Chau watched as the gate slid open, its corroded metal wheels grinding and squealing over the weathered asphalt. He hit the gas, spinning the tires, and leaving a cloud of reddish-gray dust in his wake.

As he passed through the fence line, men, old women, and children began to close in on him as he entered the mob, who began to grab at his vehicle and clothing. He instinctively placed his hand on the pistol at his hip, not knowing whether he'd have to draw it or attempt to keep it from being taken away from him. The rough wood of the weapon's handle scraped against the calloused skin of his fingers as he shoved people off with his left shoulder, then he throttled forward in an attempt to gain enough speed to get through the growing mass of humanity without running anyone over. Gunshots from the nervous soldiers echoed behind him as he sped up and switched gears, the rounds whizzing and cracking over his head.

As he escaped the worst of the horde, his eyes widened, and he felt another pang of deep anxiety. Ahead of him there was a steady stream of South Vietnamese headed opposite his direction of travel in every manner of transportation imaginable. It was a chaotic, disorganized mob. Against the backdrop of the dusty street, its surrounding greenery, and rundown alabaster building fronts, moved crowds of people on foot. Others limped or were running, and others still were riding on impossibly-loaded mopeds, motorized cyclos, or overburdened cars, buses, and trucks. He saw one family pushing their small children and a stack of overstuffed suitcases in a worn-out wheelbarrow with a barely inflated tire. Agitated voices pierced the knocks and pings of his engine, and even though the crowds weren't as dense as they were at the gate, Chau couldn't go very fast. He found himself leaning on the horn and yelling for people to move aside.

He had to get to Mai and their children. The Jeep's tires vibrated unevenly over a road littered with shoes, empty weapons, and trash. In some places, worn olive-drab South Vietnamese Army fatigues could be seen laying in heaps atop their helmets, combat boots, and white socks. Chau surmised many soldiers had abandoned their uniforms and fled in their undergarments, fearing execution at the hands of the North Vietnamese. It looked as if entire units had abandoned anything that appeared "military" and made every attempt to fade inconspicuously into the masses. It made him feel uneasy traveling alone in his own uniform in an obviously military vehicle.

As he pressed forward toward his family, people on every side yelled and pleaded with him to let them climb aboard his vehicle. Doing his level best to ignore their cries, he pressed his horn and accelerated onward as quickly as he could. It was indeed bad on the streets of Saigon. The two miles to his wife were a desperately long distance, and he didn't even want to think about what it might be like getting back.

April 29th, 1975
NGUYEN HOME, SAIGON
2:30PM

"Tuan!"

Mai wasn't one to raise her voice very often, but she was near hysterical with her youngest brother.

"Put another change of clothes in that pillowcase...and *hurry up!*"

She was holding her son, 18-month old Trung, trying to force him to drink one more bottle. It also kept him from running under her feet as she made final arrangements to depart. Fortunately, Trung was calm and not caught up in the chaos. Tuan ran into another room and dug into a small chest to follow his sister's instructions. He and his brothers were notorious for getting into mischief together, but Mai had made it clear that this was no time to mess around—she was on the edge of shouting and her brothers generally knew better than to cross her when she was like this. Usually very collected, she knew how to be a steamroller when she had to be.

That's how it had been on this day—she'd sent Son to the kitchen to make sure his sack had enough food to get them through the next day or two, and Dzung was pulling a few baby clothes from a drawer in Mai's bedroom. There was no telling where they would end up, or when their next meal would be.

"Mai."

Hong Van Nguyen, Mai's father, calmly emerged from one of the dimly-lit back rooms of the home. A quiet and modest man, he was the longtime owner of a rubber plantation near the Cambodian border in Phuoc Long Province, producing raw materials for large foreign companies like Goodyear, Pirelli, and Michelin. He'd raised acres of rubber trees from seedlings — a lengthy and laborious 12-year process before they could produce anything that could be used or sold. It was his baby.

"Mai," he said again, surprisingly serene as he stood in the kitchen doorway. "I will stay here."

Stunned, Mai could only pause and stare, unsure how to respond.

"Take your mother."

Hong had been back and forth for a week, painfully mulling whether he'd stay or go. Even as they'd been preparing to leave the evening before, her father was still torn between family, a successful business, and what he felt was desertion of his homeland. When their attempt to depart was abruptly halted, she hoped it would encourage him that it was time to go, assuming they'd get another chance. But the man was clearly unconvinced. However unlikely the probability, her father was determined to stay and attempt to run his trade after the communists inevitably took over the government.

"But Ba," Mai pleaded, "your business will not survive! You need to –"

"I will not go with you," he said, calmy but firmly cutting through her words. "I have decided to stay here."

15

He stared at his daughter's eyes as they welled up with tears.

After a long pause, he continued, "Your mother has prepared her suitcase and is ready to leave. We will be together again soon."

The frustrating week that Mai, her mother, and Chau had spent trying to convince him, plus years of living under his roof had taught her there was little point in fighting such a proud and stubborn man. She momentarily broke her composure with a loud sob. Her father tenderly put his hands on her shoulders and kissed her forehead.

"I love you," he said. "It will be all right."

He took the baby from her arms.

"Go get the last of your things together," he said quietly. "I will take the baby for now."

Emotions flooded into her aching heart, but she knew it would only be minutes before Chau arrived. She hoped her father was right — that it *would* be all right. Looking past his slender frame, she noticed her mother, Dat. A petite and beautiful middle-aged woman, she wasn't much older than Chau. Known for her stunning smile and quick wit, she stood at the ready, dressed in a simple white áo cánh and loose-fitting black pants. In her hands was a worn and fading mustard-yellow Samsonite suitcase. Mai looked back at her father the man who had always made her feel so safe as a young girl, and nodded.

"All right."

She stiffened and applied an almost clinical focus on the task at hand, doing all she could to bury her emotions. It was a time for action. On the opposite side of the narrow front room of the house were photos from her wedding and a few other pictures of the family. Mai hadn't thought of bringing them when she'd first organized her belongings but knowing it might be her last opportunity to save something of the family's past for her children, she gathered them up, removed them from their rickety frames, and handed them to Son. She refused to allow this nightmarish situation to deny her children their roots.

"*Do not* lose these," she threatened firmly, emphasizing her seriousness by jabbing her thin finger at the middle of Son's face when she said, 'do not.'

He nodded intently and carefully placed them between a notepad and two small books he had in his sack.

Then in an instant, activity inside the home ceased upon hearing the sounds of a vehicle rapidly approaching down the alleyway beside the house. Dzung ran to the front door and flung it open, amplifying the sounds of skidding rubber tires on gravel and a tinny-sounding horn.

Chau had arrived.

Once outside the house, Dzung dashed across their tile courtyard, past Hong's queen flower tree on its outer edge, and opened the large metal door to the street with a rusty groan. On the other side, Chau spun the tires in the potholed asphalt and the jeep heaved into the large open area before coming to a stop as he killed the engine. Mai's brother closed the doors with a dissonant *gong* behind him, then set the large bolt with a loud, grinding squeak.

Chau could barely get out of the driver's seat before Mai tackled and embraced her husband as tightly as she could, feeling the rigidity of his flak vest jabbing against her ribcage. She collided with him so hard that his steel helmet fell off and clunked on to the ground, its brown leather straps flailing as it came to rest in the dusty grit that lay on the tile at their feet. The family was soon outside, and without delay they began loading their few belongings into the grimy vehicle. Mai couldn't let go of Chau.

"Thank God," she whispered, rubbing her hand up his sticky, sweat-covered neck and through the short-cropped hairs at the base of his skull.

"I am OK, Mai," he said into her ear, "but we need to go quickly."

She put her hands on his cheeks and kissed him before she could even look at him. When she pulled away, she felt a slight sense of shock as she gazed at his face. Chau was pale as an apparition; there were dark purple circles under his eyes, the whites of his eyeballs bloodshot, and a visible layer of sweat-streaked dust coated his greasy forehead. There was a trace of dried, rust-brown blood under his bottom lip where he'd been digging at it with his teeth, his zipper-laden flight suit smelled like sweat, and he could have used a razor. Mai's husband had really been through the wringer, and from the looks on her family's faces, everyone else thought it, too.

Mai's father interrupted.

"What is it like on the streets?" he asked Chau.

"Bad," he answered gravely. "Things have fallen apart."

"But what about the direction for people to stay in their homes?" Mai asked, confused.

Relative isolation in the house, away from the main streets and cushioned by the courtyard had kept the family from directly viewing much of the anarchy that had been unfolding around them. They'd been holed up inside because officials in Saigon had declared martial law several days before. The Nguyens followed the rules; when they were told to hunker down in their home, that's what they did.

"There is no law, Mai," he answered, just a little coarsely. "The city is collapsing."

The rumble of what must have been several large trucks caused the surface of the courtyard to vibrate.

"Go," Mai's father said matter-of-factly.

Everyone knew that if there was any breakthrough of North Vietnamese forces, it was a near certainty that Chau would be shot because of his status as an enemy combatant. To make matters worse, it was an unspoken truth that his family would probably be executed as well, and it would be a whole lot more obvious who they were if they were all captured together.

Chau turned to the Jeep as Son helped his mother into the front seat. Dat refused to let go of her suitcase, holding it tightly to her lap as she looked at Chau as if to say, *'don't touch it . . . this is mine.'* He reached down to pick up his helmet, then absent-mindedly put it on as he climbed in, snapping the worn leather chin strap into place.

"We need to go."

The mid-morning sun beamed past nearby buildings and trees onto the torn vinyl seats as Mai and her brothers climbed in. Springs and protruding foam rubber poked at the backs of their legs, and they struggled to get comfortable as Mai's father handed baby Trung over to her. Young Truc then clambered in and took a seat on Mai's lap next to her brother. Chau turned the ignition and the Jeep choked and gasped before turning over, finally shaking the vehicle's entire frame as the engine fired up. Hong only watched numbly. Mai's lower lip quivered, and she covered it with her hand, doing her best to subdue tears. She didn't want her children or her brothers to see her cry. Her father leaned to whisper something in his wife's ear over the clicking and clacking of the engine, then he kissed her cheeks one after the other, moved to the courtyard gate, and pulled it open with a roar of screeching metal.

It would be an agonizingly swift goodbye. Chau and Hong nodded at each other as he hit the gas pedal. As the family lurched forward and through the gate, Hong touched his chest with his hands as he stepped backward, nodding as if to say, *I will see you again.* The staccato squeal of the tires on the courtyard surface echoed in Mai's ears as they prepared to leave their life in Vietnam behind forever.

Once in the narrow alley, Mai's gaze turned to Chau. In the madness of their departure, she tried to find anything to give her comfort, so she focused hard on his strong shoulders and arms as they moved the wheel of the Jeep. They were features that were some of the first she'd noticed when they'd first met what now seemed like centuries ago. Her mind briefly flashed to the intense joy of their wedding day five years before. Chau had worn traditional matrimonial clothing, dotted with a large pattern of solid, colorful circular designs which traditionally signified the groom's Imperial rank. Wearing it was a requirement to be allowed to "dwell in the family house." A torrent of conflicting emotions washed over her. How dramatically things had changed.

Chau's vehicle bounded violently on to the frenzied street at the end of their small block. As they entered the busy thoroughfare, a chill came over Mai that gave her goosebumps, despite the tropical heat. Her heart pounded in her ears. She'd heard Chau say that things were bad, but what she was now seeing turned every idea of the orderly world she learned about from her father upside down.

Chau said it would be anarchy out here, but she never expected this. It was a period of martial law in Saigon, but clearly many had attempted to take their destinies into their own hands. The street was wall-to-wall people—a sea of humans moving at different speeds and directions through the shallow canyon created by tall trees and dots of vibrant jungle shrubbery, ratty telephone poles, and shabby low block buildings. Mai's ears rang with the sound of engines small and large, punctuated with the crowd's yelling.

As Chau pressed the horn and made his way through the throng, a moped buzzed by with three people holding on for dear life, narrowly missing a large stake-bed truck heading the opposite direction packed rail-to-rail with bodies. Mai smelled the harsh odor of the truck's exhaust as her eyes briefly came to rest on a small boy only a few yards to their side, seated on the street next to a young woman lying on her side. As they passed, Mai thought the child couldn't have been older than six. It was like slow motion. His eyes were red and wet with tears as he tried to help his dazed mother—dirty, alone, and sluggishly trying to pull herself forward. Her destroyed tunic had been cinched to mid-thigh, exposing the broken end of her destroyed femur– pressing hard from inside her skin and doing its best to break through. Nauseated by the growing bloody plume of yellow and purple, Mai knew there was nothing that could be done, and that it could just as easily be her and her child. The woman's emotionless face appeared ashen and cold as blood swelled from the hemorrhaging in her devastated limb.

They probably wouldn't make it.

Chau nearly hit the edge of an unused fruit stand on the side of the road as he avoided a man and a young boy. On another part of the wide and tumultuous street a teenage girl, dressed in filthy calf-high pants and flip-flops, pulled a weathered red Radio Flyer wagon. In it, an elderly woman was doing her best to stay upright, one hand clutching a small light blue sack and the other hanging on tightly with gnarled white knuckles. As people moved toward the airport or the wharves along the river, hoping to get out of town, a heavy and anxious feeling of dread hung palpably in the air. Chau incessantly honked and did the best he could to steer around the masses.

"Get out of the way!" he bellowed.

Hands slapped on his hood and windshield as Tuan held tightly to one of the vehicle's thin roll bars with one hand, and his packed pillow case in the other. His older brother Son leaned over the side and joined Chau in yelling for people to move, and at one point even found himself smashing the hand of a twenty-something young man as he desperately ran alongside them, grabbing at the hull of the vehicle.

Chau reached a small open area and gassed it quickly forward, avoiding the base of a large shade tree that had grown outward into the road. As he lurched, Mai could see her mother in the front seat being jolted back and forth, her spine intermittently coming off the seat, then slamming back into it as the rough suspension rolled over bumps in the road. Each one caused a blood-curdling springy-metal squeak underneath its ragged foam rubber.

In places, their tires moved unevenly over trash and debris, and as they made their way past small businesses, it became evident that looters had been at work. Cheaply-made shop doors hung from their hinges at wild angles and large glass windows were broken wide open. People were exiting from any opening they could find carrying every kind of commodity imaginable—clothing, food, and even kitchen appliances. It was a horribly disordered sight that shocked and numbed Mai, who grabbed Trung and Truc as tight as she could.

Chau came upon a larger swell of people and abruptly slowed, leaning on his horn. He nearly went into a skid as several men turned and angrily stopped him next to an eight-foot wall off the passenger side of the jeep, cursing and demanding he stop and take them too. Without hesitating, Chau reached to his side, rapidly unsnapped his leather holster and removed his Colt .45 pistol, tapping it loudly on the hazy windshield as if to say, *"just try me."* It shocked Mai to see him draw his gun, especially when he fired two shots above the heads of the mob as it surged in front of them. The loud report threw baby Trung into tears. The bulging crowd let out a collective cry of distress and instinctively ducked, then parted to let the Nguyens through.

Chau was met with another fairly open space on the street and pushed his gas pedal to the floorboards again, gaining speed for more than half a mile. He slowed when it appeared he would run headlong into another cluster of people, so as he decelerated he fired another shot into the air. It wasn't good to keep shooting—he only had a limited number of rounds, and he'd need them if the vehicle became overwhelmed. A hole briefly formed as the crowd cowered from the gunfire and Chau drove through it without delay, the back wheels spinning out on the hot, sandpapery surface in the process.

It was almost too much for Mai to process. This was her city—her home—and even though throughout her childhood she'd been aware of the war, this was unlike anything she'd ever seen. It was surreal, shocking, and disturbing, and she knew the images she was viewing would stay with her for years to come.

Chau leaned his head over his right shoulder.

"We are getting close!"

His words were barely perceptible over the ringing in Mai's ears, but she could see the bright white of his teeth as his lips parted to form the words, stretching the rusty spot of dry blood on his stubbly chin into odd shapes.

The spiraling barbed wire of the base's perimeter became visible in the distance as Chau revved the engine and aggressively steered to get around a smaller crowd that stood in his way. Mai could see a large mob standing against the perimeter fence and people filling the gate area. The crowd had grown considerably in the half hour since Chau had left. Rocks and other objects sailed through the air, thrown by angry citizens at the troops trying to maintain what order they could at the ingress area, and over the tinny pinging of the Jeep's engine, gunshots could be heard in progressive, desperate attempts at crowd control.

Trung fussed as his father reached over the passenger seat with his pistol and fired again, hoping to keep from agitating the gate sentries who surely heard the firing. The hordes parted once more as Chau's Jeep moved forward, bouncing and bumping over the societal detritus under their wheels.

"Only about a hundred more yards!" Chau called to his family.

The throbbing mass of humans became so thick and irate as Chau got closer to the gate that Mai wasn't sure they'd get there without being overrun. The filthy, heated faces of her fellow South Vietnamese barked angrily at them as they inched nearer to their destination. They were near the gate now, but still smack in the middle of the mob. Two men leaned on their hood as a third approached the back seat, then grabbed at Son.

"Má!" Son called to Dat, frightened to death.

His mother was in the front seat—too far to reach him. Mai

reached for his hand and caught it at the last minute, toppling her whimpering baby son onto the seat next to her in the process. She urgently wrenched Son back in, engaging in a mortal tug-of-war with his attacker. As she grunted and pulled with every ounce of strength she had, the raw exertion filled her eyes with swirling stars, but she was able to bring her terrified brother back into the vehicle.

"*Chau!*"

Sensing the struggle in the back, Chau pointed his weapon at the man, but before he could shoot, the deafening crack of M-16 assault rifles filled the air. The crowd immediately backed off as two gate guards laid down several gunshots to allow Chau to pull forward. He raced the last fifty yards, then through the serpentine-patterned concrete barriers to the gate.

They had made it.

Mai watched as sweaty and haggard soldiers deployed between the throbbing crowd and Chau's Jeep, which was now stopped. Wearing flak vests and helmets, the guards' expressions were nervous and scared as they tightly pressed the stocks of their rifles into their shoulders. Their barrels were pointed downward at forty-five-degree angles, but the un-safed weapons were ready to be raised in an instant to put a bullet into anyone that dared cross them. Mai turned back toward Chau, who had quickly started engaging in a heated argument with a sentry.

"...and I told *you* that I was coming back! Now let me –"

"Negative, sir!" he responded abruptly, making a slit-throat motion across his neck with his left index finger, "The base is *closed!* There are no airplanes left! Turn your vehicle around *now!*"

"*NO!* There is one plane waiting for us! *OPEN THE GATE!*"

More gunshots rang out from behind them as the large crowd repeatedly heaved forward. Chau stopped talking, his hands at ten and two on the steering wheel, squeezing it with frustration. He stared intensely forward at the closed, locked gate, in a pause of this battle of the wills. Mai wondered if jamming the gas to crash the fence open might work. After all, what did they have to lose?

No, she thought, *bad idea*. She kept it to herself.

The force of the small Jeep might not be enough to knock it down and furthermore, Chau might end up getting himself and his family shot, or at least break the perimeter open, creating an opportunity for his waiting airplane to be overrun. He reached into the zipper pocket on his right upper thigh. Mai watched as he dug through its contents and removed a small plastic sandwich bag with a thick roll of green money inside. After briefly staring at it, he handed it to the sentry.

"Take it," she heard her husband say.

It was as if that single moment took place in the eye of the tempest blowing around them in every direction. The astonished soldier paused, then did as he was told, wrapping his grimy fingers around the bag. His gaze broke from the lock he had on Chau's dark brown eyes as he stared at the object that had just been placed in his hand. A small, green *"100"* was visible—American dollars. He looked back up at Chau, speechless. Chau spoke, but Mai couldn't hear his words. But she could read his lips:

Please. Let us in.

The guard quickly got his bearing, pocketed the money as discreetly as he could, and then turned to his cohorts.

"OPEN IT!"

The gate slid open over more bursts of eardrum-shattering

automatic weapons fire, and before the guards could extend it to its maximum breadth, Chau sped inward without looking back. With the crowds behind them, the family was safe—from the crowds anyway—on the airfield for the first time. Smoke from still-burning aircraft billowed skyward in twisted brown-black pillars as Mai absorbed the images of the destroyed world around her. She'd been to Tan Son Nhut before, but what she saw now was nearly unrecognizable from what she remembered. Frond-less palm trees with bits of their splintered wood were randomly scattered about. Grass, rock, and chunks of dirt were thrown erratically in places where artillery shells failed to meet their targets. Cinder block buildings were in various states of destruction, many of them reduced to nothing but broken walls and smoking rubble. If the color had been drained from the scene, it could have resembled a post-nuclear moonscape. The harsh smoke lingering in the air from the most recent attacks hit Mai's sinuses like a hammer. Truc began sneezing, and she knew her kids might have been affected too.

As they approached a cluster of buildings, Chau slowed and drove off-road, cutting a path through a short stretch of Vietnam's trademark red clay to make his way around some rubble that blocked the road. Mai and her brothers stared aghast at the scattered pistols, rifles, and knives nearby where people had thrown them over the days prior. It was no secret that armed passengers weren't allowed to board airplanes, so many abandoned their weapons where they stood. Things were happening so fast.

The world around the Nguyens raced by in a blur. Despite the noise, Trung had mercifully ceased crying, apparently distracted by the dramatically changing scenery. The plumes of smoke from the communist attacks of the night before were more visible now that they were close to the unobstructed airfield, climbing ever upward as Chau approached the nose dock.

"That's our plane!" he said loudly, pointing at the hangar in front of them.

Absent any real way of changing Trung's cloth diaper, the front of Mai's blouse and pants were now soaking wet with his urine. Through the murky wiper marks on the Jeep's windshield, Mai could see the facility's massive doors had been slid open, creating a gaping rectangular hole dotted in the middle by the inverted 'T' shape of the C-130's rear stabilizer. It was not a terribly organized scene. Civilians were everywhere, abandoned vehicles, bicycles, and other types of transportation dotted the ramp and surrounding areas.

Will this many people fit inside the plane? she thought.

Several armed, uniformed men were ushering some of them onto the plane through a small and stairless crew door near the nose as well as up the rear cargo ramp. Soldiers that were on-hand—presumably some of the remaining base personnel that hadn't yet fled—were doing their best to hold back the mob that was desperately trying to get on board. Chau reached the expansive concrete apron that lay in front of the building, quickly crossing it and skidding to a stop about fifty feet from the mass of people.

"Everybody out and follow me!"

With intense resolve, Chau raised his right hand up to hold his helmet in place as he exited. Mai worried it could get dangerous trying to get the family past the crowd and on to the aircraft—no doubt the frustrated mob would be unhappy seeing people who just showed up getting on ahead of them…and it was obvious that not everyone would be able to get on board since there were already a large number of people in the rear hold. Chau quickly jogged to the Jeep's passenger side to help Dat with her suitcase, but she bluntly refused assistance.

"I can carry it myself," she told him firmly, making clear she wouldn't give it up.

The casual observer might have thought it perversely funny, but it was all she had left, and they may never be back to Vietnam. It was as if everything the family ever owned was destroyed in a devastating house fire and the suitcase represented the only worldly possessions she had left.

A few vehicles and one or two motorcycles and scooters were scattered about near the opening of the hangar. Mai wondered how quickly the plane could be moved, since most of the trucks and cars appeared to be blocking its way. As she tore her eyes away from a large, canvas-capped two-and-a-half-ton troop carrier, she could detect the *'tick-tang'* of the cooling metal motor under the small, battered hood of Chau's Jeep. In the distance, the deep booming sound of communist artillery could be heard, prompting Chau to nervously look to the northern horizon. A sudden enemy attack would endanger everyone and threaten their way out.

"We need to move," he said firmly as the angry shouts from the crowd filled the air a short distance away. "Son, help your sister."

Son, who was already on the tarmac, took baby Trung from Mai as Chau jerkily lifted Truc, standing on the back seat, and placed her on his left hip. Dzung and Tuan had already gotten out and were moving away from the Jeep.

"Má, are we going to fly on that airplane?" Truc asked, innocently looking at her mother with her finger in her mouth.

She was more fascinated by the large aircraft in front of her than she was by the large, nervous crowd or the ominous thuds of artillery in the distance.

"Yes, honey," Mai answered as tranquilly as she could, "and Ba will fly it for us. It will be exciting!"

Walking as rapidly as they could, Chau led them across the debris-strewn flat concrete of the apron to a man in his early thirties standing about a hundred feet from the bottom of the open rear cargo ramp. He and Chau briefly bowed, then turned to Mai as the sound of the crowd became more prominent.

"Vinh is flying with me today."

Through her husband, Mai had known Major Vinh Do for several years. The two flew together during the darkest days of the war in the late sixties on both combat and training missions, and he and Chau had come to know each other like brothers. He was a short man with a dry sense of humor and exultant face that could light up a room, but he was also fiercely protective of his country and known as an intelligent and competent airman. Vinh was also brusquely unafraid to share his opinions, which were often quite direct. Today, his normally gleeful face was all business, projecting a strict sense of necessity from under his shabby steel olive drab helmet.

"We are going to bring you up the ramp, Mai," he said methodically over the noise of the crowd. "Keep the children close because these people may become dangerous. We have checked to make sure nobody is armed, but it is possible we did not find all the guns. Follow me this way."

Vinh led the family towards the cargo ramp of the C-130 and came upon another airman in a flight suit, his sleeves rolled to mid-arm. The oversized helmet he wore nearly covered his eyes, and he kept having to push it up his forehead while trying to help marshal passengers up the incline.

"Quan!" he called before turning back to Mai. "This is Quan Lac, our loadmaster. He is here with his family and will make sure you get on safely."

"Here, let me help you, ma'am," he said politely.

Quan turned to Dat intending to take her luggage but was met with the same insistent response that her son-in-law had received only moments earlier.

Chau put Truc down on to the ground, then squatted down to look her in the eye.

"You and Má are going to go in the airplane now," he said softly. "I am going to fly it for you, but I have to go get ready first, OK?"

"OK, Ba."

Chau stood and kissed Trung on the forehead, then leaned toward his wife.

"You will need to go up the ramp, Mai," he said, regaining his seriousness. "I must go now and pre-flight the aircraft before we can leave."

"Please be careful," Mai replied rather worriedly.

"We are going to be OK," he said, then kissed her on the cheek, turned, and jogged between the crowd and fuselage toward the plane's nose, absently reaching up again to hold his helmet on.

As he hoisted himself into the side crew door of the aircraft, Mai's mind flashed back to the wedding day again. Chau was resplendent in his traditional groom's garb. She could remember the softness of the skin on his face and his gentle smile as he looked into her eyes while they repeated their vows, and–

Shouts from the crowd became more pronounced as several soldiers demanded they stay back from the immediate area, and suddenly the crack of a gunshot rang out, startling Mai and her mother. A number of agitated middle-aged men were demanding to get aboard the plane and harsh words were being exchanged, but they were roughly held back by the soldiers in an attempt to continue an orderly boarding. There were simply too many to get the entire group on board.

Quan nodded at Mai, then turned to guide them up the open rear cargo ramp, which was dotted with worn patches of rough 'non-skid' tape to prevent falls on the slick sheet metal floor. The Nguyens dutifully followed, going up the angled aluminum and into the shadowy cargo bay. As they entered, the stench of sweaty humans attacked their noses like stale roadkill on a hot day. The large space was about half-filled, packed shoulder-to-shoulder with people, and Vinh's crewman maneuvered them through the crowd to a small space about two thirds of the way toward the front of the cargo bay. Beams of light penetrated the hot, steamy air, lighting a sea of black-haired heads, throbbing around in terrified anticipation of what might come next. Dat found a small spot at their feet and put her weathered suitcase down on the floor, smashing Son's big toe in the process.

"Ow!" he cried loudly, tears welling up in his eyes from the pain.

His mother apologized profusely, squatting down to look at his toe, which had started oozing blood. Mai was oblivious to her younger brother's pain, distracted instead by the more pressing need to get her children situated in the confined area, which lacked any kind of real seating. People continued to board, and the tiny spot they were standing in became progressively smaller.

"I am sorry," Quan confessed to Mai, "the door on the front of the plane is missing, so it will be a noisy ride."

Mai nodded in understanding, satisfied to be relatively safe with Chau and their children.

"I am going to go help more people get on," he continued, "after we are in the air, I will be in front near the bottom of the steps that lead to the flight deck."

He patted her shoulder then forced his way aft through the dense pack of individuals between him and the lowered ramp. The urine-soaked front of Mai's clothes had begun to dry but it was still a damp and disgusting mix of warm and cold. The rancid dirty-diaper smell didn't mix well with the oppressive air either. More gunshots were suddenly audible from outside as guards did their best to hold the crowd back, while crewmen continued to quickly usher in more passengers from the rear. With the hold ever-more jammed with passengers, their surroundings slowly darkened. All they could do was stand in place and wait, hoping for a small slice of comfort as they readied for their flight to who-knew-where.

It was all happening so fast. So very, very fast.

Mai was glad they were in a space that was clear of the ramp—she didn't want to be anywhere near it when it was eventually raised. Moments later, a small whine could be heard as it was brought to a flat position, still remaining partially open. As the sound filled the air, they were stunned by three consecutive deafening blasts from communist rocket fire that impacted nearby. The hair on the back of her neck stood straight as the color drained from her face and people began screaming in terror.

We are being attacked! she thought.

Just then, four more rockets landed—this time closer to the hangar. Voices inside the aircraft became more alarmed as Mai, barely able to see past people and the half-raised ramp, witnessed chunks of concrete being ejected into the air in a large and frightening ball of fire and thick smoke. Bits of debris rained down on the immediate area, some of the smaller ones landing on the rear of the plane with a sickening clatter. She tore her eyes from the scene trying to keep herself and her mother upright amidst the constant jostling of bodies. She and her fellow citizens were about to become refugees...“stateless” in the eyes of the world.

There had to be three hundred or more people inside. Then with a shudder, the immense lumbering airplane stirred unexpectedly as a towing vehicle moved it from the hangar. Sunlight stabbed into the bay from the open front and rear ports as they slowly left the confines of the spacious nose dock and turned one hundred and eighty degrees. Within moments it slowed to a rest and soon afterward, a throaty vibration filled the cargo area as the superstructure began to shake under their feet, growing louder with each passing second. Chau had started one of the engines. The four-propeller aircraft shook forcefully as the remaining ones began to turn, the blades beginning to spin faster. A slight breeze entered through the still half-open rear ramp, replacing some of the horrid smell with the odor of spent explosives and airplane exhaust.

After what seemed like an eternity without moving, Mai again felt motion, then a more forceful shuddering as the immense machine’s RPMs ramped up feverishly. The droning sound became deafening as the engines turned faster, and she watched as her aging mother lowered her chin to her chest and plugged her ears with her index fingers. Mai held tight to Trung, who was crying, but nobody could hear. Once again, they felt the terrible thud of several more rockets hit the ground nearby. A number of women let out startled screams, only barely able to hear the explosions over the engines, but they could certainly feel them. Mai knew that one rocket finding its target anywhere near the hulking aircraft could damage it and render it unable to fly … or worse, destroy it completely and kill everyone inside.

Will we be able to get out of here? she thought. *Could this be the moment of our deaths?*

Off to a slow start, they began taxiing, slowly picking up some ground speed as they headed toward the runway. Through a small nearby window port, Mai could see people running next to the aircraft; often it was just a hand, or a foot, or a terrified face with an expression that pleaded *'please don't leave me.'* Every bump and bang could be felt under their feet as the smooth tires bounced over the debris-strewn taxiway, and Mai couldn't tell if the lurches were a result of running over rubble or if it was more rocket impacts.

As they rolled down the taxiway, the high-pitched wail of the ramp mechanism once again pierced the thunderous purr of the engines, lifting several people with it who couldn't find room elsewhere in the bay. Mai and Dzung watched in horror as two struggling women who were unable to get clear were caught in the closing ramp. With nowhere else to go, their heads came to rest between its edge and the tail section as it closed, crushing their skulls like watermelons. People cried out in sheer horror as the resulting splashes of gore covered those standing nearby, and blood and gray matter rolled sickeningly down the closed, upright ramp.

Just then another incoming round hit the ground to their left, close enough for the passengers to hear the explosion. The aircraft rocked and bits of concrete could be heard raining down on its outer skin. With the bloody ramp now closed, what little light still existed in the hold was still enough to highlight the smoke that continued to fill the space.

Mai gazed forward, barely able to see the steep cockpit stairs embedded in the forward bulkhead, winding about eight feet to the right up into the flight deck on the platform above. She was able to catch the sight of Chau grasping a handhold near the missing crew door trying to speak over the noise with a man near the bottom step, who was tossing luggage and bags out, presumably to lighten the load and make it easier to get airborne.

The sunlight lit the smoky air entering the small opening and struck his face, highlighting the shoulder patches on his flight suit, his sweat-soaked hair, and dark eyes. Those eyes — so placid and kind, even amidst the insanity of the moment. She watched him as he threw off his flak vest, unzipped his flight suit, and rolled the top of it down to his waist, exposing a sweat-soaked black tee shirt. Chau climbed up the narrow, refugee-laden steps, before disappearing urgently on to the flight deck as they continued towards takeoff, and freedom.

Moments later, the dim bay lights flickered as the plane lurched to an abrupt halt. Mai wished she could see outside better, silently wondering if the rubber of the tires under her feet could have come from her father's plantation.

Why have we stopped? she thought.

They sat unmoved as another communist rocket hit the ground, shaking the floor and rattling the passengers deep in their chests. It was close.

Chau, she prayed. *Please fly us safely.*

2

April 6th, 1975 – twenty-three days earlier
CIA OFFICES AT THE NGUYEN HOME
8:45 AM

CIA Chief Special Agent Charles Sterrett, called Chuck by those who knew him, was alarmed at the buzz that had started filling his office about an hour earlier. The upper floor of his multi-level apartment the US Government rented from the Nguyens served as a low-profile 'base' for his small three-man CIA detachment, where he and his small team of agents had quietly moved in a few years before. Hong Nguyen had rented the space out to Americans for the better part of a decade, and it was a great setup for the low-profile operation, especially because Sterrett lived on the lower floors with his Vietnamese wife, Lien, her mother and brother, and their infant child. Their downstairs living areas shared a wall with Chau and Mai's bedroom, and if the antenna arrays the agents maintained on the roof didn't draw too much attention, Sterrett thought they might be able to keep things discreet enough that he could pass as an American who simply worked for the US Embassy.

Their KY-3 secure phone had been ringing off the hook all

morning with semi-frantic calls from his boss, Senior CIA Supervisor Robert Frailey, in the Agency offices at the US Embassy across town. The worried discussion centered around fresh reports of North Vietnamese Army forces and Viet Cong moving southward from areas below the border. Despite the fact that nothing was reported in the South Vietnamese press, things had gotten steadily busier in Saigon for the CIA since the end of March when the communists crossed the border.

The citadel city of Hue had fallen to the North Vietnamese on March 26th, and most people weren't surprised when Da Nang, only sixty or so miles to the south, became the next target just four days later. The twin defeats were alarming, and intelligence updates began coming in far more frequently afterwards, especially since Da Nang went dark exactly one week ago.

Hue fell relatively quickly, but Da Nang was particularly ugly. South Vietnamese soldiers had not only abandoned their posts, but in many cases also their families in their hysterical attempts to escape. The speed of the capitulation surprised even the most senior US officials. While the last plane out of the city landed at Tan Son Nhut, knowledge of its arrival was kept as close-hold as possible to avoid panic. It didn't take long, however, for chit-chat about what happened to start spreading through Saigon's citizenry. The underground rumor mill was quickly taking over, and Sterrett knew that if the local press wouldn't cover it, distrust of the administration in Saigon would only grow.

When peace was reached in 1973, President Nixon promised President Thieu that the United States would come to the aid of South Vietnam in the case of northern aggression. They didn't. Instead, American forces began to leave South Vietnam as fast as they could. Now—two years later—Hue and Da

Nang were gone, and the Embassy was starting to discreetly authorize the evacuation of non-essential Americans. This included some workers and their families, plus a smattering of local national citizens that worked for the American government or US companies. The US Air Force began sending in two to three C-141 or C-5 charters per day to move passengers to Australia, Guam, and other safe locations where they could arrange travel back to the United States or elsewhere.

Sterrett, Frailey, and their agents also knew that the Embassy had set up an evacuation control center at its Defense Attaché Offices, ostensibly to maintain a measure of control and clear information flow, but also to ensure that the right messaging was pushed to the outside world. The last thing US Ambassador Graham Martin wanted was to communicate to the Thieu government that the Americans were abandoning South Vietnam in the face of communist aggression to their north. Things were calmer at the beginning. The idea to be communicated publicly was that this was only precautionary ('prudent' in the words of the ambassador) and was not cause for alarm. Sterrett and his detachment played along.

Given the situation and increasing chatter from the South Vietnamese underground following the Hue and Da Nang disasters, he had initially thought things were surprisingly composed in the city, but it didn't last. Within forty-eight hours of the discreet announcement of non-essential evacuations, President Ford declared the initiation of Operation 'Babylift.' Sterrett found it perversely funny that while the ambassador was trying to keep 'prudent' evacuations under the radar, the president was making big announcements about sending babies back to the continental US. The DIA-run action was intended to move more than ten thousand Vietnamese 'orphans' (which was really code for 'half-Vietnamese children of former US servicemen') out of the country.

Sterrett and his agents kept themselves distantly abreast of the effort, part of which included something called 'Plan Alamo,' a mysterious DAO-led scheme that would utilize their facilities as a big evacuee holding area. Most other agents in area dets similar to Chuck's didn't know much more about it, and both the DAO and the Embassy weren't discussing it. This left some a little skittish—were things really going to get so bad that there'd be a need to concentrate evacuees under a plan with the word 'Alamo' in the title? More alarm bells began to ring when the Air Force presence kicked up—within days of Ford's announcement, nearly thirty Military Airlift Command flights began moving in and out of Tan Son Nhut every day. Sterrett didn't think the distinctive buzz of gargantuan C-5 aircraft filling the skies every hour would inspire confidence that the Americans were going to hang around. It was hard not to be cynical.

For Sterrett, the icing on the cake happened just one day ago—on April 5th—when a Babylift C-5 suffered explosive depressurization after takeoff at 23,000 feet over the South China Sea just beyond the coastline. A number of faulty locks on the rear cowl doors of the aircraft failed, causing them to blow off in flight. When they did, a number of passengers were sucked out of the doomed airplane. Flying debris severed control cables to the tail section, resulting in catastrophic hydraulic failures directly affecting the crew's ability to maintain flight. To their credit, the pilot and co-pilot were able to keep some control and turned the jet back towards Tan Son Nhut. But on approach, they lost what little they had left and crashed into the dike of a rice paddy barely two miles short of the runway. The massive aircraft broke into four pieces and of over three hundred people aboard, nearly one hundred fifty died, including more than seventy children.

Complicating matters was the fact that the crash site was not near any passable roads. Recovery operations had to be conducted by helicopter, and fire/rescue personnel weren't even able to reach the site to extinguish the flames and smoke that erupted when the plane's wing tanks ruptured. To make things worse was the fact that the location where rescue was taking place happened to be at the scene of a skirmish between ARVN and Viet Cong forces not even twenty-four hours before, which made recovery extremely contentious—there was no telling if violence might erupt again.

Sterrett was sure that the crash was the last nail in the coffin of the now-very-dead missive that the 'Americans would protect the southern government from the communist threat.' It had turned instead to an unintended message of stark abandonment. With so much noisy air traffic over the course of each day, a crash, an acrid-smelling pillar of smoke that drifted into the city, and a very obvious superfluity of helicopters and southern military personnel at the rescue site, the message of calm and steadfast support collapsed. Any normal Vietnamese citizen could put the pieces together, not to mention be angered that almost a hundred kids had died in the mishap.

The KY-3, an antiquated piece of communications equipment, allowed secure telephone communication between two points, but it was a clunky piece of 1960s technology. The guts of it existed in a 3-foot high safe-like gray cabinet with a small receiver that stood conspicuously next to Senior Operative Jessie Flounders' desk. To get to it, one had to wade through the copious clouds of Flounders' cigarette smoke which when mixed with the thick morning air created a dense blue cloud that floated at shoulder-level in the small space. If it were a perfect setup, the KY-3 would have been in an interior closet, but most Vietnamese homes used external wardrobes to hang clothes and closets simply didn't exist. Sterrett loved serving in the CIA, but hated using this archaic secure phone, which when in "secret" mode, made it sound like the user on the other end was speaking through a wet washcloth while making popcorn.

It rang for what seemed like the tenth time that morning, filling the room with its annoying buzz.

"Rusty!" Sterrett called. "For the love of God, can you please pick that thing up?"

"McClay here!"

Field Agent Michael McClay answered with slight annoyance, silently listening to the sender on the other end. Sterrett and his agents had always called him 'Rusty,' because it seemed everyone else did. An FBI agent before he joined the CIA community, how he got the nickname was a mystery, and he kept the story to himself, refusing to explain it to anyone when asked. Sterrett thought it might have been because of his thick red mustache and bushy ginger hair, or maybe because the only deodorant spray that worked for him was Old Spice, which was pretty hard to come by in Saigon. The result was a slight body odor that smelled like the sun-baked, faux-leather insides of a rusty old car that had been sitting in someone's driveway a little too long. He was the loveable smart ass of Chuck's detachment—always quick with a snide remark—but fiercely loyal to his country.

"Right, switching to a secure line now."

Sterrett knew Rusty hated the phone too. Even though it sat next to Jesse's desk, it was always a contest to see how long

each of them would let its annoying ring persist before someone cracked and just answered. Rusty had less patience for the
god-awful sound than Jesse did, so he was often the one who
gave in to make it stop.

"OK," he said, "I'm showing you 'secret.'"

Rusty listened intently while Sterrett, sitting at his desk
making notes on a yellow legal pad, peered distractedly over at
his subordinate.

"Northwest of Kon Tum now?"

Sterrett's concern began to grow. Kon Tum was a small mu-
nicipality near Pleiku, well to the south of Da Nang. Northern
forces must have been moving quickly.

"What about good guys?" Rusty asked. "Any radio comms?"

There was a long silence as he received the Embassy's reply.

"OK, roger that. Out."

Rusty roughly hung the plastic receiver on its brown resin
cradle, creating a semi-metallic 'ping' that echoed in the room
like the plink of a golf ball.

"Kon Tum?" Sterrett sighed with a stoic yet concerned
air — his eyes were laser-focused on Rusty. "They're getting
closer — Embassy's nervous, aren't they?"

"It's just initial reports from a couple informants in the area,
Chuck," Rusty answered. "Sounds like it may only be extreme
forward elements, but people are a little nervous there."

"Well, that ain't good," Jesse muttered over his desk as he
shuffled paperwork distractedly, a freshly-lit Camel bouncing
between his lips as he spoke.

Jesse's short, flat-topped hair bristled with sweat. During the
two tours he served during the war in the late sixties as an enlisted
Marine, he took on a mastery of dark humor and understatement.
Chuck Sterrett had worked with him for a while and figured he

knew him pretty well. He thought maybe Jesse's unique disposition was a result of his combat experience in the Tet Offensive during the Battle of Hue as a junior squad leader—some of the most violent urban fighting of the war. Sterrett had worked with a lot of military veterans over the years, and they all shared a dark, yet humorous sarcasm that tended to minimize the gravity of serious situations. Jesse was no exception.

It was endearing, yet sad, but Chuck held Jesse's experience in high regard. As an agent, he thought it gave the guy an edge at his job that separated him from his peers and endowed him with an insight that agents with civilian backgrounds simply couldn't bring to the table. On the flip side, he knew Jesse was burdened by it, which sometimes manifested in an overcautiousness that, left unchecked, tended to result in overreaction when sound pragmatism might be the better path.

Chuck's temples began to perspire, his heart was beating faster inside his ribcage, and his sixth sense began poking him in the gut like an ice pick. He sensed an odd change—like something drastic was starting, and it flashed him back to his childhood in Ritchie County, West Virginia just outside Parkersburg. As a pre-teen kid, Chuck was incorrigible, especially when he and his older brother were out of school in summer. One steamy July evening after everyone was in bed, the two boys decided it might be fun to sneak over to the train tracks near their family home to see if stories about a ghost along the North Bend rail line that led through the Silver Run tunnel nearby were true—some woman had been killed there in the late eighteen hundreds. At least that was the legend.

It was that night, for the first time, that Chuck became aware of a strong, tingling sense deep inside him that might be the harbinger of something imminent and ominous. He ignored it at the time, but while walking along the railroad ties inside the tunnel, his brother's shoelace caught on a steel spike jutting up from one of the thick wooden cross ties. During their efforts in the dark to free him, a train could suddenly be heard speedily approaching, and its headlamp quickly illuminated the entrance ahead of them. Within moments, it filled the entire tunnel. Ironically, the locomotive's lights helped them to free the shoe, and the boys were able to get into one of the safety cavities along the damp, 19th-century brick wall seconds before the huge engine thundered past them.

In the noisy breeze of the passing railcars, Chuck realized he better start listening to his gut. It was also when he first noticed his extreme propensity to sweat. The tunnel shaft was chilly and dank, but he was profoundly warm. They never saw any drifting spirits that night, but Chuck figured they nearly became spirits themselves and that was enough.

That same unexplainable intuition he felt in that tunnel so many years ago was once again lingering in the back of his conscience.

"What kinds of numbers are we talking about, Rusty?"

"Don't know yet," he answered matter-of-factly, "but there's been some harassment of local farmers. Sounds like a little banditry too, roughing up some of the men in the area, you know...slapping the women around."

"Kidnapping?"

"Maybe."

"*Shit.*"

It was a bad sign. It was barely a week since Da Nang fell. In the chaos of that battle, American-supported South Vietnamese forces had crumbled into nothing. Chuck knew it was likely that whatever there was that had stood in the communists' way farther to the south stood a strong chance of being flattened as well, as the enemy pressed for more southern targets.

"Anything on the good guys?"

"Not much."

Rusty was a little aloof.

"But there have been communist radio interceptions that make it sound like whatever's there isn't putting up much resistance. That they're retreating so fast the commies are having a hard time keeping up."

"Propaganda," Jesse said underwhelmingly.

"Think?" Chuck asked. "What's the southern military saying?"

"Crickets," Rusty said.

American financial and materiel support of the South Vietnamese military had dried up significantly since the US had left Vietnam in early 1973. Since then, it was well-known that the ARVN was woefully underequipped and that their morale was in a death spiral. Indeed, it had been on full display at Da Nang, and silence from South Vietnamese uniformed leadership wasn't giving Chuck a lot of confidence. It meant Jesse was probably wrong—this wasn't propaganda.

April 6th, 1975
NGUYEN HOME, SAIGON
9:00 AM

Dzung Nguyen released the bolt on the courtyard's screeching metal gate that opened to a small side street in front of the family home. He was looking for his brothers, who had walked a few blocks down the busy avenue nearby about an hour before to obtain some helium balloons for a little weekend mischief. The hinges, in bad need of grease, groaned with a metallic agony as he pulled the tall gate into its open position. It caused a brief, but intense vibration that seemed sure to rattle the door off its moorings, bolted deep into the concrete block of the outer walls of their compound. As he peeked his head around the edge of the opening, the noise of the main street—less than fifty yards away—filled his ears under the muggy morning shadows of the Southeast Asian sun. It was just after 9am in Saigon, and it was beginning like any other Sunday morning—with the three Nguyen brothers postured to stir up some trouble.

When Tuan and Son rounded the corner into their small alleyway, Dzung saw Tuan's fist clutching the strings of about fifteen colorful balloons floating above his head. There was a roguish grin on his face, presumably because he knew what they were preparing to do. Dzung, the main rabble-rouser of the three brothers, produced a small soiled rag and a black Bic lighter that had been balled up in his fist. It was about to be a good morning.

"Come on!" Dzung motioned impatiently to his brothers.

Tuan and Son quickly turned into the courtyard as Dzung closed the gate behind them with a metallic crash that reminded him of an old Chinese gong. The boys weren't doing a great job staying quiet—they didn't want to alert anyone that they were up to no good. Hopefully their older sister Mai, who was scarier than their mother when it came to discipline, wasn't tipped off by the racket.

They moved to a small spot near the little queen flower tree that grew next to the house on the west end of the courtyard. It was a good location because with April underway, large buds that would soon turn into beautiful pink blooms were thick.

The boys knew it would be hard to be seen from the second and third floors of the house.

"OK, rip me off a piece!" Son whispered excitedly.

Tuan grinned wide with delight, bouncing up and down on the balls of his feet with nervousness as Dzung tore a small swatch of fabric. He handed it to Son before taking one of the balloons from Tuan's hand, then wrapped its string around his left index finger to keep it from floating away. Son then pulled out a small pocket knife and cut it to roughly six inches in length, tying the end around the fabric in a tight knot.

"Ready?" he asked his brothers with a mischievous half-grin.

"Yes!"

Dzung grabbed the black lighter and moved deliberately under the overhang that separated the first and second floors, then lifted the length of rag close to his chin. Striking the lighter twice, he produced a flame on the second attempt and raised it to the frayed edge. It immediately started burning and he hurriedly let it go before running back to his brothers under the tree.

The three boys peeked their heads from under the branches in anticipation as the basketball-sized rubber sphere glided slowly up the wall of the house, the quickly-growing flame moving at a rapid pace up the short string. As it began to rise past the window of Mai's bedroom, the small orange fire abruptly found the bottom of the balloon, blowing it apart in an instant, emitting a sharp report which broke the relative silence of the courtyard. From inside the house, the boys heard a startled young woman scream, the echo of the booming pop still bouncing off the inner courtyard walls.

"*DZUNG!*" came the aggravated response from inside.

Of course it was Dzung—Mai must have known. It was *always* Dzung. The boys suppressed giggles at each other, doing their best to stay quiet. Smiling widely, Dzung readied a second balloon.

"Quick, give me another one!"

He cut the next balloon's string and tied on a second strip of dirty fabric then handed it with the lighter to Son, who rapidly shuffled back under the overhang. After glancing upward to check for someone leaning out the window, he lit the rag, and released the next balloon before racing back to the tree with his brothers, anxiously awaiting the second blast. As it reached Mai's window, it popped loudly.

The deafening noise seemed louder than the first. As it rippled across the courtyard, Son laughed audibly, watching the bits of shattered balloon and pieces of burnt cloth float to the ground. From the window, Mai could be heard again cursing her younger brothers, who softly chortled from under the budding tree.

"Tuan," Son said quietly, "your turn!"

Dzung grabbed the balloons from Tuan and secured them to one of the tree's small brown sprigs, leaving him with a single green one that he began tying the next tiny piece of rag to. Tuan could barely contain his excitement as his older brother finished trimming the string and tied a knot around the scrap of material. He then raced to the overhang and lit the makeshift fuse, immediately letting it sail up the wall. Within seconds, the green balloon blew up with another ear-shattering crack. Deeper inside the house, Mai shouted something unintelligible, dotted with *"TUAN!," "SON!,"* and *"DZUNG!"* That she was yelling from farther in the house was a bad thing—it meant she was probably on her way to the courtyard to come after them.

Their very irate older sister emerged from the house's main

door, her hair wet from bathing. She wore a knee-length white linen robe that rippled behind her as she bee-lined straight for the tree. Her face was a twisted manifestation of fury, and a string of borderline indecent speech emanated brashly from her lips.

"WAIT UNTIL BA GETS HOME!" she exclaimed, stomping toward them.

Dzung and Son scrambled up into the tangled branches to escape her wrath, but Tuan, the smallest and slowest of the three, didn't make it in time. Reaching him as he tried to join his brothers, Mai raised her right hand and laid a whopping *'smack'* on the side of Tuan's right buttock. As he struggled up the tree, her hand swiftly found another target, this time on the inside of his left calf.

"OW!" Tuan cried in pain.

"COME DOWN FROM THERE!" she bellowed.

Just then, a small black and red object sailed out of the tall branches and passed Tuan's left ear with a mild hiss. Dzung saw it but wasn't aware of what it was until it hit the tiles of the courtyard next to Mai's bare left foot. It seemed that Son, who'd hidden a small package of ten firecrackers in his pants pocket, had lit it and tossed it at his sister. The connected fuses of the small charges loudly exploded in quick succession, popping like an angry machine gun next to Mai. The deafening sound reverberated over the whitewashed outer walls of the Nguyen home. A shocked Mai jumped, dancing and yelping amongst the flashes and flying bits of firework.

"COME DOWN!" she roared over the boys' peals of uncontrollable laughter. *"YOU ARE IN DEEP TROUBLE!"*

Suddenly, the courtyard's metal gate swung open with its juddering squeal. Hong Nguyen emerged from the small street in front of the house next to the olive-green Jeep he had purchased from the US Army before they left in 1973. He angrily froze when he saw his three sons and Mai. Dzung watched as Mai stiffened, fixing her gaze on their father as he returned to the driver's side to pull the vehicle into the courtyard and park. The Jeep slowly halted next to the queen flower tree where the boys were stranded, and Mai edged carefully out of the way. Hong switched the ignition off and sat still in the driver's seat, absorbing the unusual scene in his courtyard: his three boys in a tree, his daughter standing in her robe, half-bathed and barefoot, and a colorful array of helium-filled balloons tied to a small twig amongst the budding flowers.

"What is going on here?" he calmly asked.

"Ba," Mai said after a pause "you won't believe what—"

"I do not think I want to hear this," Hong interjected calmly, but clearly frustrated with the juvenile conflict between his children.

Mai, Son, Dzung, and Tuan stared blankly at their father, all keeping their mouths shut to avoid *real* trouble.

"Boys," he continued in a calm, yet firm tone, "come down from my tree. Son, close the gate and go inside."

Hong stepped out of the Jeep and put his hands on his hips as his sons began coming down from the tangled branches of his beloved tree.

"Tuan," Hong said, pointing to the scattered bits of balloon and firecracker, "pick up that mess."

As the boys exited their relative safety, Son made his way to the gate. As it squeaked closed, Tuan got his feet on the ground and began moving toward the scattered bits of debris under directly under Mai's second floor window.

"Dzung," Hong stated sternly. "I do not want to see any scorch marks on my tile. Get a sponge and clean it."

Hong then turned his brusque stare toward Mai.

"Inside."

She wasn't happy that she got roped by her brothers into suffering her father's frustration, but she knew better than to talk back to him.

April 6th, 1975
CIA OFFICES AT NGUYEN HOME
9:25 AM

Chuck was sweating like a sinner in church. It would sometimes drive him crazy, but he was glad he didn't smell like Rusty. A drop rolled from the thick hair above his eyebrow as he walked toward the office's avocado-green West Bend coffee percolator for a refill when the KY-3 buzzed to life again. Jesse Flounders reached to pick it up, but Chuck, who was in the vicinity anyway, beat him to it.

"Sterrett."

It was his boss, Bob Frailey, at the Embassy.

"OK, going secure."

Chuck turned a large metal key, which enabled the 300-pound telephone to establish a secure connection. It took several seconds for it to run through its 1960's-era cryptologic protocols in each terminal to establish a protected connection. As the internal encryption-decryption mechanisms did their work, the line went dead for a moment, and a few seconds later Chuck heard the familiar hiss of the safeguarded line.

"I gotcha showing secure, Bob."

"OK, showing secret here too," Frailey responded white-noisily in Chuck's ear. "Chuck, we've got a fresh report of some fair-sized movement near where the Cambodian-Laotian-Vietnam tri-border area. They're obviously using parts of the old Ho Chi Minh trail on the other side."

"Any friendlies nearby?" Chuck asked.

"Not in any great number," Frailey responded coolly. "What was there has already retreated southward like the rest."

"Any indication of where they're headed next?"

"Not clear, but there are also rumors they may be digging in in a few places," Frailey continued. "We've got at least two sources in the area that reported hearing heavier vehicles or machinery. Couple of spots."

"Tanks?"

"Could be," Chuck's boss responded, "but more likely it's earth-moving equipment. They might be reinforcing some of the Cong's old bunkers or doing something with the tunnel systems."

Chuck paused quietly and wiped a fresh drop of perspiration from his eyebrow.

"What do you think it means?"

"Well," Frailey answered with a long sigh, "it probably means they're setting up shop for the long haul."

"Anything else about the harassment of the locals?"

"Still happening."

"You worried, boss?"

"I'd be lying if I told you no," Frailey responded. "Also, you should know that the last time we talked to Ambassador Martin about what's going on, we recommended he take plans off the shelf and start posturing for a full evac in case we have to get outta here."

"What did he say?"

"He didn't wanna hear it. Said we need to stick to the

non-essentials and called what we're already doing 'a matter of prudency.'"

"Any chance he'll agree to trying to get the high-risk nationals out?"

With the communists coming south, everyone knew most senior South Vietnamese officials were at significant risk—civilian leadership, military officers, intelligence operatives, and others who had worked with Americans during the war and throughout the years after. The US Embassy assumed there were nearly seventeen thousand of them, but it was a rough figure and there was no comprehensive list of actual names. If seven or more family members per person were figured into the mix, the number exploded to one hundred and nineteen thousand. If any were captured in a hostile takeover—including family members—they all stood a good chance of imprisonment or death.

"Zero."

"Hmph," Chuck grunted.

"Yeah, I know," Frailey replied with a dash of cynicism. "There'll be NVA tanks at the gates of the Embassy before Graham Martin decides to try and get anyone out. And that isn't even including Americans."

"Yeah, we'll be dead or in some sort of crappy prison right there with 'em."

Ambassador Graham Martin had lost a son during a combat operation in the Central Highlands during the mid-sixties. He had a lot invested in a free South Vietnam and seemed pretty much in denial about the potential for danger to Americans and their South Vietnamese counterparts. Most who worked inside of or with the Embassy knew he'd be damned if he was going to voluntarily remove the entire American presence from South Vietnam.

"Maybe," Frailey replied.

"What does Glenn think?"

Tom Glenn was the ambassador's National Security Agency station chief and was senior to Bob Frailey.

"Well, he asked him what he thought about us talking to the wardens across the city," Frailey continued.

"...and?" Chuck hung on his boss' words.

"Well, let's just say the response from the ambassador was bloody."

Chuck thought of his family, who basically fell into the 'non-essential' category. If the communists ever got close to Saigon, he'd have to get them out of the country. And what about Chau Nguyen? As a South Vietnamese Air Force officer, his entire family would be in danger too.

"Bob," Chuck began, "there's a lot of folks here who have supported us. I'm not just talking about the military guys...I mean civilian informants too. This is a big network."

He was sure his boss knew where he was going with his line of thinking.

"...and you know, some of us guys have families."

"Yeah...you thought about getting them out ahead of you?"

"Yeah."

"Well, if you're gonna say anything to McClay and Flounders, keep it close-hold. And don't say a word to your wife. Not yet. An order for a full evac will probably happen, but it's gonna have to get really bad first."

"OK, but there's still all those high-risk folks."

...which included Chau.

"Chuck, you know as well as I do the Embassy doesn't have an all-inclusive list of names. Who do you know? You'd be ahead to start making one of your own if you haven't already."

"Would I be the only one doing that?"

"No."

Chuck got the picture. In not so many words, Bob Frailey made it pretty clear that there could be some on the Embassy staff already thinking about gearing up for possible movement of the people who would be big targets—maybe even under the radar, which would be in direct defiance of Ambassador Graham Martin.

April 6th, 1975
NGUYEN HOME, SAIGON
9:30 AM

"Dzung."

Thirty minutes later, Hong Nguyen was still a little agitated that his sons had been tormenting their older sister. He and his wife Dat knew it was just part of being boys—and in fact, also knew that they got their orneriness from their father, who had also been known to stir up similar trouble with *his* siblings as a child. Dzung was the brother with the edge and was prone to push it a little further than Tuan and Son. At least he got it honest.

"You and I are going for a ride today."

The boys had come inside a short time before and were straightening themselves after cleaning up the mess they'd made together earlier in their father's courtyard.

"Where are we going, Ba?" Dzung asked nervously.

"The plantation."

Hong Nguyen's gigantic rubber plantation was at least six hours away into the mountains near the Cambodian border over often-rough roads, but once or twice a month, he would travel there to check on his operation and make sure his workers had what they needed to get the job done. He knew Dzung would normally be happy to go, but under the circumstances, he probably wasn't sure what to expect. Maybe they'd pass some partially-clothed women — the route to the plantation was usually dotted with indigenous Degar people, a mystical tribal society whose women often went topless. Usually, Hong asked his sons to avert their eyes, but like any young kid, the boys usually managed to sneak a peek anyway.

"I need to check on things there and bring some food," Hong said indifferently, "and you and I are going to talk."

Dzung remained silent.

"We will leave in thirty minutes," Hong continued.

April 6th, 1975
THREE HOURS NORTHWEST OF SAIGON
1:00 PM

Hong Nguyen hadn't said a word to Dzung since he'd emerged from the small, family bakery with two armfuls of brown paper-wrapped French baguettes. Since then, they'd long since left the last vestiges of Saigon and had been traveling steadily northwest on the elevated gravel and dirt roads surrounding the rice paddies. A medium-sized slaughtered hog lay in the rear bed of the Jeep, wrapped and covered by ragged burlap. It wasn't unusual for Hong to bring food to his plantation workers.

He knew his boys could tell when he was unhappy with them, because he didn't speak to them very much. It wasn't because he was trying to scare them (even though it usually did), he just needed time to come down off the emotions of having to discipline his kids. The longer he stayed quiet, the more upset the boys figured he was... and the more they feared his wrath. It had been three hours since the bakery—a long time for that kind of heavy silence—and Dzung, sitting mutely in the passenger seat, was nervous.

The vehicle began to emerge from the low river flats and agricultural land below the rolling foothills and approached the eastern side of the lushly jungled hills that hid the plantation on the other side. The once-straight thoroughfare meandered and became rougher under the hazy blue sky, and despite the breeze rushing past their ears, the heavy air caused their shirts to show perspiration. The long stretch of macadam they were leaving behind them had been surrounded extensively with rice crops, water buffalo, and people in wide, conical 'non la' hats, but by now, verdant green jungle began to take over as the agriculture became sparser. There would be a smattering of farms ahead of them, but the red dirt road would increasingly wind them through the luxuriant wilderness, its leafy green vegetation, tall trees, and palms covering the narrowing road like a long railroad tunnel.

Hong looked at his son. Tiny breaks of sunlight broke through the high branches, randomly tracing tiny shadows across his face while beads of sweat dripped slowly down his temple. Turning his eyes back to the road, he stared stoically ahead for a moment, then broke his long silence.

"Dzung."

His son didn't answer, instead gazing forward, braced for what he must have thought was coming.

"Do you understand what is happening in our country?" he asked.

Dzung turned quizzically to his father as the passing jungle grew thicker. It was not the comment he had expected. Hong looked again at his son, searching for a splash of understanding, but he didn't find it.

"What do you mean, Ba?"

They began to come down a long and gradually opening hill, headed toward a few farms on a narrow reddish-brown valley below. They were more than half-way to the plantation, and it straightened out for a stretch as it passed a few dilapidated farm structures, then took a sharp right-angled turn before winding back into the jungle.

Hong was taciturn for a moment, then broke his silence again.

"Our country is in danger, son."

This conversation wasn't going to be about balloons and fire-crackers.

Hong continued quietly, barely audible over the sound of the wind, engine, and crunching gravel.

"My employees at the plantation have seen enemy soldiers passing through. Mostly they come at night. There is also talk about large armies to our north, and that they are heading in our direction."

Dzung looked scared.

"What will happen if they come here?"

"I do not know. But we will trust in our government to defend us ... at least for now."

"Will we have to run away?" Dzung asked.

He hoped his son's words weren't prophetic. What boy of that age would have instantly assumed fleeing their home might be necessary? Perhaps he could read into things more than Hong thought he could.

"No," Hong responded. "I do not believe it is time for us to leave. But your mother and I have been making a simple plan to get to safety if we have to."

Vietnam had been immersed in conflict for the better part of three decades, and unbeknownst to all their children except Mai, Hong and Dat had kept evacuation plans for a long time. It was just part of life in a war zone, but he never though he'd have to seriously consider putting them into action. Saigon always felt relatively safe, since much of the fighting occurred miles outside the city, especially in the seven years since Tet. In fact, there hadn't been any violence in or near Saigon for almost four years. All the same, Hong and his wife had a few small bags they kept packed with a change of clothes and some personal items.

"Where would we go?" he asked, his voice sounding troubled as the Jeep finished descending into the small valley plain.

"I am not sure," his father answered. "If we have to leave, we might first escape to Thailand or Malaysia. After that I do not know."

Hong paused, as if uttering the word *escape* to his son made it that much more likely to happen.

By now, they were passing the tiny farms that Dzung had seen earlier from the higher vantage point. He wasn't looking very closely at first, but from what he could tell by some distracted glances around, there weren't any half-naked, colorfully-dressed women in the fields. In fact, there weren't any women at all.

Or men.

The place looked deserted.

"Ba, I do not see any people. Where is everyone?"

Hong saw it too, and quickly became alarmed. He slowed

his Jeep to a crawl to get a look around a little more safely. Not a soul. Something wasn't right.

"We need to get out of here."

Hong pressed the gas pedal to turn around and momentarily gained some speed just ahead of the right angle in the road but didn't get more than fifty feet before slamming on the brakes, throwing the un-belted Dzung from his seat and into the steel dashboard.

The vehicle idled and coughed as Dzung's hand went to a small spot high on his forehead, pulling it away to see a bit of blood from where it had met metal. He quickly pulled himself upright, then looked out over the Jeep's hood.

Hong had come to the violent stop to avoid the unthinkable. In the crook of the tight ninety-degree bend that led the road back into thick vegetation and large trees, helmets became visible amongst the underbrush—some light green-colored and worn, and a few tan-looking, newer and even a little shiny. Over the engine there were voices yelling, when out of the thickness of the low growth, two helmeted men emerged clad in dark clothes and sandals. One held an AK-47 in the ready position and was pointing with his left hand to a small spot on the road, loudly bellowing something unintelligible. The second man carried what looked like a very long brownish pipe with a colorful pointed tip on the front end, which rested partly on his right shoulder. In a millisecond of the first soldier's command, the man with the pipe went down on his knee and leveled it at the vehicle.

It was a rocket propelled grenade launcher.

Hong felt the color drain from his face. Animal instinct gripped his inner primitive brain and he felt a strong impulse to protect Dzung, but he kept his cool, staying reserved and still. Hong could hear his son's intestines gurgling as the boy sat frozen in the passenger seat, overcome by fear.

"*SHOW YOUR HANDS!*" came the command from the tall, thin soldier with the assault rifle before he drew a bead on them.

Sweat was dripping from under his sun-baked helmet, the small strands of hair clinging to the skin of his forehead. Dzung's eyes were wild and penetrating, his breaths quick and shallow, and Hong was hyper-aware that the man's finger was on his trigger. His mind raced, and he wondered silently if they were being stopped because they were using a green US Army Jeep. These men did not appear to be young, and it was likely they'd had some experience with American Jeeps before…probably not under the best of circumstances either.

Both Hong and Dzung instinctively lifted their hands over their heads and there was a pause between the two sides that lasted long enough to make it feel like a childhood staring contest. Except this one wasn't designed to see who would laugh first. It was suddenly evident why the small farms they'd passed only moments before were utterly devoid of people — the locals had probably cleared out for fear of getting caught in the middle of something violent.

"TURN OFF YOUR ENGINE!"

The two armed men were positioned about twenty feet off the Jeep's front bumper. Hong slowly reached his trembling right hand towards the dashboard. The ignition was just above and to the right of the steering column, and he gently switched it a quarter turn to the left. The Jeep's engine stammered off as Hong deliberately raised his hand back in to the air.

He very carefully whispered to Dzung, his teeth clenched and lips barely moving: *"Do not speak of Chau."*

Hong knew that to these soldiers, people like Chau were enemy combatants, and there was no telling what kind of punishment (or worse) he and his son might suffer if they knew a South Vietnamese Air Force pilot was one of their family members.

The man with the AK-47 began slowly advancing toward the Jeep, the muzzle of his rifle so steady it could have been on casters. His eyes locked dead-on Hong and Dzung as he walked in their direction. The bottoms of his baggy black pant-legs were dirty—like he had run through a three-inch deep mud puddle. His sandals were worn, barely covering a thickly calloused set of dirt-caked feet. As he moved to their left, the soldier with the RPG flanked the Jeep on the right. He moved with purpose and elegance, almost like he was slow dancing … his partner the brown metal tube resting parallel to the ground on his shoulder, its single multi-colored rocket protruding threateningly from its snout. When the men were within about five feet of the hood, the soldier with the rifle slowed his gait and spoke.

"Keep your hands where I can see them."

It was a loud, but cool and steady tone, his language dripping with a northern dialect of Vietnamese that Hong was not accustomed to hearing. He hadn't been anywhere north of the ancient citadel city of Hue in more than two decades, and he'd forgotten how different the linguistics were.

Hong's heart pounded in his chest and he could feel his blood pressure climbing, the fluid in his veins pulsing at his temples. His breaths were shallow, and he swore he could feel the sweat filling the glands on his forehead, gathering in tiny drops before gravity could pull them across his face, down his neck, then soak the top of his loosely-buttoned collar. His eyes followed the soldier intently, monitoring his every move as the worn rifle's nose inched closer to his center mass.

He thought of Dzung next to him in the passenger's seat. If

they were going to be killed, it would already have happened. These men must have had other plans. *No sudden moves,* he thought to himself, hoping that somehow his son would catch his unspoken instruction.

The soldier with the RPG stood adjacent to Dzung, like he was awaiting some sort of command from his counterpart. They remained silent, waiting for something to happen. It could have been their final seconds on earth.

Hong briefly took his eyes off the rifle pointed at his chest and caught a glimpse of several other men in the underbrush a few meters away, bluish rifle muzzles protruding just under their chins. Then the soldier nearest to Hong turned his rifle butt outward, wound up, and savagely clubbed him on the cheek with it. Hong's head jerked backward, and his shoulders followed. Dzung jumped in his seat with a start at the abrupt violence. Before his father could recover, the man re-leveled at Hong's face.

"*GET OUT OF THE VEHICLE!* What is your business here?"

The man grabbed Hong's collar and ripped him from the Jeep, throwing him on to the hard-packed gravelly road surface. The rifle butt had traced a purplish crisscross pattern on his left cheek, which immediately began to swell. A small cut in the middle of the lump oozed blood which began to intermingle with his sweat.

"Come," RPG-soldier said to Dzung in a hushed tone, "get out."

He handled Dzung far gentler than the other man was handling his father. Without taking his eyes off the situation on the other side of the Jeep with Hong, the RPG-soldier gently pulled Dzung towards the vehicle's grill by his shirt sleeve.

"Put your hands on the hood and be still."

He was speaking quietly, almost like he was trying to avoid the wrath of an angry parent.

"*Who are you?*" the rifle-soldier bellowed at Hong. "*Why are you here?*"

Hong, still on the ground, had placed his hands over his swollen cheek bone and was doing his best not to make any noise. Then out of the blue, the rifle-soldier kicked him in the ribcage, sending his diaphragm into a spasm and knocking the wind out of him.

"*Get up!*"

He choked and coughed, desperately trying to catch his breath from the blow that might have cracked some ribs. He was glad the rifle-soldier was wearing sandals and not a pair of hard-soled boots—the soft tissue of his toes might have saved his spleen from being ruptured. A wad of stringy mucous drizzled onto the dusty gravel from Hong's mouth as he strained for air, struggling to climb to his knees.

"*Ba!*" Dzung bellowed.

"Shh..." the RPG-soldier responded softly, "keep quiet."

Dzung watched in horror as his father was beaten.

As Hong got himself on to all fours, the rifle-soldier lifted his foot and shoved hard on Hong's posterior, causing him to tumble to the ground once more. Hong rolled over and received a kick to the kidneys, eliciting a grunt of pain. His hand went to his back, desperately trying to quell the agony tearing across his lower back.

"*Answer me!*"

The rifle-soldier pointed his gun at the center of Hong's body.

Dzung held fast. It didn't seem like RPG-soldier quite knew

what to do. Hong had once told Dzung that war brought out the worst in people. Maybe that was true of the rifle-soldier, but perhaps the RPG-soldier was a father and had children of his own. RPG-man lowered his rocket tube and moved to the driver's side of the Jeep, looking conflicted about Hong's violent beating. He reached toward his angry companion and gently tugged on his shoulder. Without taking his eyes off Hong, the rifle-soldier forcefully batted it away.

"Do not shoot him," the RPG-soldier whispered.

It was odd—he might have launched a rocket at them not two minutes before, yet here he was speaking in concerned tones and wearing an expression of trepidation at the sight of the stern beating.

Blood seeped from the corner of Hong's mouth as he struggled to pull himself up off the ground.

"My name...." he said, straining, "is Nguyen. I have...a rubber plantation..."

"Where?" the rifle-soldier replied.

His AK-47 was still pointed at Hong's head.

"Do you have food?" he asked impatiently. "*Answer me!*"

"Yes," Hong muttered with a cough. "You can have it all. But please leave my son alone."

The rifle-soldier paused, his demeanor changing from anger to insidious surprise.

"This is your *son*, is it?" he said in his northern dialect, suddenly cracking a sadistic smile.

"*Please.*"

"You are coming with us."

April 6th, 1975
THREE HOURS NORTHWEST OF SAIGON
2:00 PM

Hong held his hand over his ribs as he struggled to keep the rickety Jeep on the road. They'd been driving for what seemed like an hour, but it could just as easily only have been ten minutes. Dzung, his hands tied tightly with ragged hemp twine, was upright on the torn middle cushion of the back seat flanked by one other man. The rifle-soldier, sitting next to Hong, pressed the point of his gun into his ribcage below the right armpit. Hong's breaths were shallow and strained as he maneuvered the Jeep over hill and dale through an ever-tightening cylinder of jungle growth.

Where are they taking us?

Is my son safe?

He was actually surprised these enemy soldiers were allowing him to drive his Jeep. After all, he was a captive. Wouldn't it have made more sense for them to be blindfolded in order to conceal the location they were traveling to? So many thoughts swam through his head. Would he and Dzung be the latest South Vietnamese to disappear and never be heard from again? It seemed a likely scenario. Would he ever see his wife and family? Was this the beginning of the end? What about the rubber plantation? Was there a way to escape? He kept coming back to *'if they were going to kill us, they would have done it already.'* But was that really true?

"Where are we going?" Hong asked, his voice weak and broken.

"*Shut up!*" came the terse reply.

The Jeep bounced and bucked over the rough road, and travel wasn't quick. They were plying through mud and puddles of water in some areas as vegetation brushed past their shoulders on either side of the vehicle.

Hong, Dzung, and their captors reached a straight stretch covered by low, thick, and ever-darkening flora. A little way ahead, there appeared to be movement in the road, but Hong wasn't sure. Squinting his eyes in an effort to see, the movement became more pronounced, and he realized he was looking at several khaki-uniformed men with lightly-colored helmets moving in and out of the shadows. As they got closer, he saw that each had an AK-47 slung over their shoulders, and two of them were holding something in their hands.

Rifle-soldier sat at alert in the passenger seat gazing forward at the men in the road. Their faces slick with sweat, the soldiers on the road looked very young — maybe only a few years older than his sons — and they were now standing three abreast wearing no-nonsense looks on their faces.

"Stop here!" came the gruff command from the rifle-soldier.

Hong pressed the pedals and slowed to a halt. His captor exited the Jeep and walked with a purpose towards the three men. A brief and frank conversation took place, but neither Hong nor Dzung could hear anything over the snorting of the Jeep's engine.

The youth that rifle-soldier was talking to turned to one of the others and nodded in the direction of the Jeep, his tan helmet bobbing. One of the khaki-clad men rapidly approached Hong on the driver's side and without a word, violently ripped him from his seat by the left arm, throwing him into a patch of leaf-covered muck on the side of the road. As his foot left the clutch the Jeep lunged forward, stalling the engine with a jerk and nearly throwing Dzung from his seat for the second time.

"*Get up!*" the man bellowed at Hong angrily. "Get into the back!"

Hong looked the man in the eye, placed his right hand in the mud to raise his body and his left out with its palm facing downward appeasingly. The left side of his face had become a swollen mess of red and purple, blood oozed from the place high on his cheek where the rifle-soldier had clubbed him. As Hong started to re-enter the Jeep, the khaki soldier grabbed him by the hair and moved him aggressively towards its rear. Hong grabbed the side of the chassis and painfully lifted himself inside, doing his best to squeeze into any spot he could find between the other bodies—the back seat were made for two medium-sized men, and now there were three people crammed into it.

The khaki-clad youth who'd thrown Hong into the back then motioned for a counterpart to approach the Jeep. He held canvas fabric in his hand. He approached Dzung, then grabbed him by the ear, producing a small yelp from the eleven-year old. In an instant, the canvas was over Dzung's head and tied around his neck. A similar hood was placed over Hong, then his wrists were coarsely tied together. They were blind and left to discern what was happening around them with their other senses. The leaf suspension of the vehicle shook as people filled the front seats, and the Jeep's ignition was turned. The engine cranked to life once more.

Someone grabbed the side of Hong's head, then leaned close to his ear and whispered ominously: "If you move even an inch, I will break the boy's legs."

What the hell is happening? Hong thought.

With a forceful heave, they were moving again.

April 6th, 1975
THREE HOURS NORTHWEST OF SAIGON
3:00 PM

There was little sense of time in the midst of the confusion. The captives had been traveling the road with the soldiers in silence for what felt like hours. Hong remembered their thickly-forested route being straight before the hood was placed over his eyes, but the driver had been making turn after bumpy turn in every direction, and it even felt as if they'd gone in a circle once or twice. Maybe they had.

The Jeep slowed until the brakes squeaked to a halt. Hong heard the engine shut down and sensed people exiting the vehicle, then he was forcefully removed from his seat. He stumbled under the coarse treatment but managed to stay on his feet. He wondered how Dzung was doing but didn't dare ask.

"March," a voice ordered as a rifle barrel poked into his back.

He shuffled forward towards who-knew-what.

They hadn't walked far when a damp and musty coolness enveloped his bruised body, as if they'd been led into a cave. A man's voice near him said, *"move, boy!"* and the sound echoed hollowly like they were now in some sort of tunnel. The floor was uneven and hard—like mottled concrete—and Hong's sandal-clad feet became wet walking through inch-deep puddles of stagnant water. His nostrils were attacked with the strong, mildewed smell of mold, mixed with stale urine and human waste.

Am I going to die?

"Move!" came a rude voice from behind him.

Nearby, he heard Dzung whimper. *Thank God.* His son was still alive.

"Dzung, do what they say!" Hong's voice resonated feebly in the closed space of wherever they were.

"Shut up!" came the angry retort, accompanied by a rifle butt to his back.

"urmph!"

Hong doubled over. With his hands bound in front of him, he had a hard time stopping his fall. He went down to the rutted floor on his face before his left shoulder rolled into a puddle, soaking his shirt. Gasping for air, hands grabbed his collar and belt and he was brought back to his feet, a rifle barrel shoved into his spine. The toes of his sandals tripped on the hard, uneven surface and he heard a metal door rasp open. Before he knew it, Hong was thrust to the floor again and received a painful kick to the abdomen, leaving him winded and coughing. A hand grasped hold of the base of his hood at the neck, but not before the swift blow he'd just received caused him to vomit what little was left of his breakfast on to the inside of it.

The canvas that covered his head was ripped off, drops of his regurgitated breakfast smearing across his right cheek, then thrown across a dimly-lit room. As Hong gulped to catch his breath, he held his stomach with his bound hands and took stock of his surroundings. He stood in a stark and craggy prison cell with only a small, high window to let in some light. A dirty, tan-clad young man who couldn't have been older than twenty stood over him holding the soiled hood and a weathered Kalashnikov. He stared irritably for a moment, then exited the cell, pulling the heavy door closed behind him. The slamming sound made a strange and deep reverberation through the dank facility. Whatever light it had been letting in was quickly extinguished, but the window left enough for Hong to see a deteriorated and mud-covered concrete floor surrounded by crumbling walls, and a high ceiling made of concrete and battered wooden beams.

Where am I? he thought. *Where is Dzung?*

He sat silently for a few moments assessing his situation and trying to think of a way to inconspicuously make contact with Dzung. Was he in a similar cell? Sounds emanated from what was probably a small hallway outside the door—footsteps walking by and the muffled sounds of men talking. He couldn't quite make out what was being said, but picked up a few words…*plantation…Jeep…bread…pig…Saigon…*

His index finger—still attached to a tightly-bound hand—gently fondled his face on the place he'd been rifle-butted when they were first captured. It throbbed slightly, but what blood still coated it had long since dried and become crusty.

How long will I be here? he wondered.

He resigned to the fact that it could be for a long time.

April 6th, 1975
THREE HOURS NORTHWEST OF SAIGON
7:00 PM

Fading light entered through Hong's cell window, and he'd spent the last several hours shifting uncomfortably from one buttock to another. He worried about Dzung and pondered escape. Even if he could, when his empty cell was discovered his boy would be as good as dead. Besides, the window letting in what little light was left in the sky was too high to reach, and probably too small to crawl through. His hands were still bound anyway, and no amount of rubbing on the rough concrete walls had worn the twine enough to break free.

Despite the fact that this was April in Vietnam, Hong's sandaled feet had become chilled in the still, musty air inside his cell. He shivered and prodded the lumps on his cheek and temple and noticed that his ribs hadn't forgotten their beating either. The swelling on his face had spread to his upper left eye socket, causing his puffy forehead to protrude below his eyebrow and limit his vision whenever he tried to look upward. He pulled his fingers away, revealing a mix of blood and yellowish seepage.

He stared at the small plate he'd been brought several hours before. There had been a small piece of a stale baguette and no water to drink, but he'd ferociously devoured it. Now his stomach had begun to grumble with hunger again. Outside his cell, Hong detected the quiet footfalls of men in sandals walking back and forth, contrasting sharply with loud but muffled voices uttering mostly unintelligible conversation.

The voices seemed to get closer to his cell door, and suddenly he heard a key inserted in to its lock. It swung open and two uniformed men advanced toward Hong and brought him to his feet by his armpit and waist belt. His pain was replaced by an adrenaline rush. The men dragged him out of the Spartan room and into a poorly lit and short, narrow hall. Doing his best to look past his engorged left brow, he could see light bulbs, some burned out, hanging from frayed wires affixed to exposed copper that ran along the high ceiling.

Hong was hustled into a windowless, barely-lit room and forced into a hard metal chair. He felt a pistol pressed against his right temple. As he stared at the blank wall across from him, a calm voice from behind began speaking.

"Your name is Nguyen."

Hong did not answer.

"What is your business here?"

Hong paused, considering his response. Rather than replying directly, he tried another tactic.

"Please tell me where my son is."

With no warning, he was pistol-whipped hard across his forehead, sending his head backward and bringing tears to his eyes.

"I asked you: what is your business, Mr. Nguyen?"

Hong huffed in pain and opened his eyes wide, blinking heavily to try and dissipate the involuntary tears. He could see, but the fogginess persisted, even after several frantic flutters of his eyelids.

He regained a small measure of composure and answered: "I have a rubber plantation to the west."

There was no response from his unseen attacker.

"Please," he said. *"Where is my son?"*

"Your son is safe," came the response. "Where did you come from?"

His heart pounded with a mixture of fear and rage, and he hesitated slightly.

"Saigon."

His response generated some garbled whispering from behind, and there was a long pause. Hong thought his heart would leap from his chest and into his throat, and a quick, steady pulse of blood pounded across his forehead.

"Can I please…" Hong began, breathing heavily, "…have a drink of water?"

A door slammed in the hall, followed by the sounds of a slight struggle behind him and in an instant, Dzung was shoved into the small room in front of his father. A soldier held him tightly by the upper arm, his hands were tied, and a pistol was pointed at the right side of his chest. There was dried blood on his forehead, but it didn't look like a severe injury.

"Ba!"

Dzung attempted to go to his father but was forced back into position by his handler.

"Stand still, boy!"

The man kneed Dzung in his lower gut and he bent over in pain, his hands automatically going to an area above his groin. He coughed and sputtered, trying to catch his breath and stay upright.

"Stop hurting my son!" Hong pleaded.

"SHUT UP!" came the reply from behind him, followed by a heavy-duty punch to the mouth from the dimness.

Hong's head jerked backward again.

"Ba!"

Hong felt blood filling the voids between his teeth. Then a pistol once again pressed into his right temple. He watched his son's face contort into a tear-laced dread.

"Did you say you owned a rubber plantation?"

"Yes," Hong answered, breathing short, and nervous breaths.

"Are you affiliated with Chinh Bùi?"

Hong knew the name well—Bùi was the de-facto mayor of the small village of Làng Bi, which was situated very close to the plantation, and over the many years of his ownership and operation of the property, the two had become acquainted.

"No, I do not know him," he said, doing his best to sound convincing.

He finally got a glimpse at the man who'd been standing behind him, and by the looks of the faded khaki-green uniform and blazing red insignia on his collar and shoulder boards, he was an enemy officer—and not just *any* officer. This man appeared to be a colonel. Hong was surprised. He and Dzung must have been a pretty meaty catch for a full colonel to be interrogating them.

"You are LYING to me!"

The officer punched Hong in his abdomen, eliciting a painful groan.

"BA!"

He doubled over in the chair, doing his best to control his diaphragm and get a breath. After a flurry of pounding spasms, he drew in deeply as if he'd been underwater for too long. He coughed violently and spat out a spray of blood-laced saliva and mucous that had accumulated from his damaged mouth and lips.

"We *KNOW* you know him!" his captor shouted. "Do you want to *die* today? Maybe I will just shoot your son while you *watch*."

The colonel unholstered a pistol and racked a fresh round into the chamber. The intimidating click and crack of the slide bounced off the stark cement walls and filled the small room. He darted towards Dzung and pointed the pistol at his head.

"...no!" Hong squeaked out with a horrible strain.

"Your friend Bùi is a *criminal!*" came the bawl from the enemy officer as his pistol shook with rage next to Dzung's temple. "He organized an attack on this compound and killed many of my men!"

Hong stared resentfully, his torso flexing visibly with each wounded breath.

"I will splatter your son's brains all over these walls! You were *involved,* weren't you, Nguyen."

"No! I know nothing!"

"I am taking your son," the colonel said as Dzung's handler jerked him from behind. "Perhaps he will be of use to the Viet Cong."

"No!" Hong cried. *"Please!"*

The colonel holstered his weapon. Upon snapping the leather cover closed, he moved himself back towards Hong, put his hands on his knees, and squatted nose-to-nose with him, barely an inch away.

"What will you do about it?"

The man must not have bathed in days. His rotten body odor was overpowering as he got closer to Hong, and his breath was a putrid amalgam of un-brushed teeth, stale cigarettes, and bad liquor.

"Are you scared?" he bullied under his breath. "Because you should be."

"Please!" Hong pleaded. "Take the bread and the pig."

There was no response from the enemy officer, just an icy, threatening stare.

"I was only going to feed my workers," Hong appealed. "You can take the food."

"We already have," the colonel responded before turning to a subordinate. "Go and find the boy some fatigues."

"NO!"

"Your boy belongs to *ME!*" the colonel roared.

Dzung's captor began to drag him out of the room.

"*Wait!* No!" Hong implored again. "I have money!"

With his eyes still transfixed on Hong, the colonel raised his hand to stop the soldier from shuffling Dzung out.

Money? That got their attention.

"It is under a floor board in the Jeep," Hong continued. "On the driver's side."

The colonel stared.

"Please do not hurt my son."

April 7th, 1975
THREE HOURS NORTHWEST OF SAIGON
11:30 PM

It was dark, and Hong figured at least a day had gone by since they'd left Saigon and were captured.

"Where are we, Ba?"

Hong's whole body ached. It had been quite an ordeal, but fortunately it had been brief. He had his son. Incredibly, he also had his Jeep—perhaps it carried little value to the enemy troops because of its nineteen-forties age and state of repair, which was dubious at best. Hong couldn't even remember the last time he'd changed its oil, and often times it struggled to turn over when the ignition was engaged. They had been lucky.

Very, very lucky.

He hoped he had enough gas to get somewhere—any-where—that was safe.

"I think I know."

The soldiers and their colonel must not have thought Hong and Dzung could provide them much except food and money, and they'd been released. Or maybe their real value was in re-turning to Saigon beaten and bruised to serve as a warning to others. Hong didn't know, and he didn't much care either. His laborers—if the enemy hadn't already seized his plantation and captured them—might be hungry, but his boy was safe and that was enough. Perhaps he didn't want to believe the stories about enemy encroachment were true, even though he'd discussed escape with Dzung—maybe that was why he tried to go to his plantation. Maybe it was some unconscious desire to make sure his livelihood was still intact amid the alarming rumors he'd heard. Only now did he realize it was a bad idea—Dat told him as much, but he'd insisted on going, and she'd refused to fight him.

It was hard for him not to castigate himself—he should have moved faster when they noticed the empty fields just before they were stopped, still hours away from his beloved rubber trees.

Idiot!

His son was nearly pressed into service by the Viet Cong. They could have been killed. He tried to portray an outward appearance of calm, which was made easier by the darkness.

The enemy had kept Hong and Dzung in their cells for hours, when suddenly they were hooded again and removed. They were eventually thrown into a vehicle, then driven in silence to a remote location in an area in a large, flat rice-producing region. Before abandoning them next to their Jeep, still bound and hooded, a soldier warned:

"If you come back, *we will kill you.*"

After the soldiers' engines died off, Hong waited for a short while and was able to cut his hands loose on a sharp edge he found on the Jeep's frame, then he freed his son. Once they could see, Hong didn't recognize where they were, but he wasn't willing to cause Dzung any more anxiety by telling them they might be lost. They survived and they'd find their way. The sun had long since set, but Hong used the dim light from the waning crescent moon to try and determine their location. He had a fairly good sense of direction and figured with rice paddies all around them, they were closer to Saigon than they were to the mountains. The regions to the north and west of the city had been producing the crop for centuries. He figured it was likely that's where they were, and if he could find a village or a road sign, he could find their way back.

They drove through the dark in silence, slowly traversing a succession of low dikes that separated each paddy from the other.

"Do you still hurt, Ba?" Dzung asked.

Hearing his son's stifled emotion, Hong glanced briefly at him and placed his right hand tenderly on his shoulder.

"It is OK, Dzung."

That's when the dam broke. Dzung couldn't hold his tears back anymore and the boy wailed into the darkness. It cut his father to the bone. Hong's eyes began to well with tears and it was all he could do to keep his own composure, much less try to comfort his son. He blamed himself.

"We are OK."

Hong turned to look at his son in the dark, then took his right hand off the wheel and placed it on Dzung's shoulder.

"Hey," he said, rubbing the boy's back and neck. "We are going home."

The traumatic and life-threatening nightmare they'd just been through would not be something either of them would soon forget. He'd told Dzung he didn't think it was time to leave Vietnam, but this horrific experience had him seriously wondering whether that was really true.

"We are going home," he said again.

How could he keep his family safe and still salvage his lucrative rubber production, which had supported his family for years, with the knowledge that South Vietnam might be facing a real communist takeover? If they stayed, would it ever be safe again? How would their relationship with Chau—a southern military officer—figure into it all?

As his son cried in the passenger's seat, Hong felt both physical and emotional agony. His cheek throbbed where it had been hit by the rifle butt, his lip was swollen, and there were sharp pains across multiple places on his ribcage and lower back. If they left the country, his family might be safer, but it would be the end of his business. Wherever they landed, he'd have to find a new means of providing a life for the people he loved. If they stayed, they might survive, but he knew their freedoms would be supremely curtailed and it *still* might spell the end of the rubber operation…or worse.

His mind raced. Dat would be alarmed when they arrived home. Would she panic? Would their American tenants next door be able to provide any information? Or would they be leaving, too? Then there was always Chau. Would he decide to leave with Mai for the sake of his grandchildren?

Hong tried to stop thinking about it. At least for now. He turned to his son.

"Hey," he said. "Dzung."

His only response was a hushed sob.

"Do you think your mother will like what I have done with my face?"

3

"Helipads?"

"Yeah, thirteen of'em," Frailey answered, his voice crackling over the static-filled line on the KY-3.

Chuck Sterrett hadn't heard a lot from any senior intelligence officials at the US Embassy compound over the last few days, and despite the recent plane crash that killed almost a hundred Vietnamese children, air traffic at Tan Son Nhut didn't seem to be letting up much. The activity of Air Force C-141 cargo jets, C-130s, and a sizable number of commercial planes was getting more and more frequent. The only thing he and his officemates hadn't noticed was the whiny buzzing of C-5s—following the Babylift crash, the fleet was grounded for the launch of an investigation, which would greatly affect any ongoing evacuation activities.

"A bunch of civilian guys from the States were here and they looked at thirty-seven buildings around town to see what might be able to handle helo landings if the base goes down and the only way we can evacuate is rotary," Frailey went on. "Hueys, CH-53s, CH-46s maybe. They picked thirteen of the best ones and are in the process of painting giant 'H's' on 'em."

"Sounds like they're putting a lot of thought into this," Chuck said. "I thought Martin wasn't interested in any talk of full evacuation?"

"Well, he's not," Frailey answered, "but I think even Graham Martin knows he needs to be prepared for the worst, as long as it can be kept inconspicuous. He doesn't want to make it look like we're bailing. The helo LZs are a 'just-in-case' measure."

"Maybe *prudent* is the word you're looking for," Chuck said acerbically, knowing 'prudent' was the word Martin had used to justify the ongoing non-essential evacuation. "He just needs to order the evac and be done with it."

"Don't hold your breath. I only hope if he decides to do it, we're not escaping and evading by then."

"The other dets know about this?"

"Yup."

The blue smoke of Jesse Flounders' newest cigarette caused him to sneeze. Chuck could tell both of his agents were listening.

"Bob, how in the hell do we maintain the impression that we're sticking by the South Vietnamese government when we're evacuating babies and painting H's on rooftops?"

"Hell if I know," Frailey answered. "I agree with you that it's a bit of a cluster."

Chuck wondered if it was possible for his cynicism to grow any larger than it already was.

"Know what I think?" he asked. "I think Graham Martin is doing what's prudent for Graham Martin. He needs to feel like the State Department sees him being judicious. But I don't think he really believes we're gonna have to leave."

Dead silence on the other end.

"Bob?"

"Yes?"

"What's the real story here? Gimme more about this 'Plan Alamo' thing I'm hearing chatter about."

Frailey was again silent.

"American citizens that live here can go home if they want, and Martin is trying to enable them to do that," Frailey answered, skating obviously around Plan Alamo. "If they work for the US Government or its contractors and are considered non-essential, or if they're family members of government workers, they're authorized to go home. Essential people like some of us have to stay here for now."

It sounded to Chuck like a rehearsed talking point.

"Chuck, you're essential but you're authorized to get your family out of here," his boss continued. "Have you thought about it?"

"Yes."

"Are you gonna do it?"

"Well, I'm leaving it up to them, at least for now, and for the moment they're staying. But to be frank, I can't really tell them everything there is to know, can I? If I could, they might think differently."

It was a frustrated barb at his boss.

"I think I see the handwriting on the wall, Bob, don't you?"

"Graham Martin has confidence the South Vietnamese armed forces will protect their homeland, don't *you*?" Bob Frailey said in equally cutting tones.

"Are you kidding? Come on."

If not for Frailey's mild acrimony, it would have been hard for Chuck to believe his boss would spout such crap about the South Vietnamese Army, which was well-known to be poorly supplied and suffering major morale problems.

"I know you see what's happening here, and you've been around a whole lot longer than I have. ARVN soldiers left Hue and Da Nang in boxers and tank top undershirts so they wouldn't be seen in uniform by the bad guys, and our government hasn't exactly been providing the military aid to help them keep the north up north."

Bob Frailey was a well-seasoned agent and military veteran, and Chuck knew he wasn't usually one to toe the party line if he thought the party was dead wrong. He was more than certain there was something his boss wasn't letting on. The present conversation only made it more evident.

"And what about these high-risk South Vietnamese guys?" Chuck asked point blank. "We're not doing much of anything to help them leave, and if the commies were ever to get a hold of them, they'd never be heard from again. These are our allies, Bob. Friends that you and I both know and have worked with. Don't we give a shit about them?"

"The high-risk guys are expected to stay here and defend their country, Chuck," Frailey entailed. "If we were to enable them to leave, we'd be encouraging violation of South Vietnamese law. It's desertion. You think Martin would agree to be a part of that?"

"I don't know."

"Yes, you do," Frailey responded. "And as for us, for right now we are here and going nowhere."

"You really think that's what Martin's got planned for them? Nothing? He's not even quietly posturing! No list of names if we had to act quickly to get the important ones out of town. Damn the law!"

"All I can tell you, Chuck, is that Graham Martin is quietly planning for the worst but hoping for the best."

"Well that's a little vague."

"I get your frustration, but you need to be careful."

"Right. Let's hope he does the right thing if it starts getting bad…and I don't feel real good about any of this."

Bob Frailey paused again.

"I know. Me neither."

April 8th, 1975
LE QUY DON SCHOOL, SAIGON
8:38 AM

Tuan Nguyen shifted uncomfortably in the chair of his wooden two-student desk at the Le Quy Don School in downtown Saigon. His father and Dzung weighed heavy on his mind—they'd come home in the wee hours that morning with their faces bloodied and bruised. His mother's panicked reaction when they arrived had awoken the whole house. What happened to them? Initially frantic, his mother—strangely—acted like nothing was amiss when Tuan got up to get ready for school. He'd asked several times what had happened and didn't get an answer until his father became annoyed and said, 'we just got into a small accident in the Jeep.' Tuan wasn't sure he believed it.

When he snuck outside to look at the vehicle, he found it undamaged, save for the same wear and tear that had been present before. Dzung wouldn't tell him anything either, which was highly unusual. He wasn't sure what it all meant, but he knew whatever it was had really scared his brother...and Dzung didn't scare easy.

But right now, that wasn't the problem. Today was test day, and it was the biggest one of the year.

Son and Dzung had already completed their courses of study ahead of the summer break, and Tuan was the last to finish. He hated tests, and even though school was a place he could always come to see his friends, he wasn't big on getting up every morning to attend class. All he wanted to do was go home so he could stir up trouble with his brothers, and the only thing that stood between him and lighting firecrackers in the courtyard of their house was his test. He should have been focusing on the paper in front of him, but he couldn't stop daydreaming as he stared at the well-worn gouges and chipped ink well holes in each corner of the ancient wooden desks. Tuan's nine-year old brain was sure that the classroom's furniture must have been as old as the school itself, which had been built under French Imperial rule a hundred years before.

Despite a decent breakfast, his stomach was already growling, and his rear end throbbed on the dark, hardwood surface of his seat. In another attempt to shift around and get his hind quarters comfortable as he struggled to focus on his test, he bumped elbows with his desk mate—a boy named Hanh who was the biggest kid in the class. He was a tall and husky bully who had thin, beady eyes that barely shone through his facial fat rolls. He shot Tuan an ominous look threatening physical pain if he didn't stop shaking the seat they shared. It wasn't unusual for Hanh to pick on the smaller students in the class, and Tuan was the smallest of them all. Why did the teacher put them together at this desk? Summer couldn't come fast enough.

Thirty minutes earlier, his teacher Mrs. Linh Nhu, an authoritarian and curt woman in her thirties, handed out the final examination of their year, giving them strict instructions to complete it within the allotted hour-and-a-half time limit. Her tall and thin frame, half-moon glasses, and salt-and-pepper bun exemplified the stereotypical dictatorial teacher, despite her fairly young age. Mrs. Nhu made it clear that a failure to pass her final test could result in a repeat of the entire year's coursework, or at least being forced to attend summer school. Tuan was no dummy, and after she tried to scare the children into compliance the first day of school, he grew numb to her. As a result, his mind often drifted.

Through the long, thin holes of the slats high up the classroom's outer wall, he could see the narrow leaves of a nearby takian tree against the blue morning sky, rippling in the light breeze. The high 15-foot ceiling of the somewhat austere, whitewashed classroom dwarfed the students below, whose uniforms consisted of white shirts and black shorts or skirts, accented by faux-leather sandals on their tanned feet. Each student's tan canvas satchel sat at the foot of their desks, most of them a worn, russet color. A wide black chalkboard stood sentry at the front of the room under the cracked plaster walls. Above their heads swung bare bulbs, casting faint shadows on the desks in the slow-moving air.

Located at in the former "European Quarter" of Saigon, the Le Quy Don school was built in the 1870s at a hectic intersection adjacent to the South Vietnamese president's home at Independence Palace. It was smack in the middle of one of the busiest sections of the city, and the incessant commotion of crossing guard whistles, traffic, and the mundane chatter of city life permeated the fabric of Tuan's classroom beyond his capacity to ignore it.

A tropical breeze lazily traversed the cavernous space as the open door that served as a gateway into the building's tree-lined courtyard provided a thoroughfare for the moving air, gently lifting the corners of everyone's test papers in the process. Students found themselves holding them down in order to write. Tuan brought his focus back to the long legal-length sheet in front of him. In the Saigon school district, end-of-year assessments consisted of everything from math problems to vocabulary, and like many of his fourth grade classmates, he found sitting still for a full ninety minutes difficult. But Tuan knew discipline was expected in Southeast Asian society, and he wasn't ready to face punishment from his father.

He completed an addition problem and began moving on to the next, but not before looking up at Mrs. Nhu, who stood with her arms crossed, dutifully gazing over the class while standing between her clunky, honey-colored desk and the chalkboard. Towards the front of the class, Tuan could see the rear profile of a girl named Thao—the most beautiful female student in the class, in his opinion—and though he'd deny it to his brothers, he always got a weird fluttery feeling in the pit of his stomach every time she looked at him.

He forced himself to look down and get back to the test. As he dove into a list of words to match with their definitions, he paused for a moment.

What was that sound?

His eyes left the paper again and his senses detected something that felt out of place. It was a strange whisper that could be detected over the commotion outside—almost like white noise. Was he hearing things? If not, this wasn't something he'd been used to hearing at school. A quick look around didn't reveal anything amiss, so he slowly and cautiously refocused on his list of words.

But the funny sound persisted.

Noise on the street seemed a little quieter, too, as if people who were deep in conversation or engulfed in the bustle were suddenly distracted by something else. The peculiar whisper became slightly louder and almost hollow-sounding… like the sound of a seashell held over the ear at the beach. Tuan raised his head and watched Mrs. Nhu, who appeared to be hearing it, too. She walked towards the open door leading into the quiet courtyard, the noise growing in intensity. Her hands absent-mindedly moved to her hips as she looked outside. There was no denying it. The odd sound was there, and it seemed to be getting louder.

Tuan took his eyes from the teacher and noticed nobody was paying attention to their tests. Everyone heard the growing crescendo, which was quickly becoming thunderous. Mrs. Nhu moved under the overhang outside the door, just within his view. Sunlight gleamed from above and she began looking up, raising a hand to shield her eyes. Tuan turned toward Hanh, his oversized desk mate, who was looking towards the high slats in the walls before he looked back at him. A confused look crossed his face as if to say to Tuan, 'what *is* that?' It was an unusual sight to see Hanh's face painted with a concerned look and not a threatening one.

As the sound began to overcome the ambient noise of the street and classroom, there was sudden activity outside the door, punctuated by the tones of several teachers talking more frantically.

It was an aircraft—Tuan knew it now.

Living close to the air base, he knew what they sounded like, but he'd never heard anything like it while he was at school. He looked for Thao in the front of the room, but her seat was empty. Along with several other students, she was now standing in beside her desk, her eyes darting towards the teacher.

Then within a split second, the noise went from quizzical and bearable to nearly deafening...and what happened in the next second was like a slow-motion nightmare.

Mrs. Nhu whirled around and ran back inside, bellowing, "*DOWN!*" as the earsplitting sound of a jet fighter passed low overhead with lightning speed. Students dove for the floor as a chest-rattling vibration ripped through the formerly serene classroom. Hanh's large frame rolled like a giant panda bear under the comparatively tiny desk, his mouth screaming something that Tuan couldn't hear above the earsplitting clamor. Tuan held his breath as dust and bits of plaster fell from the ceiling, the smaller grains peppering his and his classmates' black shorts like baby powder. It penetrated Hanh's hair and eyebrows, instantly aging him fifty years and reminding Tuan of his grandfather. Every one of his muscles tightened underneath his skin, and his mind conjured up the sensation of his mother's arms tightly enveloping him.

Oh, how he wanted to be home.

The floor shook with a low rumble for what felt like an eternity, as if a hundred heavy trucks were driving past. The thunderous, screeching roar of the engines produced a painful ringing in Tuan's ears. He felt disoriented as the jet peeled past the school. Tuan forced his eyes open as the cries of his fellow students now reached his eardrums. He saw the familiar faces of his friends, who only moments ago were filled with the hope of childhood fun, now twisted with terror. With children huddled together looking left and right, Tuan surveyed the scene, relieved to be sheltered under the desk, even if it was next to Hanh.

Chalky dust filled his nose. Then, amidst the terrific confusion, a sudden bright flash lit the school as a massive explosion ripped the wall slats from their moorings, littering the room and its inhabitants with flying bits of plaster and wood.

April 8th, 1975
CIA OFFICES AT NGUYEN HOME
8:40 AM

"What the hell!"

Chuck Sterrett and his CIA agents jumped from their seats, startled at the sound of the unexpected boom. The jet that released its munitions on Independence Palace was not assigned to northern communist forces—it belonged to the South Vietnamese Air Force. That much was clear after Chuck and his agents received a call from one of their local contacts at about 8:30 a.m. A fighter out of Bien Hoa Air Base to the northeast had deviated from its course right after takeoff.

Human intelligence was always a tricky business because it counted on relationships with local people who often held split loyalties. Chuck's 'HUMINT' informant at Bien Hoa was an early-20's South Vietnamese airman that worked at Base Operations. When he called Chuck, he was trying to keep his nervousness in check (presumably so it wasn't too obvious that he was passing on potentially sensitive information), but it was obvious the guy was a little agitated.

It wasn't a huge secret that there was fighting to the far north, and Chuck and his agents were aware of the recent uptick in fighter activity out of Bien Hoa and Tan Son Nhut, who'd been launching missions to stave the communist tide. Hearing fighters overhead from time to time, especially recently, wasn't necessarily out of the ordinary. But fighter activity directly over Saigon with accompanying explosions was highly unusual.

Bien Hoa told Chuck that three fully-armed, American-made F-5E fighters piloted by South Vietnamese airmen had just taken off, but one had unexpectedly taken a different route than its formation immediately after leaving the ground. Red flags had instantly gone up in Chuck's mind. Could it be another defection? Intel channels had been acknowledging there'd been large numbers from the South Vietnamese military who'd been scared into going over to the other side...but today's activity had apparently become an unanticipated bombing in the city.

While official news sources in South Vietnam were communicating mundane bulletins as if nothing was amiss, the Embassy's intelligence apparatus had been transmitting that the ARVN had been on the ropes ever since Da Nang fell. In the last couple days, Chuck and his agents learned that in some areas to the north of Saigon, leaflets had even been circulated by northern forces with all sorts of messages. Consisting of anything from "surrender or we'll kill your family" to "come join us, brothers," military personnel and citizens across the South were getting antsy, and now it appeared the potential for a major problem had become all too real.

The young enlisted airman at Bien Hoa told Chuck that a south Vietnamese lieutenant named Nguyen Thanh Trung had taxied his F-5 to the end of the runway to take off as part of a 'three-ship.' Chuck immediately thought about the surname 'Nguyen,' which in Vietnam was as common as 'Smith' was in the United States—the same last name as Hong's family, whom he rented his residence from. The triple-aircraft formation's official mission was to attack communist positions some distance to the northeast. In order to carry it out, each was equipped with four 250-pound bombs hung under each of their short, razor-thin wings. As they moved into takeoff position, Lieutenant Nguyen reported an afterburner problem, and momentarily delayed his departure. His two counterparts were ordered to proceed on their mission without him, but after the second pilot was airborne, Nguyen unexpectedly moved into launch position and followed with an unannounced departure. He tore into the sky and quickly diverted from the planned northerly route where he should have joined his formation.

The blast that happened only blocks from Chuck and his agents wasn't enough to rattle the windows of their offices, but it definitely got their attention.

His desk phone rang.

"Sterrett!" Chuck answered.

"He may not be finished!" a voice called on the other end.

It was Chuck's contact at Bien Hoa.

"What do you mean?"

"We think he still has bombs!" the airman answered, panicked.

Chuck's thoughts turned to Da Nang and the enemy activity moving in their direction. But it was all still so far north — hours in a Jeep. Most intel reporting had expressed alarm about enemy movement and the disregard of the Paris Peace Accords, which was condemned by President Ford, but there hadn't been warnings about any sort of direct danger to Saigon yet.

" . . . and he is over the sea!"

His gut was tugging at him again, just like that night with his brother in the Silver Run Tunnel.

April 8th, 1975
LE QUY DON SCHOOL, SAIGON
8:40 AM

The classroom erupted into chaos. Tuan's ears rang as the air surrounding him filled with shouts and screams from students and teachers alike. The floor tile was covered in bits of plaster that had been shaken loose from the ceiling in the blast. He noticed that the building had shuddered so much that all the desks had moved, their feet tracing short paths through the dust that had landed on the floor. As he looked around and brushed the bits of debris from his face, he looked for Thao, finding her under her desk crying. Her tears had traced lines through the powder on her cheeks.

Tuan was shaken from his confused state by Hanh, who grabbed the collar of his white shirt, forcefully shaking him, bawling, *"Get out of here!"*

The bully's face was a bizarre mix of terror and anger as he quickly got to his feet, pulling Tuan with him through the atmosphere of tumult, confusion, and fear. Their class-mates were quickly making a disorganized beeline towards the door to the courtyard, and the air was filled with the slowly decreasing echo of the bomb's thunder, street noises, and alarmed human voices as dust continued to fall from the ceiling. The overhead lights swung as Hanh dragged Tuan towards the door.

"Come on!" he shouted.

Students pushed and shoved in the panicked rush. Hanh and Tuan squeezed into the frightened crowd, slowly trying to make their way onto the sidewalk outside and into the courtyard. As they emerged from the packed doorway, three terrified students behind them knocked the two boys to the gravelly concrete, causing Tuan to scrape both of his elbows. Hanh quickly pulled him to his feet and drew him into a grassy area where Tuan lost a sandal. Bedlam took over as teachers and school staff lost all control in their attempts to herd the hundreds of kids into manageable groups.

The sun shone brightly into the increasingly dusty center of the facility, which was covered in lush green grass, palms, and concrete with tropical shrubbery in the center. In the middle of the area was a worn statue of the school's namesake, Le Quy Don—an 18th century Vietnamese philosopher—his stone face, a stark contrast to the disorder gushing from the classrooms. The uproar continued as students ran in every direction, including towards the tall main iron gate, which a quick-thinking staff member had closed to avoid a flight of children into the harried and potentially dangerous street.

Hanh had let go of Tuan's collar and ran off, while the shocked fourth grader tried to make sense of what was happening around him. In the din, teary-eyed and sandal-less girls cried and embraced tightly, bright white school papers floated on the grimy breeze, and teachers called to each other in an attempt to gain control of the situation. Grit and the steely aroma of fireworks filled Tuan's nostrils like when he was knocked to the ground a second time by another rattled student. This time he landed on his shoulder, grass-staining the white shirt his mother had hung clean on the clothesline just the day prior. He quickly scooted out of the way to avoid being trampled, got to his feet, and made his way toward a group of students gathered near the center statue. There was Thao.

"What is happening, Tuan?" she shouted in a barely-controlled tone as he approached.

All Tuan could do was worriedly stare back at her. In the brutal confusion of the school courtyard, Tuan felt his first sense of fear that he was, at least for the moment, totally on his own.

April 8th, 1975
CIA OFFICES AT NGUYEN HOME
8:41 AM

"Dammit!" Chuck muttered, as he hung up the avocado-green rotary phone.

"What the hell was that about?" Rusty McClay asked.

Chuck's spooked agents stared at their boss.

"Looks like we may have another defection, but this guy might have tried to take a few of his countrymen with him."

The agents absorbed his words and the explosion that had just reverberated through the room.

"We've got a Lieutenant Nguyen from the VNAF who just hijacked an armed F-5. I think what we just heard was caused by something that came off his wing."

There was a pregnant pause as he allowed his agents to let it sink in, while he tried to figure out what to do next.

"OK, I need each of you on the phone NOW. Engage every contact you've got. Supposedly this guy is over the ocean and I want to know *exactly* where and what his heading is."

Years of service leading agents in the CIA had turned Chuck Sterrett into a master delegator. He had also established himself as a guy who handled himself well under pressure. His agents in the small detachment loved and respected him because he instinctively knew what to do when a tenuous situation demanded it. Best of all, when he was off-duty, he knew how to throw back a few 33's, the ubiquitous South Vietnamese lager, and enjoy life.

"I want to know everything about Nguyen Thanh Trung. Where does he live? Who's his family? How long has he served in uniform? I'll get on with the Embassy and see what I can dig up."

"OK, boss," Rusty responded with a cooler demeanor as he picked up his phone's handset from its cradle.

Chuck noticed his loose, white button-up tropical shirt was showing some growing perspiration rings under his arms. The sticky, tropical Saigon humidity poured in through the half-open windows and condensed on the walls, which were dotted with specks of black mold. The room was filled with a steaminess that was intensified by the smoke from Jesse's Camels, and its blue haze mixed with the staid, muggy air. But for the large fan in the corner that Rusty brought in the day before, it would have been smoggier than Los Angeles during an afternoon commute.

Chuck could see the distress on Jesse's face. As the agent kicked into action, it was obvious he was trying to hide his anxiety. Chuck knew Jesse had heard plenty of explosions in his day, had lost friends to many of them, and he couldn't help but wonder exactly where the man's mind was at this particular moment. He'd told Chuck once that being shelled, which was probably a lot like being bombed, was one of the worst things someone could endure in war, because nobody ever knew where a round would land.

Chuck moved quickly to the KY-3. Inputting the Embassy's number on the rotary dial was fairly painful, as the numbers for the US Government's local switch network seemed to always have a lot of 9s in them. He felt like he called the CIA offices at least five times a day and had Bob Frailey's extension memorized, cranking out the digits as fast as he could using the thin metal finger wheel. On the other end, Bob Frailey finally picked up.

"Bob, it's Chuck."

"Lots of stuff going on Chuck, hope you have something for me," Frailey responded, sounding a little stressed. "You ready to go secure?"

"Initiating now," Chuck replied.

The standard long pause followed as the cryptologic innards of the phone did their work.

"I'm showing you secure on my end, Bob."

"OK, you're lit up secure here too," Frailey replied, his voice warbling on the other end. "Tell me what you know."

"We think it was a South Vietnamese pilot named Nguyen Thanh Trung," Chuck explained. "I've got a source at Bien Hoa who called me just after he took off. He was supposed to be on a bombing run with a three-ship to the north but broke off and aimed for downtown. It sounds like he may be somewhere over the South China Sea right now and indications are that he had several munitions, but we only heard one detonation out here. What did he hit, Bob?"

"He tried to hit the Presidential Palace."

"Holy shit."

"We think he only released two bombs," Frailey went on, "one didn't explode and the other landed in a grassy area and didn't damage anything."

Chuck felt a momentary relief.

"What about you guys?" he asked. "Everything OK? You're real close to the palace."

"Yeah, we're all fine," his boss responded, "but that's not all."

There was a short pause before Frailey went on.

"The radar station at Tan Son Nhut has been tracking him for the last few minutes. He's headed back and may be lining up for another run."

"Are you guys evacuating the building?"

"Not yet."

Chuck began doing logic problems in his head.

"If he only released two of his bombs ..." Chuck said carefully, deep in thought. "An F-5 carries four, so that means ..."

" ...he's got two more targets," Frailey finished.

"Bob ...what the hell is he gonna hit next? You guys need to get the hell out of there!"

April 8th, 1975
LE QUY DON SCHOOL, SAIGON
9:05 AM

Tuan had only been at the statue with Thao and her friends for a few minutes. She was terrified but had stopped crying. Despite his fear and uncertainty, Tuan momentarily forgot about it all when Thao grabbed his hand. The uneasiness of their predicament was briefly replaced by a curious romantic thrill that traveled up his spine like a white-hot bolt of electricity.

"I do not know what has happened," Tuan had said to her with a faux bravado, "but it will be OK."

Thao stared back with a confused look. Teachers and staff were wearing thin masks of self-assurance and had found limited success calming the crowd of students enough to bring things under control.

On the gated end of the courtyard, the school's headmaster, Dr. Dac Kien Anh, spoke through a battery-powered bullhorn.

"May I have your attention please!" he spoke into the microphone.

A few heads turned, but many were still crying. The clamor of alarmed voices remained at a fever pitch.

"Students!" he continued.

He pressed a button several times which blared a piercing tone to quiet the masses. It worked somewhat, but what persisted mixed with the clamor that continued on the street, intermittently overpowering his small device. He hit the button again and held it for about five seconds. Students close to him plugged their ears to block the shrill sound.

"Attention, students!"

Teachers who had been desperately trying to manage their classes began to shush, doing their best to silence the noise, and the din probably quieted as much as it was going to.

"We do not know what is going on outside the school, but it appears there has been some sort of explosion nearby," Dr. Anh continued, barely hiding the shakiness in his voice. "It is very important that you listen to your teachers! Each of you must assemble with your class outside the doors of your classrooms so we can get a head count!"

Out on the street, motor scooters buzzed by like mad wasps, car horns blared every few seconds, and sirens of emergency vehicles began to sound.

"Gather with your teachers and await further instructions! We will provide more information shortly."

Tuan and Thao looked at each other with relief, thankful for the momentary halt to the anarchy. Someone had finally brought about some relative calm, and the situation seemed to be settling down, even if it was still fragile. Tuan looked toward his classroom door and found Mrs. Nhu standing there calling out to a small number of her students as they trickled over to her. He couldn't hear her but could tell by her movements that she was attempting to line those that had returned up against the wall.

Tuan was barely aware that he was still holding Thao's hand. Without saying a word to her, he led in the direction of Mrs. Nhu. Children walked quickly in every direction, no longer running, but moving with a purpose. He suddenly remembered his skinned elbows and looked down at his right arm. There was a trail of sticky red blood and he was suddenly cognizant of the annoying pain. He didn't want it to happen again, so he picked his way carefully through the throng.

"Hold on to me, Thao," he said, barely audible enough for her to hear.

Tuan began to lead Thao through the swarm of young humans, but before he could get very far, the hollow sound of jet fighter engines began to fill the courtyard again. Before anyone could react, a jet roared overhead out of nowhere for the second time, causing enough rolling vibration to shake the leaves on the trees in the courtyard. Frightened students and staff scattered for cover, and the open space was thrown into pandemonium. In the confusion, Tuan lost hold of Thao's hand.

He swung his head in every direction looking for her.
"*Thao!*"

She was nowhere to be found. He ran for Mrs. Nhu. Before

the deafening sound stopped, two more deafening explosions shook Tuan's world.

April 8th, 1975
CIA OFFICES AT NGUYEN HOME
9:05 AM

"Sonofabitch!"

Items on Chuck's desk vibrated as the house shook with two perceptible shudders, reminding him of a small earthquake he once experienced on assignment in California years before.

"Let's hope that wasn't the embassy," Rusty commented.

The sounds of distant sirens could still be heard from somewhere downtown through the open window slats, but it was difficult to discern the direction they came from.

"Hard to tell," Chuck said, listening to the outside noises for something more.

He looked back at his agents.

"Keep looking for info."

As his agents went back to their phones and notepads, Chuck dialed his young HUMINT contact at Bien Hoa. The line hissed, then began to ring in the distinctive tone of the Southeast Asian phone system, which was very different than the States. There was a click and a Vietnamese airman answered in his native language. Being married to a Vietnamese girl and living with her family had helped Chuck become somewhat conversational. He was nowhere near fluent, but he knew enough to understand the basics.

"Bồ hành sự!"

'Base Operations.'

The young man sounded a bit frantic, but alert and in control.

"It's Chuck," he said. "Do you have anything new? We need to know as much as possible about the pilot! I've got his name, but nothing else."

"Minute..." the kid said in heavily-accented English.

Chuck got put on hold for what felt like ten minutes but was probably only about fifteen seconds before the line went live again.

"We think Lieutenant Nguyen is traitor," the kid explained quietly, as if to avoid letting anyone know he was talking about something he wasn't supposed to.

"OK."

"We not know, but a pilot said Nguyen's father was killed by Saigon police," he went on. "He very angry about that. He said he retaliate."

Chuck soaked it in.

"How long has he served?"

"Eight years."

"Do we know where he is?"

Chuck's agents could be heard in the background having conversations of their own and he plugged his ear with his little finger to hear over them through his receiver.

"He fly northeast but we do not know where he go. There is fuel site he might go to, but we not know."

"Fuel site?!"

"I not know anything else. I sorry."

"OK, I'll call you later," Chuck responded then hung up.

"He's going where?" Rusty was saying over the phone in the background. "A petro site?"

Chuck immediately perked up his ears.

"What?" Chuck said, hoping Rusty would answer, even though he was rapaciously writing down some notes.

It sounded as if Chuck's source was being corroborated. Rusty completed the note he was on, then raised his hand towards Chuck without looking, extending his index finger as if to say, 'hold on a second.'

The KY-3 phone began to buzz annoyingly in the background, mixing with the noise from outside and adding to the cacophony in the room. He felt like they were in a bizarre and chaotic limbo, balancing the noises of what had to be utter chaos downtown, and the sound of Rusty's voice talking on the phone. Jesse dropped his cheap, black and silver Skilcraft pen and made for the KY-3's handset while Rusty wrapped his call. Chuck was fixed on 'petro.'

"OK, thanks," Rusty said before hanging up.

As he finished his note, Chuck interrupted as the secure phone continued to rattle.

"What did they say?"

"Looks like he might be headed for a small petroleum storage facility way up north, Chuck," Rusty responded. "Just a guess — it's far, but that's the direction he's going and there's an austere landing strip."

"I heard the same thing. What in the hell is he gonna do there?"

Rusty shrugged as Jesse answered the phone.

"Flounders!" Jesse yelled into the receiver. "Yup, going secure."

There was a long pause as the unit was switched into secure mode.

"Yup, gotcha secure on this end. Standby one."

There was a brief pause as Jesse covered the mouthpiece.

"Chuck!" he stated matter-of-factly, "I got Frailey on the line here."

"They didn't evac?" Chuck asked as he moved over towards Jesse's KY-3.

"Bob," Chuck said, "why the hell are you guys still in the building?!"

"The decision was to shelter in place," Frailey responded in a frustrated tone. "Word was we'd never get everyone out in time, and we could be in more danger out in the courtyard anyway."

"Well, what the hell? Did the RSO make that call?"

"Doesn't matter, we're OK."

"Well," Chuck said, "it is definitely a defection. We think he's headed towards some sort of fuel farm to the northeast."

"We know."

"Evidently his daddy was shot up by some Saigon cops a bunch of years ago, and he's been pissed about it ever since," Chuck explained. "Told one of his buddies he was gonna take some kind of revenge. This must be it."

There was a pause.

"Damn," was Frailey's only reply.

"I know."

The line popped and clicked as Bob Frailey took it in.

"Bob—what do you know?"

Frailey sighed.

"Well, we're thinking this might have been planned for a while."

"Why's that?"

"Didn't know about his dad, but one of our listening sites to the north just picked up an NVA radio signal that was congratulatory. Called the pilot 'a brother.'"

"A *brother*?"

"A *comrade*, Chuck," Frailey continued, "and it sounds like he has been since about '69."

"What did he hit downtown?"

"He took another shot at the palace. No news on casualties. Can't guess what he's gonna be doing at the fuel site if that's where he's going, but if this was planned, he's probably meeting his commie buddies there," Frailey continued. "Or maybe he's headed farther north.

"That was my thought."

"Are there any good guys up there, Bob?" Chuck asked, the wheels in his mind turning.

"Yeah, they're close," Frailey answered with a sigh, "but I doubt they'd be able to get there fast enough to do anything."

The South Vietnamese army hadn't been putting up any real fights in recent days and weeks anyway. What would they do even if they *could* get there?

"Keep your ears on, Chuck. Call me if you get something new."

April 8th, 1975
LE QUY DON SCHOOL, SAIGON
2:30 PM

Over the last several hours things had calmed for Tuan, who's normal school day had become shockingly disorganized. What began as a dreaded final exam had turned to the shrill sound of fighter jets, several explosions, and complete bedlam at his school. Teachers and staff had not allowed their students to return to the classrooms, instead seating them along the inner walls of the courtyard with their classmates. If it hadn't been for Thao and several of her friends sitting next to him, Tuan might actually have been bored. He sat near her with his sandals off, silently soaking in the scene around him. The street remained noisy, and whatever was going on outside the school's walls had abated somewhat, at least for the moment. Thao, who also seemed to have forgotten the utter terror from earlier that morning, was ignoring Tuan and talking with her friends.

It wasn't clear what had happened, but it was quite obvious something monumental had taken place. Growing up in Saigon, Tuan had always been conscious of the war that was taking place in his country, but until now it hadn't come home to him—at least since Tet in sixty-eight, which he didn't remember. He'd heard frightening snippets of his father's stories about driving to the rubber plantation, but Saigon had always seemed relatively safe.

Palms rustled as a warm breeze swirled through the open piazza. It was actually a little peaceful, which was a strange contrast to the sandbag nests that had been put into position near the yellow and red South Vietnamese flag hoisted on the flat roof of the school. Tuan could hear clinks and rattles from the long belts of machine gun ammunition as a large platoon of soldiers settled into several strong points on top of the building with all manner of weapons and rifles. The weird sounds were only partially muffled by the sandbags that made up the gun emplacements, and it created an odd discordance that mixed uneasily with street noise.

Horns blared, and scooters buzzed by unseen outside, and but for the activity on the roof, it seemed things were returning to some semblance of stability. Some of his classmates might have felt a little safer with armed soldiers above them, but all Tuan wanted to do was go home.

His stomach rumbled and he thought it would be nice to get some food. With his hunger growing, he noted that students were slowly trickling out of the tightly-controlled gate, flanked by soldiers with M-16 assault rifles, as families began to take them home. When the gate closed, it made a steely *'shok'* sound as the men secured the bolt just under the handles. He turned to Mrs. Nhu, who stood at the door to the classroom. Her hands rested authoritatively on her hips as she scanned the courtyard.

"Teacher? Will we finish our tests?"

Mrs. Nhu looked down at Tuan with a cool glance.

"I do not know, Tuan," she responded. "We are waiting for instructions."

Tuan watched as a young woman, perhaps someone's older sister, walked out the courtyard gate with another small boy from a lower class. It sure looked like he was going home for the day.

"Some kids are going home," Tuan replied, but Mrs. Nhu ignored him.

He turned to Thao and her friends.

"I think people are going home, Thao," he said. "Do you think we will finish our tests?"

"I heard they're closing the school," Thao answered.

Tuan wondered if his family even knew what was going on. Had they been called by the school? Was there a radio broadcast that instructed parents to come pick up their children? Nothing was clear.

Minutes later, Mrs. Nhu was signaled over to the gate area by an office staff member. She quickly walked over, nodded, then looked toward her class, dutifully seated along the concrete wall.

"Thao!" she called, then motioned for her to stand and come to her.

The teacher said something to her that Tuan couldn't hear, and Thao nodded. She jogged back over to the area where she was seated only moments before.

"My brother is here," she said to her friends and Tuan as she grabbed her school satchel. "See you later."

Thao was going home. He watched as she walked toward the gate. A quick glance around the inner sanctum of the school revealed several students napping, which suddenly sounded like a good idea to Tuan. He sat in bored silence for a short time before deciding to lay on the cold concrete, his head supported by his own worn brown canvas satchel, which had a fraying shoulder strap and a tarnished steel buckle. In the distance, the *whup-whup* sound of a helicopter echoed off the interior walls. Within minutes, he was drifting.

He awoke after what only seemed like a few minutes to hear his name being called. What time was it? The crowd in the courtyard had thinned considerably, and there were only a few students left from his class. The sun had changed position in the sky, and it started casting a golden late afternoon glow into the schoolyard, illuminating the leafy foliage a bright green around the center statue from behind. Most of the area was in shadow. How long had he slept?

"Tuan."

It was Mrs. Nhu.

"Come here, please," she said, sounding somewhat annoyed.

Tuan grabbed his bag and rushed over to her, almost losing his balance in his immediate post-nap state.

"Your sister is here."

"But what about our test?"

"No test today."

Tuan looked toward the gate. There, signing a piece of paper held on a staff clipboard, was Mai. He ran over to her.

"It's time to go home, Tuan," she stated flatly.

"What's going on outside?" he asked.

She ignored his question and grabbed his hand, seemingly in a rush to get out of the school.

"Come on."

She dragged him through the exit and on to the uneven sidewalk outside. As Tuan heard the metal gates close behind him, he was stunned to see a street scene awash in dirty, olive-colored military vehicles. Two helicopters — the first he'd seen — approached from down the street, then peeled off toward the Presidential Palace adjacent to the school.

"Mai," he said, "what happened here?"

A pall of smoke was coming from the direction of the grassy property of the palace, but he couldn't tell what was burning with the tall trees and palms obstructing his view.

"Someone bombed the Palace. Come with me, I have my Vespa up the street."

As Tuan and Mai walked quickly thorough cigarette smoke-crowned soldiers, an impossibly-overloaded olive-drab jeep sputtered by, it's uniformed riders bristling with small arms. A small tank maneuvered only ten yards or so beyond them, and Tuan could hear the piercing squeaks of its tracks under its metal wheels. As it approached, he could feel its weight shaking his feet through the asphalt and realized he'd never been close to a tank before. It had never occurred to him they were heavy enough to shake the ground.

As they wound down the uneven sidewalk and around the low trees that lined the street, Tuan could barely keep his sandals from catching on the edges of the damaged, cracked bricks, which were coated with a patina of dirt and blackened chewing gum, long since spit out by years of passers-by. As an uncovered truck slowly drove by, Tuan and Mai got a lung full of bitter diesel exhaust and the odor of old canvas, worn leather, and green paint.

They reached Mai's scooter, which was propped against the wall inside a tiny alley flanked by leafy vines. She pulled it out on to the sidewalk.

"Get on," she said, "let's go home."

It was the last time Tuan Nguyen would see a school in Vietnam.

4

April 14th, 1975
TAN SON NHUT AIR BASE
8:30 AM

A roar filled the air as two fighters launched from Tan Son Nhut's runway. The hazy morning sunlight poured into the window of the modest office, and Chau stifled a shudder as he read what Major Vinh Do had just handed him. His old friend and co-pilot had run across an unusual and ominous dog-eared paper banner and was wearing a look of grave concern.

Brother soldiers, regional soldiers, and popular forces: it's time for the Americans and President Thieu to pay for their crimes. If you still hesitate, you will be punished by the uprising force.

"I found it last night on a wall near the base perimeter," Vinh said.

Chau was pallid.

"This is bad, Vinh."

How long had the sign been hanging there? Who put it up? The obvious target audience for the message was South Vietnamese uniformed service members. It was the first one Chau had laid eyes on, but not the first he'd heard about. There'd been a lot of rumors and several days before, he'd earwigged a senior aircrewman telling a story about a leaflet that a friend of a friend of a friend had found, which supposedly read something like, "*The puppet government of Thieu is collapsing. Come back to the people and save the country, your families, and yourselves.*" Combined with the noticeable uptick in flight operations—particularly fighters and American airlift—his head was swimming.

Even after his father-in-law and Dzung returned home a week before with their faces badly hamburgered, he had still been hoping against hope that what he'd been hearing was only paranoid gossip. Banditry and rogue vestiges of the Viet Cong had long operated in areas near Hong's rubber plantation since the end of the war, so was a kidnapping and beating really that surprising? He'd been suppressing his alarm about it and tried to convince himself it wasn't a surprise at all, but now that he was looking at something tangible, his hopeful optimism was vaporizing.

No...something was happening.

There'd been a lot of chatter in the ranks about Hue and Da Nang and fighting in the central highlands the week before, but there was never any official verification. There'd even been gossip that the enemy was close—very close—but it was all just talk. Wasn't it? It was certain the media wouldn't carry any stories about it. And as far as the bombing near Tuan's school, intelligence analysts at Tan Son Nhut said it was just an isolated incident. After all, similar instances of defection had happened before. It was just more of the same...right?

If there were any veracity to what he had until now blindly trusted were just tall tales and fear, surely the Americans would have taken some sort of action. Wouldn't they? Most of their forces had left South Vietnam two years before, but like many, he and Vinh were confident President Nixon's promise to stand firm with the south would be honored, even though the man had left the Oval Office in shame two years prior and a new executive was now in charge. Reliable information was hard to come by and it was frustrating.

"You know what I think, Vinh?" he asked, fearing that if he said what was on his mind, it would become fact. "I think the stories about the North are true."

It was the first time he'd uttered his concerns aloud to anyone. An American C-141 taxied on the tarmac at the airfield not far from their work area, the whining engines filling the air with noise. Vinh didn't respond. Perhaps he didn't want it to be real either. But there it was … out there.

"Do you hear that?" Chau continued as the airlifter rolled. "Americans are leaving. For a week we have been told these flights are humanitarian missions bringing in supplies and taking orphans out. But do you believe it is only Americans and babies on those planes, Vinh?"

Chau's pallor was turning to a flush, and he felt a stitch of anger.

"See this?"

He shook Vinh's banner in his hand.

"We do not have the full story and we will not get it from the Air Force or from President Thieu on the television. And what about the fighter traffic? Does it not seem like more than usual? Where are they going?"

Vinh wouldn't look at Chau.

"Our people are leaving Saigon, too, Chau," he finally commented. "I did not tell you, but my wife has two friends who departed on a boat with their husbands and families earlier this week."

It was only more confirmation of what Chau was at last believing as truth.

"And now we have this poster," Vinh worried aloud.

Vinh's banner was quickly becoming the last straw for Chau. It was like a switch had finally turned on a bright light in his mind. For the first time in his military career, his confidence began to quickly collapse, replaced by anger and doubt about his government and its leadership. He gnawed on his bottom lip and scathingly wondered if Vinh's poster would be called another 'isolated' incident by his government's intelligence analysts.

Hmph.

At that moment, he made up his mind that he wouldn't discuss this with his wife, at least not yet. Nothing good would come out of alarming her.

"Chau," Vinh started again. "If the enemy is really coming south at the speed we are hearing about, we need to act."

Chau was silent.

"Would you stay in Vietnam?" Vinh asked. "Or flee?"

Flee.

The utterance of the word was like striking a bell, and its echo rang slowly through the room.

Taking action or doing something about the situation was one thing but dropping the word "*flee*" was another thing entirely. Living in a war zone, it was always in the back of everyone's mind. But now the word hung large in the small room like a cloud of poisonous gas.

"It has crossed my mind before," Chau admitted. "I have a family. So do you."

"On the other hand," Vinh said, "there have been no intelligence reports of –"

"Vinh, please spare me the Air Force talk. Why would our military intelligence tell us there was a growing danger to the north?"

Chau was agitated—not with Vinh, but with the entire situation that they were being forced to piece together on their own.

"We are military, but we do not fly combat missions anymore. Only training. We do not have a 'need to know' about much."

He paused, turning his gaze out the window, taking in the two large, white globular radar domes that partially defined Tan Son Nhut's skyline, lit brightly in the sun. Beyond them, the C-141 airlifter's four jet engines were now whining at the end of the runway as it lined up for takeoff.

"What about Hue and Da Nang?" Chau asked.

The Da Nang stories were punctuated by loose talk of an aircraft full of South Vietnamese troops that had fled, landing at Tan Son Nhut—soldiers that had reportedly left the northern city in the wake of a forceful communist takeover.

"What about it?" Vinh responded, sounding a little perturbed. "Have you seen any haggard troops here that say they left our cities in northern hands?"

"No, but I have heard the talk. I sense…that something is not right, Vinh."

Chau didn't want to talk about it anymore, but he couldn't stop the gears of his mind from turning. Now that reality seemed to be setting in, he wondered if it might be too late to take action. If communist forces really *were* coming south…would he and Mai actually do it?

Flee?

He knew as a South Vietnamese pilot, he would be considered an enemy combatant, which put his life and his family's lives at risk. Chau Nguyen was a patriot and had fought for his country for a long while, witnessing terrible things that no human should ever have to see in their lifetime. Vietnam was home. It was true that he and Mai had kept a perfunctory escape plan, but he never seriously thought they'd have to use it.

Flee.

The American C-141 throttled forward at the far end of Tan Son Nhut's runway, taking to the air in a flurry of sound and exhaust before fading into the distance. Chau and Vinh were interrupted when their office door was flung open. It slammed shut with a peal of squeaking metal from the aging, over-painted hinges, and both men rocketed to their feet as Colonel Giang Trung, Tan Son Nhut's Director of Operations and all flying activities, stalked in.

"Show me today's airlift schedule," he barked.

Giang was a brusque man not known for tenderness or beating around the bush. He'd seen his share of violence over the years, lost his family during fighting in the sixties, and many thought it hardened him to whatever compassion he ever may have had, although he was definitely no lover of the Communist North Vietnamese. His visit to Chau and Vinh was fairly routine for this time of the morning. As the man in charge of Tan Son Nhut's flight operations, viewing the day's C-130 mission schedule was a standard practice for Chau and Vinh as the day's duties were carried out.

"Yes, sir," Vinh answered robotically.

Moving quickly to a desk in the corner of the room, he began shuffling through a stack of papers and stiff, dirt-brown file folders. The colonel sat in a worn, gray-cushioned swivel chair and removed his flight cap, revealing a sweaty V-shaped red mark on his skin where it had been covering his forehead. Wiping the perspiration from his tanned brow, he made a half-hearted attempt to straighten his soaked salt and pepper hair.

Chau sat back down near his superior officer and his chair's springs groaned. He pondered what his boss would think about Vinh's communist banner.

"Colonel," Chau began gently.

Giang turned his head, his bronzed and leathery face looking half-annoyed. Chau didn't say anything, but instead slid Vinh's sign across the desk toward him.

"What is this?"

The colonel picked it up by the edges, lifting it slightly off the metal and faux-wooden surface of the workspace. Chau thought he heard him stop breathing.

"What *is* this?" Giang asked again, his bearing suddenly sounding uneasy.

"Vinh found it last night, sir."

"Where?"

"On a wall not far from the main gate."

He and Vinh weren't always privy to non-airlift and non-training operations, but as the director of all flight operations on the base, Giang was. He *had* to know something was going on. How could he not? Was he hiding something? The colonel's expression went back to one of stern business.

"This is nothing," he said dismissively, letting the sign slip casually from his fingers and back to the desk surface. "Probably a local teen trying to scare people."

"But sir — how can we be —"

"I said '*it's nothing.*'"

But it was obvious to Chau that it wasn't. Giang's demeanor said it all.

April 14th, 1975

CIA OFFICES AT THE NGUYEN HOME

9:45 AM

Jessie Flounders hung up the phone with a grimace.

"Chuck, we've got some new developments."

Chuck Sterrett watched Jessie extinguish his spent Camel into a mound of cigarette butts in his golden-brown, cheap pressed-glass ashtray. Despite the steady din of the electric fan in the corner, his blue second-hand smoke hung in the air. Trying to suck in oxygen through the pall was like inhaling cold maple syrup. An aircraft from Tan Son Nhut could be heard on takeoff in the distance as it took to the sky—Chuck couldn't tell if it was a passenger liner or a C-141 full of babies.

He and his small team were still processing vague reports of North Vietnamese movement south of Da Nang. The last friendly airliner that had left the city two weeks prior, which was heavily damaged in the escape, was no secret to Chuck and his agents, and it concerned them—on board had been a plethora of "friendly" ARVN soldiers, some of whom had left their families behind in their haste to get out before being killed. The news had been shared by US officials with some of their South Vietnamese military counterparts, although it wasn't widely distributed. But with the passengers released into the public, he knew rumor would travel—and with the inevitable large numbers of refugees expected to come south ahead of communist military activity, it probably wouldn't be long before Saigon became a nest of fear, panic, and chaos.

What a joke, Chuck thought, but didn't say aloud to his agents. *Plenty of people already know what's happening.*

The small detachment was also very much aware that the

south had been launching fighters to attack enemy positions to the north from Tan Son Nhut and Bien Hoa Air Bases, but there was limited detail provided on how far they were going or what their targets were, only that strikes moving 'farther south.' Chuck thought the reports were unusually nebulous and he didn't like it. In addition, his agents came across uncorroborated intelligence the day before of enemy movements in some of the country's coastal areas, but there was no significant outward concern or an expressed desire from the Embassy to respond in any way. Chuck knew people at the compound were pulling evacuation plans from the shelf, quietly reviewing and updating them even though the mission's leadership hadn't directed it. If he were working there, he knew that's what he'd be doing. He also figured US military entities in the Pacific region would be reviewing and updating evacuation plans of their own—plans that complimented procedures in every country around the globe that had an American presence—but there was no discussion about it yet, at least not that he'd been privy to.

"Got a report just now from our detachment in the north of town."

Jesse paused and looked away as if in deep thought.

"What?"

"Several locals have reported leaflets."

Rusty McClay perked up his ears.

"What kinds of leaflets?"

"Well..."

"Hell, the good guys have dropped leaflets, Jess," Chuck said. "What do they say?"

"Communist messaging."

A hot flash of alarm shot through Chuck like a lightning bolt.

"How are they getting here? There haven't been reports of any northern aircraft dropping anything in our area."

"Don't know," Jesse continued, pulling a fresh smoke from a newly-opened pack, "but they're there. Probably being distributed via some kind of underground."

"Well hopefully the bad guys are still a ways off, even though we're hearing they're 'getting closer.'"

Chuck sarcastically made 'quotation marks' with the index and middle fingers of each of his hands.

"How could stuff like this be getting around so close to town?"

"Hue's or Da Nang's refugees," Jesse answered. "Or maybe…the bad guys are closer than we think."

The KY-3 buzzed with its annoying clatter, and Rusty squeaked out of his chair to answer it.

"McClay," he answered as Jesse struck his Zippo.

After a brief pause, he could be heard responding: "Right, going secure now."

Chuck's mind processed the idea of leaflets in areas on the edge of Saigon. There'd been reports of enemy operatives in the city for years—both confirmed and unconfirmed. It wasn't new. He also knew about leaflets being distributed up north and refugees leaving those areas, but up until now, he wasn't aware of anything this close. Maybe they *were* making it through the refugee network…or maybe the communists *really were* close. It was frustratingly hard to tell with the limited info coming out of the Embassy, and the HUMINT networks had become sketchy of late.

Rusty interrupted Chuck's thoughts.

"Hey Chuck," he said with the palm of his hand covering the secure phone's handset, "you got Bob Frailey here."

Chuck backed his worn, gray-cushioned rolling chair away from his desk, stood, and made his way to the encrypted phone.

"You're already secure."

"Chuck, Frailey here," came the garbled voice from the other end. "Have you heard about the leaflets yet?"

"Just got word from one of the northern dets. What do you think it is?"

"Not sure yet," Frailey continued, "but naturally we're concerned."

"Have you confirmed it?"

"Yes, but it isn't clear what the mode of delivery is. They're obviously not being airdropped."

"What about mortars?"

The North Vietnamese Army and Viet Cong had used mortars to distribute leaflets both during the war and since the 1973 cease-fire, and there were a handful of reports that they'd used this method in the Da Nang area earlier in the month. The rounds weren't severe enough to damage, just enough of a blast to blow the lid off a can of small papers, which would be launched into the air and allowed to float benignly to the ground to be found. If the enemy was close, it was plausible.

"Possible, I guess," Frailey responded in muddled tones, "but probably unlikely since there isn't any significant fighting in the area. It's more probable they're being sent out through the underground. Refugees or something."

Another aircraft could be heard rumbling off the runway at Tan Son Nhut. A passenger liner for sure.

"Anyway, we just got done with the daily intel brief with Ambassador Martin."

"How'd that go?"

"Well, you know," Frailey chuckled incredulously, "it was the standard 'nothing to worry about' and 'probably just an exceptional case.' Martin's gonna deny there's a real threat until he's got a commie leveling a rifle at him."

"I don't know about this, Bob," Chuck said hesitantly. "We know the commies are moving, and even though it looks like they're still kinda far off, don't you think it's pretty clear what their ultimate target is?"

Bob Frailey paused with a heavy silence. He wasn't telling Chuck the whole story and Chuck knew it.

"Bob, we've got helipads identified, we're moving babies and non-essentials, and there's this uber-secret Plan Alamo thing that nobody wants to talk about. The palace was bombed by a defector. Now we have leaflets. What's the deal?"

Silence.

"Where are the bad guys, Bob?"

Frailey didn't answer.

"Hello?"

"Yeah."

"Listen, don't you think there's a pretty clear and present danger?"

"I don't know," his boss mumbled, frustrated.

Skepticism filled Chuck's soul like a stale cup of hours-old coffee, and he found it hard to keep himself to a whisper to avoid upsetting his agents. There was no privacy and he didn't doubt they were tuned in to his half of the conversation.

"I know we don't get much here from the New York Times or NBC, but what are we seeing now? Our wire sucks. Are we getting the full scoop or not?"

More silence. Chuck was getting pissed.

"Something's funny here. You know, an old college mentor once told me to 'listen to your gut, because it's usually right,'"

Chuck said with clear irritation. "There's a buzz here, and don't tell me you're not feeling it, boss. All we've got is cryptic talk of movement, and then we're told not to worry?"

Chuck swore he heard crickets chirping on the other end of the line.

"Are you hearing me?"

"Yeah," Frailey replied.

"I'll be straight with you," Chuck finally whispered into the mouthpiece so his agents couldn't hear. "We joke about it, but this whole Graham Martin thing makes me nervous. I know damn well the words 'full' and 'evacuation' have been dropped inside the walls of the Embassy—and often. He *knows* what's going on, so why is he so reluctant about getting the essentials outta here? And why is information so spotty? My gut is screaming at me that we at least gotta get the high-risk locals out and we need to start yesterday. What's your gut telling *you?*"

Another long pause from Frailey.

"Bob?"

"Mine tells me it's the right move," he finally relented.

"Well, do the wardens know that? If they do, you better not let Martin find out. He'll have a shit."

Again, no response from Frailey. What was he hiding?

"You guys gotta be looking at our evac plans for a big movement out. Don't tell me you're not."

"There are a few folks," Frailey huffed, not confirming anything about the wardens.

Chuck lost himself in thought for a moment, considering the gravity of it all. Bob Frailey hadn't said much about essential American personnel evacuating Saigon, and this was the first time he'd basically confirmed it may happen, or at least that it was being discussed on the down-low. The KY-3 line popped and hissed.

"Boss, are you gonna tell me anything?"

"Sorry," Frailey answered somewhat dreamily. "Just thinking."

"Are you *finally* saying something solid to me about a full evac or getting the high-ranking guys out? I hope to God you are."

Chuck failed to hide his whispers (such as they were) and when he looked up, he found Jesse and Rusty staring with a pair of uneasy expressions.

"All I said was evacuation *plans are being looked at*," Frailey confirmed firmly through the muddled phone line. "You know as well as I do that they are on the shelves and have been for a long time. That's what it is, OK?"

"Ok, fine. *They're being looked at*. But what does that mean? We still don't have a list of the high-ups and their families, right?"

"No," Frailey said feebly. "There's still a chance the good guys could pull this one out."

Chuck knew his boss didn't really believe that.

"There are a lot of them between us and the north, and even without our help, they may have enough force to repel the communists and send them back to Hanoi."

Oh, bull SHIT, Chuck thought.

"Right," he said heatedly. "Bob?"

"Yeah?"

"There's something you're not telling me. For the love of God, a guy at Da Nang tried to ride the nose gear of the last plane out of there, panicked that he wouldn't be able to leave, and he died in the process."

Chuck knew Da Nang was a terrific scene of panic. Absent some significant western intervention, there was no way the south would hold up long against a similar onslaught on Saigon.

"You know what I know."

At 37 years old, Chuck Sterrett had been in the business long enough to trust his feelings, and there was definitely more to this.

"OK, we'll follow up later," Frailey said.

"OK, out."

The call abruptly ended, and Chuck hung the receiver on its resin cradle with a louder-than-usual *crack*.

"Um…Chuck?" Rusty said with a touch of sarcasm, "you wanna fill us in here?"

"They're just looking at *plans*," Chuck reiterated, repeating his boss' words. "Everything's OK."

Jesse Flounders looked a little queasy.

"Hey Chuck?"

Sterrett, who was clearly agitated, had moved to the window to look out and think for a moment. He'd seriously been considering bumming one of Jesse's cigarettes, but decided against it.

"I haven't said anything, but…"

Chuck turned to look at Jesse, who was sitting still at his desk with his elbows on his knees, starting at the floor.

"…it's just that I got this letter from my mom the other day," he went on.

Both Chuck and Rusty knew Jesse's story. His mother was still living back in his hometown of Gaithersburg, Maryland—by herself and often consumed with worry absent the strong support she'd had from Jesse's father, a World War II veteran who'd died of a heart attack a few years before. As the youngest of three brothers, Jesse was the last to leave the home and his mother did her best to stay sane in the empty nest that had only gotten emptier since her husband passed away.

"You actually got *mail?*"

"I didn't wanna say anything, but..."

Jesse hesitated as Chuck looked impassively at him. Mail came every couple of days through what remained of the military APO system, and agents would usually pick theirs up on weekly Embassy runs to distribute at the detachments.

"Seems the TV networks have been reporting some pretty crazy shit back home."

Chuck looked back out the window. The American press...In an odd twist, Bob Frailey's intelligence personnel in Saigon didn't see much of their own home country's newspapers, or many other domestic media sources for that matter, at least not lately. There was American radio in Saigon, but it never said much, and most of what could be found in the Embassy were ragged, weeks-old *Newsweek* and *Time* magazines that made their way to the US Mission when shipments of goodies arrived to stock the compound's small commissary. Copies of the *New York Times* and *Chicago Tribune* used to make it fairly reliably, but in the last couple weeks it had been sporadic at best, even if it came from someone's family member. The CIA got regular updates over the wire and while messages often referred to media articles, the information was still compiled by the intelligence services.

In the place of a steady journalistic news flow, gossip and sometimes even tall tales would often fill in the blanks. In the current environment in Saigon, that gossip could become a tough thing to deal with and still keep a solid continuity of operations. Everyone knew the communists were moving south, but nobody seemed to talk about how fast they were going or where exactly they were.

"Stuff about communist forces coming at us at a pretty stiff pace," Jesse explained.

"Nothing we didn't know, Jess," Chuck affirmed.

"Yeah?" Jesse responded somewhat absently. "Try Qui Nhon and Tuy Hoa."

That got Chuck's attention. Rusty too. Qui Nhon and Tuy Hoa were halfway to Da Nang. Until now, neither site had been named as a location threatened by the north. Now there was 'intelligence,' as it were.

"*My mom* knows more than we do."

Chuck didn't respond.

"She's nervous," Jesse said.

"I bet."

"I keep pretty quiet about it, Chuck, but you know I've seen things get bloody. It isn't new to me. Tet was a slaughter, and that was with a lot of us, and a lot of heavy weapons. I know we have guns here, but a 1911 ain't gonna do much against NVA tanks."

Jesse had only spoken to Chuck about his war experience on a handful of other occasions and it was brief every time. He never asked about it and because it came up so infrequently, he knew Jesse was deadly serious when it did.

Chuck's det kept three .45-caliber M1911-A1 pistols on hand, but three agents weren't the Army. There were long guns at the Embassy, but little heavy weaponry and even if it *were* there, it could never be enough to fight off a large and determined enemy force.

"What's the real picture here, man?" Jesse asked, sounding

frustrated. "You didn't exactly whisper to Frailey. I mean, maybe I'm embellishing but sometimes it feels like a damned information blackout. For God's sake, *we're supposed to be in intelligence.* Am I missing something?"

Another large jet tore overhead from the airport, temporarily filling the sky with the whine of engines.

"I'm telling ya—this note from my mom's got me seriously wondering," Jesse said. He was paid to think critically, and that's exactly what he was doing. "She's not gonna make stuff up, ya know? There's something happening at a higher level of classified that we haven't been read in on."

"I don't know, Jesse."

"Don't you smell some bullshit? Because I do."

April 14th, 1975
DOWNTOWN SAIGON
1:00 PM

As the tropical early afternoon heat of April began to lay over the small market area like a thick wool blanket, Mai picked up a bouquet of Da Lat roses from the bustling row of roadside street carts and put them to her nose, allowing the scent to transport her miles away, even if only for a moment. She and her mother had just finished lunch at a busy noodle stand near their home; the smells of garlic, cilantro, ginger, and beef broth were a welcome reminder of something normal after the unease of recent weeks.

First, it was her father and Dzung being attacked and kidnapped in the jungles to the north, and then the unnerving bombings near her younger brother's school. Over the last few days, the swelling in her brother's face had gone down significantly, but the two incidents had her feeling a little jumpy. She'd always felt relatively safe in Saigon, but there was something else—something she couldn't quite put her finger on that gnawed away at the back of her mind. Her family had lived in a war zone for years—her entire life—and Mai knew anything could happen at any time, but nothing violent had happened inside the Resume 75% city limits for years. At least until the bombing near Tuan's school.

The feeling in the pit of her stomach that something was a little off-balance got worse at night. Despite the sensation of Chau's warm, snoring body next to her, the peals of angst hit her a little harder when she was ramping down for the day. Of course, she'd worried out loud to Chau—should they be worried about more violence? What about stories of the communists to the north? She deeply loved him, and genuinely respected him for what he'd seen and done during the war and since. He was sixteen years older than she was, and in many ways wiser and worldlier. It was true he'd been acting more stressed recently. She'd also noticed his swollen lower lip, but it was probably job stress. He hadn't been saying much, but she trusted that he'd talk to her if he was really concerned. Maybe she was worried about nothing. She did her best to suppress it all.

Her mother approached, having come from another nearby cart stacked back to front with paisley fabrics on one end and books in Chinese, Vietnamese, and French on the other.

"Smell this jasmine I bought, Mai."

Dat had always been a very sensory person and loved fresh fragrances in her house in the springtime, especially if it was the herbal kind. Every year since Mai was a little girl, her moth-

er always had a small herb garden in a planter in their courtyard—lemon grass, mint, and Thai basil were staples, and one
year she even tried to grow ginger, although she didn't have
much success. Mai suspected that was where she got her own
love of aromatics my wife Beatles.

She plunged her nose into the wide, dark green leaves of
the pungent blooms, rolling some of it between her fingers to
release its fragrance, inhaling the intense, earthy bouquet. It always brought her back to her childhood.

"Mmm...," she said, "it smells wonderful, Má."

"This would be so delightful in the kitchen."

Mai reached into her bag to get money for the roses and
noticed a small storefront near a large shady tree on the sidewalk. She remembered it—a small shop with a window full of
gold and silver jewelry, earrings, and watches. She would infrequently stop there, but today its lights were off, and the window
displays were bare.

She gazed in confusion at the old woman she'd been about
to pay.

"What happened to the jewelry market?"

"Oh," she replied, "they left."

"Left?" she asked, not expecting that answer. "Where did
they go?"

It was puzzling... and she thought the woman looked a little
worried. It was almost as if she might be feeling the same nagging, almost unconscious doubts as Mai.

"They left last night," the old woman responded. "We do not
know where, but there are some who sell here that are trying to
leave Vietnam."

Mai gave a forced smile and handed over her money as if
nothing was wrong.

"There are several other stores and carts that have also left," the old woman added, waving her hand down the street.

Looking around, Mai suddenly realized the market area she stood in did not seem as busy as it normally was, and it hit her that a large seafood stand that was always located nearby—its workers hocking fish, prawns, squid, and even fresh bananas and mangoes from time to time—was missing entirely. Her mother started back towards her, and the young 24-year old did her best to quell the fresh anxiety she felt.

"Thank you."

The two women turned and walked silently down the street I need a deal as Mai looked around. Ahead of her to the left was another establishment that appeared shuttered, the lights inside unlit. Even though slightly fewer people seemed to be around, those that remained didn't seem to be acting very much out of the ordinary. Things just felt...odd.

"Má," Mai said with a sense of phony calm. "The woman at the flower stand said some people are leaving Vietnam."

Dat looked around again, saying nothing.

"Do you not see fewer people? Look at the shops," Mai said, capturing her mother's undivided attention. "Some are closed and locked. The fish stand is gone."

Her mother could only regard her silently, as if surprised at Mai's concern.

"Where are they?" Mai asked. "It is a Monday and they should be here and open. Why are they not?"

"Oh, it's nothing, Mai," Dat responded with a casual wave of her hand. "Come on, we should get home."

At twenty-four years old, Mai still paid significant deference to her mother. Over the years of her childhood—like any youth—Dat's words carried weight. Besides, Chau would have mentioned something. Maybe she was just worrying too much...percentbut what was it that nagged at her? The thought of the marketplace not teeming as it usually did...the closed businesses...

Yet nothing about any danger had surfaced in Saigon press or radio. Her gut tugged at her. She suspected her mother might have felt the same thing, but she decided not to ask any more questions.

April 15th, 1975
US EMBASSY, SAIGON
1:00 PM

After a night of fretful sleep, Bob Frailey had been feeling uncomfortable throughout the day. He sat pensively at a small desk inside the Embassy SCIF, its hard metal chair cutting into his pelvic bone, causing a dull ache in his lower back. He was finding it hard not to dwell on Ambassador Martin's state of stubborn denial, which scared him to death. The ambassador was aware of what was happening to the north, but he wouldn't allow anyone to spend much time on it beyond classifying it at such a high level that it couldn't be shared outside the embassy walls.

By God, we're not leaving.

Several days prior, he was in a meeting with the ambassador and leadership from the 9th Marine Amphibious Brigade, who'd been tapped by the US Military's Pacific Command to be prepared to provide rotary airlift — if it became necessary — for any major evacuation of Americans from Saigon. The whole idea of the conference was to nail down the final pieces of a plan for high-risk Vietnamese evacuations and a full American evac in the event a decision was made to get everyone out. But Martin didn't seem concerned about posturing. The whole thing seemed like an aggravation to the man, and it wasn't exactly productive. Fortunately, Frailey was able to quietly engage with the DAO on their establishment of 'Plan Alamo,' which Martin was aware of, but also insisted be kept as quiet as possible for as long as possible.

Frailey knew a communist takeover of Saigon wouldn't be something any of them would easily escape from. Like Jesse, he'd seen what all-out bloody conflict looked like. A World War II veteran, Bob Frailey had served as a paratrooper in the 101st Airborne. During the Battle of the Bulge he'd spent a week in a foxhole on the perimeter around Bastogne, Belgium, enduring some of the most frigid temperatures in European history. Shelling was frequent and "tree bursts" would often occur when enemy rounds exploded above the ground at about chest level. It was one of these that resulted in a hellish incident that Frailey would never flush from his memory. During a shelling, he witnessed one of his friends vaporized in a cloud of pink mist as a round came screaming into a nearby tree, splintering its trunk at the speed of sound ... and his buddy too. Nothing remained but the blood and gristle that covered the snow, and Frailey's face and field jacket. The young man was gone — lights out. Now — over 30 years later — it still woke him up at night. He didn't want to get caught up in more violence because Graham Martin threw the switch on a full evacuation too late ... or didn't throw it at all.

With more than two decades in the cloak-and-dagger world of intelligence operations, Bob Frailey was used to keeping secrets. But one thing he despised was keeping them from his proxies and friends in his detachments, especially when it was critical information. The KY-3 conversation he'd had with Chuck Sterrett the day before hung heavy on his conscience, because he knew the guy was frustrated. He was right to be, and Frailey knew he would be too if the tables were turned. And it wasn't only about Chuck—he had agents in other locations that were hearing from their own sources, the chatter about Plan Alamo, and coming to conclusions similar to Chuck's.

The CIA detachments across Saigon knew enemy forces were coming south, but exact locations were elusive. The dets would also soon find out about the north's aim to be in Saigon by Ho Chi Minh's birthday on May 19th. Now they were moving down the coast, along the western border with Cambodia, and had reached points north of Saigon that were dangerously close by—another bit of information that hadn't yet been widely shared.

As quiet as possible for as long as possible my ass, he thought...especially knowing Chuck's landlord and son had recently been kidnapped and beaten.

It was a struggle to keep it all quiet because he knew full evacuation was about the only thing that was left—the overrunning of Saigon was inevitable. The big questions were: 'when do we start sending the high-risk South Vietnamese out?,' 'when do the rest of us leave?,' and 'are we too late?'

The immovable ambassador, of course, continued to all but insist that none of it was necessary. Frailey and many others felt it was a complete repudiation of the obvious. Many Americans in Saigon were wise to the rumor mill and had already been leaving town for days under the ongoing 'non-essential' evacuation that Martin had sanctioned.

The high-risk Vietnamese issue struck a particular nerve in

Bob Frailey, and he'd come to a fateful decision, which if discovered, would look a lot like mutiny. A week prior, along with one or two other senior people inside the Embassy, he'd recruited a young agent named "Mosey" Copenhaver who worked in the building to begin quietly coordinating the movement of senior local nationals out of the country. It was an effort in complete defiance of Ambassador Graham Martin's instructions that a 'full evacuation wasn't on the table.'

He knew he'd have to tell his agents—he needed their help, and it would have to be done soon.

No, *immediately.*

He picked up his phone, and the first call was to Chuck Sterrett. The earpiece produced the familiar *beeeeep* ringtone of the Southeast Asian telephone network.

"Sterrett," came the response on the other end.

"Chuck," he sighed. "I need you to come to the Embassy first thing in the morning."

April 15th, 1975
TAN SON NHUT AIR BASE
2:00 PM

Chau shuffled through the day's flying schedule as a passenger liner tore through the wild blue overhead. More air traffic. The sense that something urgent was happening tugged at him hard, and his thoughts about getting out of town hadn't abated—if anything, they'd increased. Mai had mentioned the night before that some shops in the market she'd visited with her mother in downtown Saigon had closed their doors because their owners were presumably deciding to leave the country for safer environs. All the signs pointed in the same direction—and it wouldn't be long, Chau thought, before he and his family would be caught up in it. The thought made him queasy.

The office doorknob wiggled, then timidly swung open as Vinh walked in, moving slowly and almost ghost-like.

"Have a good lunch with the wife, Vinh?" Chau asked, trying to sound as normal as possible.

His co-pilot made his way to Chau's desk, his normally bronzed face cold and gray.

"What?"

Vinh wordlessly handed him a business-sized envelope, his hands shaking like leaves in the wind. Chau read the type-faced name and address on the front. There was no postmark or return address, but it was directed to Vinh at his home residence and had a frayed opening at the top where it had been unsealed. Chau turned his eyes back to Vinh, confused.

"Open it," he said.

It was almost a whisper.

Chau reached into the envelope and pulled out an off-white, tri-folded piece of paper. It was a typed letter, devoid of any handwriting at all.

SOUTH VIETNAMESE LIBERATION FRONT
PEACE – NEUTRALITY – INDEPENDENCE – DEMOCRACY

TO: Vinh Do, Major, VNAF
Tan Son Nhut Air Base, Saigon

Major Vinh Do: We write to inform you that you are guilty and have sinned against our people and our Fatherland. The victory of Revolutionary forces is imminent, and we appeal

to you to repent and leave the enemy military organiza-
tion. Do not procrastinate. Release your beast of burden, be
wise, and do not continue your fight against the Revolution,
which will only result in further crimes against our people.
Do not commit to being used as a puppet of America, or
the Revolution will be forced to take a very severe attitude
towards you. We know who you are, and where you live.
We know you have a family, and we severely condemn and
warn you. You must quit your work immediately, and if you
do not, you will be punished.

April 12th, 1975
Liberation Troops of Saigon

Chau felt the sudden urge to vomit the bowl of noodles he'd eaten for lunch, and his hands trembled as if the letter was addressed to him.

"*Trời ơi,*" he cursed under his breath, lifting a hand to cover his gaping mouth.

The color drained from his cheeks as he slowly raised his dark eyes toward his old friend and co-pilot.

"They know who I am, Chau," Vinh said with a quiver in his voice and tears welling in his eyes. "This is not a joke. I did not want to believe the banner, but now letters in the mail? My family and I cannot stay."

Vinh moved to his familiar desk chair and dolefully slumped into it, then put his head into his hands.

"The rumors *are* real," he mumbled.

Chau hadn't received a letter like Vinh's of course, but he might as well have. He was in much the same position, but he could be in even *more* danger than Vinh — after all, Mai's father

139

was renting a large portion of their home to Americans...who were pretty likely CIA. It wasn't that hard to figure out—although he'd never been in Chuck Sterrett's office areas, he had seen the antennas, dishes, and cabling on the roof. What else might it have been but a part of some sort of low-profile communication network? He never asked, but it was definitely out of place and hadn't been there before Chuck moved in.

His guts grumbled with nervousness, then Vinh brought him back to earth.

"Chau, what are we going to do?"

The urge to remain silent didn't last, and Chau was overtaken by a feeling of determination. The anger at his senior leadership and government returned with a fury, and it was a great motivator. The enemy would *not* be the masters of their destiny, and neither would Colonel Giang or his contemporaries. Perhaps the resource they needed might well be literally right next door to him: Chuck Sterrett. If he wasn't CIA, Chau was certain the man must know *something*. They would not show Vinh's letter to Giang—in all likelihood, it would only be met with stern disregard anyway, just like his reaction to the banner.

"First, we need to find out the maintenance status of all our aircraft."

Vinh regarded Chau quizzically.

"We will not do anything yet—not today," Chau continued.

"I do not get your meaning, Chau."

"My friend, we will not be here long, and I want to know what is available for you and me to fly out of here with our families, and as many of our countrymen as we can fit in our bay."

Vinh was dumbfounded.

"You mean leave Vietnam?"

Chau nodded.

They'd only rolled around the word 'flee' a day or two prior, but there wasn't any discussion of actually doing it.

"But how will we—"

"This letter is another indicator, Vinh," Chau interrupted sternly. "The banner, the kidnapping of my father-in-law, all of it can only mean that…"

"…that we need to go."

"It all adds up very clearly, at least to me."

"What do you propose?"

A C-130 pealed overhead, having just taken off over the base's twin radar domes and a pair of red and white radio towers. Chau thought of the word the Americans always used for their old workhorse airplane. Known as the 'Hercules,' his western friends cheered the C-130 as 'the four fans of freedom' during the war. *Indeed*, Chau thought. Four of those fans could mean freedom for himself, Vinh, and their families.

"Tell me the status of everything," he said. "Then we will visit with my American neighbor."

Vinh had met Chuck Sterrett before and shared Chau's belief that he wasn't just some low-level Embassy employee.

"Good idea."

It felt good to be doing *something* even if it was small, because it gave them a sense of purpose. Vinh turned and dutifully marched to a tall four-drawer filing cabinet next to his desk, pulling the top one open with a roaring metallic growl. The dusty odor of old paper filled his nostrils as he thumbed through files, jammed into their container.

"Let me find the update from this morning."

Vinh searched through the tightly-packed mass of folders.

"Here it is," Vinh said, pulling a crisp manila dossier from the large cabinet.

Sitting back at his desk, he opened it to reveal a sheet of paper with inked notes, x's and checkmarks showing a short list of tail numbers, each with a small red, yellow, or green hole-punch-sized sticker next to it. He ran his calloused finger down the list.

"One down for maintenance waiting for parts...one in the US for overhaul at the depot...three off-station...one on the ramp scheduled to go to Bien Hoa."

Chau nodded as Vinh picked the phone up to dial the maintenance supervisor. He could hear the ringing in the earpiece from across the room.

"Vinh here," he started. "I need to know updated aircraft status."

A pause as Chau left his desk to come look over Vinh's shoulder.

"Yes, I know you just gave it to me this morning. I need it again."

"Vinh," Chau whispered wide-eyed and nervous, moving his hands in a tamping motion. "Do not alarm them."

Vinh ignored his friend.

"Right..." he said in to the phone, "one fully-mission capable that's still on the ramp?"

Another pause as Vinh processed the information and took notes with a stubby pencil.

"What about the one in the hangar that is missing the cargo bay man-door? Do we have any update on when the parts will arrive?"

Vinh furiously scribbled a note next to a red-stickered tail number.

"What is the estimated time to repair once we receive the new door?" he asked curtly into the phone.

He underscored what had already been written in his own untidy scrawl, *To be determined—parts: USA.*

"Thank you."

As Vinh hung the receiver back on its cradle, Chau chimed in.

"Personnel door is still in the United States?"

"Yes."

"And we still do not know when it will be here?"

"That is correct."

Chau pondered for a moment. The look of fear and alarm had left his face and was replaced by one of resolve.

"Our airplane is the one with the missing door," he said. "It is the only one that can be flown that nobody will suspect. We must forget about the ones that are working."

"Why?"

"We do not have as much control over them," he answered. "They are all scheduled for missions and will keep getting scheduled. We need to keep them that way to make things look as normal as possible. The one that is waiting for the door is grounded and it will be for a long time, which will make it easier for us to quietly get it ready."

"You want to fly with no door?"

"We will stay at a low altitude," Chau responded. "Is it otherwise ready to fly?"

"Well, yes but –"

"If we do this correctly, nobody will suspect we are even considering leaving, and if they do, they will not suspect we would use a broken plane."

Vinh only stared.

"Where will we go, Chau?" Vinh asked. "The Philippines? It is a long way, and we cannot exactly fly a planeload of people over the ocean with a missing door. Are you sure this is the right one?"

"It will not be used without it. We could stay on top of the parts status, but you and I both know the door will never come."

"Yes, but do you not agree we should avoid flying over open ocean with a hole in the side of our plane?"

"We will go to Thailand."

The conversation momentarily paused as a pair of fighters took off, the deafening noise filling the office.

"Vinh," Chau said, as the jet noise gently dissipated, "we must keep things inconspicuous. Giang *cannot* know."

But his co-pilot was distracted.

"Chau," Vinh started, "do you still think there is increased fighter activity?"

"It does seem so."

The sound of the engines continued to die in the distance as the planes got farther away.

"The fighter shelters have looked a little emptier than usual, I think," Vinh said.

"I know," Chau answered quietly. "On my way out today I plan to drive by the fighter unit. I want to see what is hanging from their rails."

"Do you think they are hitting targets?"

Chau gnawed on his bottom lip as he stared answerless—but knowing—at Vinh. He tasted blood.

5

"Shh!" Son whispered to his two brothers.

The water tank on the roof of the Nguyen home was a great place to cool off for three boys who didn't have access to a swimming pool. The brothers were good at being sneaky — better than most kids of their ages.

Son climbed a tiny staircase on their home's top floor to open the small steel hatch to gain roof access. It made very little sound as he gingerly unlatched the bolt. *The slower the better,* he thought, preparing to lift the door. He knew if he opened it gently, he could avoid the distinctive rusty squeak it usually produced — he'd found from previous experience that pushing the two-foot square door created far less noise when done gradually.

"What is everyone downstairs doing?" Son whispered nervously.

"Still talking," Tuan answered quietly. "All I hear is some boring stuff about airplanes."

Chau had come home about an hour before, and Son had

noticed he'd looked a bit more worn and haggard than usual. At thirteen, he had become more attuned to changes in the behavior of the adults in his life, and over the last week or so he'd noticed an unmistakable deviation from the norm. It was pretty clear to him that something was different than usual, but he didn't care enough to be worried about it. Right now, he just wanted a dip into the cool water of the makeshift pool he and his brothers would sometimes use to swim in.

"Come on!" Dzung whispered. "Open it!"

Son cautiously lifted the trapdoor, and a beam of late afternoon sunlight landed on his face, highlighting his greasy hair and the thin layer of black peach fuzz on his upper lip. Dzung followed as Son raised himself out to the flat surface of the Nguyens' roof. The silvery-black tarred covering, hot from a day's worth of stifling sun, was squishy and gave slightly under his feet.

"Hurry up!" he whispered to his brothers.

Dzung quickly hoisted himself up as Tuan's head emerged, the slight breeze tousling his sunlit hair. Son reached down and grabbed his hands to lift him on to the roof, then carefully closed the hatch. It was always better to go on the roof later in the day—coming in at an angle, the piercing solar rays were less likely to come through the hatch and into the upper level of the home than if the sun shone in from directly overhead. Any noise or change in brightness levels might be noticed and alert an adult to their surreptitious activity. Most of the time, Hong and Dat were strict about a child being on top of the house without an adult present—three stories above street level was a long way to fall, and the boys had been busted before.

Son was already at the water tank. A large, corrugated aluminum structure, it was capable of holding several hundred gallons of water to supply the domestic needs of the family, and a small human could stand up in it if they wanted to. At four-foot-six inches tall, the water surface usually came to Tuan's chest, and all three boys could fit inside it quite easily. Son climbed the small ladder on its side and lifted the hinges on the metal door on top of the tank, emitting a low-grade squeak. The noise didn't concern him—with the roof access port shut, the family would never hear it.

Sitting on his hindquarters on the edge of the flat-topped tank, Son removed his shirt and kicked off his sandals, then swung his feet into the open entrance, allowing himself to fall inside. Drops from his small splash exited the hatch and the cold water forced him to pull in a sudden deep breath of air. Pulling himself up to peer out the opening, he watched as his two younger brothers began removing their shirts and footwear. Dzung noticed Tuan's feet were filthy.

"How did your feet get so dirty?" he asked.

Tuan casually shrugged.

"Tuan, you cannot go in the water with dirty feet," Dzung said firmly. "You *know* what will happen! All the sinks in the house will produce brown water if they are turned on. Remember?"

Dzung's facial wounds from the kidnapping were apparent to Son as he picked his shirt up from the roof where he'd thrown it a moment before.

"Stand on the ladder," he commanded to his smaller sibling.

Tuan climbed to the second rung.

"I am going to try and clean your feet," Dzung said. "Lift them one at a time."

Dzung started brushing his brother's feet as fast and hard as he could. Son, who was still watching, hoped it would produce a little pain in the process. It was somehow satisfying to watch Dzung being rough with Tuan, but it was more important not to get in trouble with their father.

"What did you walk through? Motor oil?"

The dirt wasn't coming off.

"Sorry."

"The two of you need to *hurry up!*" Son called impatiently from the opening.

Dzung looked backward at the roof's port—still closed—then looked up at his older brother and threw his shirt to him.

"Son," he said, "get this wet."

With a frustrated look, Son caught the garment and quickly soaked it in the water below before returning it to Dzung, who wrung it out and applied it to Tuan's soiled feet. He did the best he could, but there was some dirt that remained on the heels and balls of his feet.

"This will be good enough," Dzung said irritably.

He whipped the now-soiled shirt in the slight breeze to flatten it out, then laid it on the roof to dry.

"Go ahead and get in."

Tuan anxiously climbed to the top of the ladder and hung his knees into the open tank port before allowing himself to slide into the cool water. Dzung then joined his brothers in the cool water, and a whoosh of breath emanated from his lips as he slipped in.

Downstairs, Hong, Dat, Mai, and Chau were having a discussion that had become slightly heated. Earlier, Chau had informed his wife that he felt the time to broach the possibility of escape had come, and he gently started the process when he'd arrived home from work earlier. They'd only been talking a few minutes, and as Mai had expected, Hong was resistant.

"I am telling you," Chau said bluntly to his father-in-law, "I know something is going on. I am seeing and hearing things and people are getting scared."

"No!" Hong stated emphatically. "*Nothing* is going on! We are *not* leaving."

"Hong, departure activity at the base has increased. American airlift planes are very active, and our fighters are coming back with nothing on their wings. It means they are dropping ordinance—I have seen it myself. These are not just regular patrols and training flights. There are rumors of communist infiltration and movement in this direction from the north."

Mai sensed that her husband knew more, but at least for the moment was keeping it to himself.

"What about your kidnapping? What about Dzung nearly pressed into the service of the Viet Cong?"

Hong only glared; his frown punctuated by a still-ugly scab left from the abduction on his left cheek.

"…and there are other things I'm concerned about."

"Such as?" Hong answered skeptically.

Chau hesitated.

"I cannot say," he said under his breath, "I just need you to trust me."

Now Mai was sure he wasn't sharing everything. Maybe there were things he couldn't talk about, or maybe he didn't want to scare the family, but her nerves were already frayed. Leaving blanks in the story only made Mai's imagination run wild.

"We should think seriously about preparing our escape."

"Chau, I have a productive business to think about," Hong said impatiently. "I built it, I have raised my family and made a good life for them with it, and if we leave, we could lose *everything*."

"I *know!*" Chau responded forcefully, momentarily losing his cool, "but you could lose it anyway—whether we stay *or* go. Would it not make more sense to get out with our lives? Your business is not worth it!"

Hong threw his hands up and sighed.

"I do not know…" he trailed off with exasperation.

He made his way to a small cabinet and removed a glass. Reaching for the adjacent faucet, he cranked the handle to fill it for a drink. The water was murky as a mud puddle.

Hong rolled his eyes, then grumbled as he shut the sink off.

"I do not want to discuss this anymore tonight, Chau," he said with frustration. "Mai, please go get your brothers off the roof."

Mai rose from her seat and made her way for the upper level of the home as she pondered their situation. She was uneasy, but trusted Chau—after all, working on the air base every day, he had access to more information than the rest of them. What she'd seen at the market with her mother made her uneasy, but her father's insistence that things were fine in Vietnam caused a real inner conflict. Since she was a young girl, he'd always been the strong one in the family and at twenty-four years old, she was still young enough that she trusted his judgment…sometimes more than she did Chau's.

Despite his denials of the potential seriousness of the situation though, she did find it curious that he didn't go up to get the boys himself. Normally, he'd be the disciplinarian, but his aversion to doing it this time around struck Mai as unusual. Maybe something really *was* bothering him.

Reaching the third floor, she climbed to the hatch and lifted it. A golden ray of late afternoon sun lit her surroundings, and she could hear the reverberations of three young boys splashing about and laughing inside the family's water supply. When the door slammed down on the flat roof, all sounds from the tank ceased.

Mai was sure the boys knew they'd been discovered.

As she neared the ladder, talking could be heard from inside.

"Uh-oh," she heard one of them say under his breath.

"You should have cleaned your feet better, Tuan!" Dzung whispered angrily.

Mai opened the tank's lid, and the boys breathed a sigh of relief when they saw it wasn't their father.

"What are you doing!" Mai asked with a tinge of frustration. "Get out! You are lucky it is me!"

Tuan was the first to approach the opening and climb out.

"Come on!" Mai said with urgency. "Get out!"

Dzung and Son soon followed their youngest brother out of the gray vessel, and when they reached the roof surface, began wringing the water out of their shorts.

"You better go straight to your bedrooms before Ba finds you," Mai said with warning in her voice. "Maybe he will forget that he filled a glass from the sink with your brown water in it."

As the brothers threw their clothing on, she looked across the rooftops at the air base two miles away. Another passenger aircraft took to the air.

April 15th, 1975
9:30 PM
NGUYEN HOME, SAIGON

Mai laid in bed as Chau finished in the bathroom, her mind racing. Her father's words echoed in her skull—*nothing was amiss*—but it was hard to discount the concerns Chau had voiced earlier in the evening. And why was there nothing on the radio or in any other media outlet that she'd seen. Why was what her father thought so very different than her husband?

Chau emerged into the bedroom in a pair of plain white boxer shorts, freshly cleaned from washing the sweat off his body after a long day on duty. Mai noticed the contours of his slim, olive-skinned body—the svelte chest that she loved, peppered with fine hair between his pectorals...the musculature of his quadriceps. To Mai, he was the perfect image of a strong, lean man—something she'd longed for in her early youth. Now she had it. Chau was the father of her two beautiful children. She trusted him implicitly and knew he would do anything for his family.

He pulled the white, meshy insect net to the side and climbed on to the bed with his wife of five years. Without a word, he looked deeply into her dark eyes, the trait he had always told her immediately attracted him to her in the first place. Chau's mother had owned a gas station in 1969 and at the time, Mai was working in the wholesale department of Shell Oil near the Presidential Palace. Out of the blue on a summer day, Chau, who often helped his mother with her business when he was not on duty, appeared in Mai's office to place an order for fuel. She could remember how confidently he carried himself, the warmth of his smile, and the gentleness of his voice. Mai's heart skipped a beat and her cheeks flushed at the sight of this beautiful man.

Over the next few weeks, Chau started coming in more and more frequently to 'place orders for gasoline'—a thinly-veiled (and even lame, Mai humorously thought) excuse to come see her. Not long after that, he was asking her father for his permission to date his daughter. It wasn't easy—Hong was uncomfortable with the sixteen-year age difference and asked very direct questions, like *why are you not married?* and *why do you not have children?* But Chau was a hard guy not to like. Hong and Dat fell as much in love with him as Mai had, and soon after, the couple were on their first date...which was chaperoned by her parents, just like every one of them afterwards. Just in case.

Their courtship had taken place at breakneck speed over only six months. It had to, because Chau knew that Mai had another suitor. The wedding came only a few months later, and it was one of the happiest times of her life. Since that day, it hadn't been all sunshine and roses, but Chau was an honorable man in an honorable profession, protecting his country and the life he and Mai had built.

"You are thinking about your conversation with my father."

Her husband sighed, rolling on to his back to look away at the mosquito netting above their heads. She lifted herself up on to her elbow and reached for his mouth with her hand, brushing her index finger across his bottom lip.

"What are you doing?" he asked, slightly perturbed and tenderly pushing her hand away.

"Let me see your lip."

"No," he responded, turning his head away from her.

His wife reached for his mouth again but stopped short, caressing his cheek instead.

"Show me, Chau."

He said nothing. Mai knew him too well.

"You have made it raw," she said. "Let me look."

He quietly turned his face back towards her, wearing a strange look, as if he'd been caught in a lie. Mai pinched his lip slightly with her thumb and forefinger. When she peeled it off his bottom teeth, she could see in the dim light of their bedroom that it was shredded and bloody.

"Chau, I know you."

She let go as he turned away again.

"You spoke to my father about escape. I know you are worried."

He didn't immediately respond, instead reaching for the light and switching it off. The dull glow of Saigon came through the slats in their window as a slight breeze lightly moved their insect netting. The low sound of nearby vehicle engines and a far-off car horn provided a familiar, dull backdrop to their bedroom. Saigon sounded fairly normal this evening. Even peaceful. The calmness was reassuring to her, and she wondered how it could be that an unseen peril could possibly be threatening their doorstep.

"I am, Mai," he said quietly, his silhouette still in the darkness of their room.

"What have you not told me?" she asked. "I do not like this talk about preparing to get out of Vietnam."

He paused, sighing again.

"Something is not right," he said. "I should not tell you this, but Vinh found a sign."

"What kind of sign?"

"A banner…"

Mai stared at his dark form, waiting for the other shoe to drop.

"…with communist text."

"What did it say?"

"Something about Thieu's 'puppet' government and 'save yourself,'" he said coolly. "It was on a wall near the base."

"Oh, Chau," Mai replied dismissively, doing her best to hide her concern. "It's probably somebody playing a bad joke."

"That's what Giang said."

"Do you really think there are communists in Saigon?" Mai asked. "There hasn't been anything in the papers."

"The papers?" he said. "Mai, the papers will not say anything. The government does not want us to think there is anything wrong."

Mai thought of the market again. It was her only frame of reference—the only tangible thing she'd seen.

"I *know* something is happening," Chau continued. "There are rumors. I am seeing signs of things at the airfield that are not normal. People are nervous."

Mai sensed that Chau knew more, but she didn't press him.

"It will be OK," she said, trying to hide her inner concern.

"No, Mai," he said. "it will not."

His words frightened her all over again. Mai suddenly remembered the last time her older sister Nga visited from Australia. It had been more than a year ago, not long after the last of the American forces had left. It was her first trip home from studying abroad in quite a while, and she recalled that her sister said she felt that something was a little off, maybe a little less secure. When it was time for her to return to Australia, Nga—two years Mai's senior—seemed relieved to be leaving.

"I believe the time to leave Vietnam will be soon, Mai," Chau said. "Americans are already leaving, and some Vietnamese are going with them. I have seen the airplanes. Have you not heard them?"

Americans leaving? How did he know all this? She couldn't reconcile what her husband was saying with her father's denials that anything was wrong, or that there hadn't been any public announcements that people should behave any differently than normal. Then again, she *had* heard the planes...

Mai stayed silent, unable to respond to her husband's portentous words.

"I have not said very much to your father," he continued, "but..."

"But *what?*"

"I have an airplane, Mai," Chau responded. "Vinh and I can fly us to safety."

The extreme magnitude of his words hit Mai with abrupt suddenness, and she felt a spasm of heat in her gut. This was their home. Would they *really* have to leave?

"Leave Vietnam?" she asked trying and failing to hide her quickly escalating fear.

"Yes."

Escape.

Flee.

"But...how do you have an airplane?"

"There is one that has a missing forward door, but we can still fly it," he explained. "It is in a hangar right now, and since people know it is broken, I do not think many will pay attention."

Chau's words were chilling.

"But Chau, how can you *steal* an airplane?"

"If things continue to get worse," he winced, "nobody will care."

It was so much to process. Escaping Vietnam was one thing, but what would happen after *that*?

"Where would we go?"

"I am not sure. Probably Thailand."

It seemed he'd thought this through in more detail than she realized.

"I think the Philippines might be a good option too," Chau went on, "but I do not like the idea of flying over the ocean with a missing door. We will have passengers."

"Passengers?"

"We should take as many people with us as we can."

"We would be refugees."

"Yes."

"Would we stay in Thailand or the Philippines?"

"If we have to … yes. At least for a short while."

"Well, where would we go after that if we were not planning on staying?" Mai asked incredulously, leaning up on her left elbow to look into Chau's darkened visage.

"Perhaps Australia with Nga. Maybe even the United States," he said. "I learned to fly in Texas, you know. I speak English, and you could practice it too. You took some English courses in school."

Mai only stared blankly in the darkness as another car horn lightly pierced the silence of their room, followed by another plane lifting off the runway at the air base.

English. She barely used it since she'd graduated years before.

"I do not know for sure," Chau wondered aloud. "But I want you to know that whatever happens, I will make sure you and our children remain safe. I know this is unpleasant to talk about, but I will not allow us to be caught up in any chaos that might come. We can move on, and we will survive."

Mai laid back down on her feather pillow and stared into space. It was a broad statement and she didn't like hearing it.

"Saigon has been in the middle of a war for a long time, Mai."

"Yes," she said, turning her head in his direction, "but little has happened here for years."

"What about the palace bombing? What about your father's kidnapping, Mai?" Chau asked, feeling his wife's conflict and denial. "Things are crumbling now. Can you not see it? We have always had a basic plan of action in place. I am only thinking it through to the next step. It is a good idea to put a few things together for Truc and Trung. Your brothers too. In case we need to move quickly."

It was almost too much for her. If Chau was right, staying in Vietnam could be incredibly dangerous. But on the other hand, so could leaving. She silently tried to reassure herself that none of this would be necessary, and that it was all just some kind of horrible nightmare.

"We will get through this, Mai," he said.

Her brain was spinning. What would they need? Diapers for Trung maybe, some other baby items…clothes…perhaps she could fit the basics into a few small bags or pillowcases that they could grab quickly.

She would do it, she decided, because she respected and trusted Chau. But a part of her still felt her father's influence…that maybe this was much ado about nothing.

"Hey," Chau said, rolling over to look at her. "It does not hurt to be ready, right? Maybe this will be all for nothing."

But she knew he didn't believe it.

Chau stroked her fine hair, combing his fingers through it slowly. The ensuing sense of comfort Mai felt was something that she couldn't put into words, and a temporary feeling of contentment came over her.

"We will be fine, Mai," Chau said, giving her a slight kiss on the cheek.

Maybe it would look better tomorrow.

April 16th, 1975
DOWNTOWN SAIGON
8:15 AM

Chuck Sterrett drove the Embassy's early-60s model French-made Citroën through the crowded street, moving carefully around bicycles, mopeds, and women in straw hats. Many were moving rapidly, and he detected something odd. Were there more people out here today? It looked a little more congested and frantic than usual, but at the same time, the veggie carts and street vendors that he usually saw were dispersed far more thinly than normal.

Strange, he thought.

Especially with all the hush-hush ops he suspected Frailey wasn't keeping him up on. Then again, maybe his suspicious mind was running away from him. He entered a short line of vehicles approaching a police checkpoint as he got near the Embassy. It was manned by a blue-shirted police officer wearing a hat and crisp, white gloves, his whistle dangling from his collar. Chuck pulled up and the cop quickly examined his Department of State ID before waving him through.

Checkpoints were the newest thing in Saigon, and yet another indicator that things were different... even ominous. Maybe it was a remnant of actions the government had put into place after the palace bombing, but Chuck doubted it. From the serious sound of Bob Frailey's voice on the phone the day before, he got the feeling he was about to hear something that would probably be both a burden and a relief. A cyclo with a young couple in the carriage buzzed past as he rounded a corner, and the large concrete latticework of the Embassy's façade came into view. The gargantuan off-white, six-story concrete structure was the height of 1960's chic, built with security in mind after the 1965 Viet Cong bombing of the former consular facility that killed an American CIA agent. Surrounded by a fifteen-foot steel-reinforced wall, the compound held fairly well during Tet Offensive attacks about seven years before, despite a handful of enemy penetrations. The RPG hits in the perimeter wall, though long since filled and painted over, were still visible as Chuck maneuvered his vehicle around several bicycles and aimed for one of the two main gates—barred metal structures manned by several M-16 wielding American Marines.

Even though he'd lived in the city for a number of years, he always got a feeling of security when he entered the Embassy compound—like he was back on US soil. With things feeling so sketchy out on the streets, it would be good to get back inside, at least for a little while.

Bob Frailey wore a foreboding look on his aging face as Chuck walked in to the CIA work areas.

"Thanks for coming, Chuck."

His carefully-coiffed salt-and-pepper hair reminded Chuck of country singer George Jones' Brylcreamed, immovable style. Frailey stood up from behind his desk and shook Chuck's hand, his full six-foot, muscular frame on display. For a fifties-ish guy, the man was still built like a fireplug, his thick chest and large arms filling out his clothing. He was bookended by Ben Frederick, Harry Moran, and Conrad Spurgeon—all peers of Chuck who worked in detachments similar to his own in other parts of the city. Special Agent Mosey Copenhaver was also in the room, sporting a new set of chintzy faux-leather flip-flops, the latest in Southeast Asian men's fashion. Chuck had met him before at a few Embassy functions, but never worked with him. He nodded a subtle greeting at the four men.

"New shirt?" Chuck asked Frailey sarcastically.

Frailey wore a brown and white patterned top that he thought could have come right off the set of the Brady Bunch.

"Cute."

Chuck smirked, satisfied that his playful barb had achieved the intended effect.

"OK, we're all here," he said. "Let's go into the SCIF. There are some things we need to discuss that are pretty time sensitive."

Short for 'sensitive compartmented information facility,' the SCIF was a large vault within the office, used to process and handle highly classified information, and complete with desks, file cabinets, and communication equipment. When they reached it, Frailey punched in a code that opened the unremarkable but extremely heavy door. It was a twenty-four-hour, fully secured facility which was used for processing highly classified information, though only manned with a skeleton crew on night shift.

"Need you guys to give us some privacy in here please,"

Frailey mentioned to a few young agents inside the room. They gathered up some desk items and closed the door behind them.

"Grab a seat, guys."

Bob Frailey rolled a bulky green desk chair to the center of the small and dimly-lit windowless room, festooned with all manner of telephones and cryptological equipment, bulky Mosler safes, and disheveled stacks of paperwork. Chuck and his peers each rounded up a chair and sat in a haphazard circle with Frailey at the top.

"So, what's the deal, Bob?" Chuck asked with genuine wonder, and a little bit of suspicion. "Feeling out in the city is a little weird."

"Gents, it's time you get the full story from the horse's mouth. Up until now, the Ambassador's official position has been that there's very little amiss. You're aware of Hue and Da Nang, of course…the leaflets, and the defections, as well as Babylift and the surveying of buildings in town to serve as landing pads. Hard to be quiet about that kind of stuff. You may also know about local nationals leaving. And despite the ambassador's agreement to allow a lot of Americans in the city to do the same voluntarily, he's been adamant about not responding to some of the *other* things we know about. In fact, he's essentially been in denial, and it's scaring the hell out of some of us."

Chuck and the other detachment chiefs were quiet, absorbing the information.

"What I'm about to let you in on could get me fired and worse. The fact is that the situation is grave, and the Embassy has been very tight-lipped about most of it. I'll tell you that what has been made public barely scratches the surface. There's been a hell of a lot more confirmed defections than you realize — not just the Lieutenant Nguyens that are going around trying to drop bombs on presidential palaces. A *hell* of a lot—ground troops of every rank and file of the South Vietnamese Army, government officials, et cetera. They are going north in fairly alarming numbers."

"But they're not communists," Harry Moran commented.

"No, but they're scared shitless and most people would do anything to stay alive and keep their families alive," Frailey answered. "Some have been harassed by northern go-betweens and sympathizers, their families have been threatened and kidnapped, their sons have been pressed into communist service, daughters used for sex and sold into the prostitution trade, you-name-it."

"Guess I'm not too surprised."

"Well, it gets worse. These are bad guys, and the cities to our north were only the start. It's clear from intercepts of northern radio comms the target right now is Saigon...as if you haven't surmised the same on your own."

"...and it'll be a matter of time before they're knocking on the door, right?" Ben Frederick chimed in.

"Well, they're knocking on the door *now*," Frailey answered. "Have been for over a week, and people like me are worried."

"A *week?*" Chuck Sterrett was shocked.

"Vietnamese employees that work for the Embassy, US companies, et cetera are all picking up on the unease just like we are, even though most of them don't have much granularity as to exactly what's going on. The rumor mill is prompting a lot of locals to take their money out of the banks, although not everyone has been successful, and many families have already left."

"...and we don't know about this because—" Chuck began.

"Martin doesn't want a panic."

There was a heavy pause.

"It gets better," Frailey continued. "The West German Embassy is sending people home and it sounds like the Aussies may be close on their heels."

"Well when the hell are *we* leaving?" Moran asked incredulously.

"I don't know. Oh, and by the way, the PAVN is shooting to be down here and in control before Ho Chi Minh's birthday."

"When the hell is that?" Chuck asked.

"May 19th," he answered, "but they're gonna beat that deadline."

Chuck and the other agents were having a hard time hiding their distress.

"Despite the ambassador's denials of the obvious, he's basically been forced to prepare for the worst by his higher headquarters and the Pentagon. The president is quietly sending PACFLEET from places all around the Pacific just in case things get bad. If the airfield goes down, helos will need a place to go, and ships at sea are the destination."

"When do they all get here?" Spurgeon asked.

"They're already beginning to arrive."

"You said they're gonna beat the deadline, Bob," Chuck said. "Information on enemy movements hasn't been exactly plentiful—just rumors and unconfirmed stuff from a handful of sources. *Where are the NVA right now?*"

It was the elephant in the room. Frailey's guys weren't stupid—they all knew the northern army was on the move after Hue and Da Nang, but the Embassy had been nebulous about exactly *where* they were. Right in line with the ambassador's denials, Chuck thought.

Bob Frailey sighed and stared at the floor.

"All around us," he answered gloomily, "pushing fast along

the coast and Cambodian border areas for Buon Ma Thuot. They're north, west, and south of us. There's been fighting near Xuan Loc since last week."

The agents began to murmur nervously.

"South Vietnamese fighters have been hitting positions all over, but it isn't doing much, and as of this morning," Frailey continued over the uneasy mumbling, "there are villages within thirty miles of us being abandoned."

That was new. Villages only thirty miles away were being abandoned?

"Holy *shit*," Chuck said under his breath.

"A lot of South Vietnamese military leadership hasn't even been told what's happening, but gentlemen, we're facing a pincer threat. Refugees are starting to pour in, and it's only gonna get more chaotic as the noose tightens."

Xuan Loc was only about sixty miles to the northeast of Saigon, and it was strategically important. If the north were able to take it over, they'd have a straight shot through Bien Hoa Air Base, then a clear road to Saigon. And now there was a threat to the south too? Chuck and his counterparts assumed there'd been movement to the north, but didn't realize the enemy was this near, or that there was a threat of the city being surrounded. The hair on Chuck's neck stood on end.

"...and this brings me to why I called you here this morning," Frailey went on. "The bottom line is that we have fifteen PAVN divisions heading this way, and they have all kinds of heavy weaponry with them. They're steamrolling the competition and the good guys are folding and retreating faster than they can be captured."

"*Damn it*," Conrad Spurgeon verbalized what they were all thinking.

"Guys, the communists are in control of more than three quarters of the entire country," he went on, "and aside from the rumor mill that many locals, and even your sources are acting upon, a lot of them are still largely in the dark because the host nation media is silent and all they've only got the underground network to go on."

"Seems there's some intel services keeping people in the dark too," Spurgeon stated sourly.

Frailey didn't respond to the obvious dig.

"What about Ford asking Congress for all that that aid?" Chuck asked.

Chuck was loosely aware of a last-ditch military aid package the president was trying to push through Congress that might buy the South a little time.

"A couple hundred million, right? Isn't that what I heard? I have a feeling it ain't happening."

"$700 million," Frailey explained bluntly, "and you're right—most everyone in DC circles pretty much knows it's gonna fall flat on its ass. People are sick of Vietnam and want nothing to do with this place. Twenty-some years and fifty-eight thousand American husbands, brothers, and sons didn't come home from here and they're done with it all."

"Right."

"Anyway, don't worry about all that. I need you guys focusing on Vietnam," Frailey continued. "We can't control the politicians, including our ambassador. We can't even control when people like us are gonna get outta here. But we *can* affect lives here by helping the high-risk people leave. Martin isn't gonna give the order to start a full evacuation. He's convinced himself that this'll pass, but my fear is that his intransigence is gonna get people killed, so by God, we are gonna do *something*."

There it was. Mutiny.

"What are you talking about, Bob?" Moran asked with suspicion. "What're you gonna do? You want to disobey the ambassador?"

"Let me be clear, guys. I'm not *ordering* you to do anything," Frailey explained, "I'm *asking* you. Mosey here has started coordinating an ad hoc and low-profile evacuation of the high-risk folks—it's already underway. I won't force you to participate. If you choose not to, don't breathe a word of it to anyone. If you do, I'll know where it came from, and you'll go down with me."

The men soaked in every syllable of Bob Frailey's words through the slow-motion heaviness of the moment.

"Remember what happened in Hue in '68?" Frailey asked and was met with blank stares. "The NVA and the Cong were there for a month during Tet. After we broke through and pushed them out, mass graves were found. Men, women, grandmas, and kids, and they weren't killed nicely with a bullet to the back of the head. They were raped, tortured, and dismembered. There's a good chance that could happen in Saigon, especially with Americans and anyone who's linked to us."

"Have we heard about any of that yet up in Hue or Da Nang?" Frederick asked pointedly.

"There've been stories, and they're not good. This morning we had an unconfirmed report of a couple Americans captured in Buon Ma Thuot. So far nobody's been able to reach them, but it's not exactly easy to get behind an enemy line and get a good read. We got SIGINT late yesterday that mentioned beheadings."

The group let out a collective alarmed sigh.

"When are we letting the wardens know?" Spurgeon asked.

"We started alerting most of them this morning," Mosey responded. "They're contacting non-essentials and directing them not to wait until the last minute. The ones we trust most will help high-risk local nationals get out. Essentials like us are still stuck here."

"Something else you guys have heard rumblings about is this 'Plan Alamo' thing," Frailey continued. "You know about the rotary LZs. The Embassy's tried to keep it inconspicuous but we've got water, C-rats, and fuel stockpiled at the DAO. You'll see the concertina wire and the last of the sandbags go up there today, but we've stockpiled water, rations, fuel, and we think we can hold up to 1,500 for at least 5 days."

"I wouldn't wanna see those latrines," Moran commented acerbically.

"The compound has put up B-huts with primitive latrines," he went on, "and it'll definitely be a last resort. For now, this non-essential thing is gonna continue and we're not gonna get an order to run out the host nation's senior guys or their military leadership."

"What the hell is this guy's problem?" Moran asked. "Martin knows about this but we don't?"

"He wanted it kept as quiet as possible for as long as possible," Frailey answered. "and now I think you have a need to know."

He nodded before going on.

"Starting tomorrow, wardens will be distributing some small booklets about where the evac sites are if it all hits the fan. You guys are all gonna get 'em. If you hear 'it's a hundred and five degrees and sunny' followed by 'White Christmas' by Bing Crosby over the radio, you get your asses to the Embassy and we go."

"It's just such a mixed signal, Bob," Chuck said. "It baffles me—why is Martin going to all this trouble if we don't think he's gonna tell us to leave until it's too late?"

"He doesn't want to do all this. He *has* to. The direction to prep sites, booklets, et cetera is coming from someplace else," Frailey answered. "What I'm telling you is Graham Martin will prep all day long but based on the behavior we've observed from him here on the compound, he'll continue to resist making the decision to get the rest of us or the high-riskers out. Prep work doesn't mean he's gonna decide to do anything. When or if it happens, it'll be far, far too late. That's why some of us have decided to act *now* and it's in the form of getting the people outta here who'll have big targets on them in less than a month. Even if it's small, most of us believe we owe it to ourselves and a lot of other people to start making things happen faster."

"Who's 'we?'" Frederick asked.

"'We is me, Mosey, and a couple other guys that are in on it."

"OK, how much time do 'we' think we have?" Chuck asked.

A muted but genuine dread rose in his gut. After Da Nang, he suspected in the back of his mind that this day might come, but now it was right in his face. He wondered about at least getting his family out.

"I don't know. Commies are moving fast, and when Xuan Loc falls, they'll get here well before Ho's birthday party. The good guys are out of ammo, food, and gasoline and other things as simple as barbed wire and sandbags. Their morale sucks and their numbers are declining rapidly because of defection and desertion, so they'll be less and less able to put up any real fight. Hell, in Da Nang there were more than a few troops that shot at their own family members to get aboard the airplane that got them out."

"Yup..." Moran commented, still in disbelief that it had happened at all.

"God knows what happened to the ones that were left. We're talking about a growing panic that will soon penetrate our perimeter. Refugees from up north are here, and there'll be more of 'em, guys—a lot more. It'll add a pretty significant dimension of chaos as things start to fall apart here. And they *will* fall apart."

Chuck remembered sensing there were more people on the street than usual when he was making his way to Frailey's office. And what about the small groups of young men he saw outside the mission's fence? Were they refugees from up north looking for a way out of the country, hoping the Americans could do something for them? The stunned silence of his cohorts said it all. Division-sized troop movements, heavy weapons and artillery, an influx of exiles, raging fights only miles away...could it get any worse?

"I don't understand where Martin's mind is," Moran said under his breath.

"I'll worry about Martin, you—"

"Just tell us what you need us to do, Bob?" Conrad Spurgeon cut in.

"Figure out who you know and who your guys know. Who are the high-ranking people? Who's worked for or with Americans? Mosey's compiling a list but I'm damn sure it's not comprehensive. You need to add names to it and start moving people. We can help some of them get paperwork in order if we have to, get manifested on airplanes with the non-essentials, whatever. You also need to burn or shred your classified and destroy your crypto equipment. Do it ASAP.

"And guys, *we need to keep this very quiet.* Many of the peo-

170

ple that we want to help are South Vietnamese military—their leaving amounts to desertion. Of course, that's against South Vietnamese law. The state expects them to stay here and fight for their country...so consider this a black op."

Secret.

"Mosey's got copies of the high-risk names that we could come up with in-house. Brainstorm and give him more names with addresses, contact info, whatever ya got."

"When do we start?" Chuck asked, tacitly signing up the group for Frailey's 'black op.'

"What we've already got happening can now kick into high gear," Frailey answered. "There's a lot of people to move."

"How many?" Moran asked. "It must be in the hundreds."

"Way more."

Chuck wasn't an adrenaline junkie or a soldier. He'd always served in the role of a quiet professional and eschewed violence when he could help it, but the enemy was at the gates, and he knew it could get bad.

REAL bad.

"As people start to leave, it's gonna become a question of who they know that can help them. Military pilots, government officials, and others. We wanna get ahead of that if we can. *You* need to be 'who they know.'"

Military pilots. *Chau Nguyen.*

"We're probably not gonna be able to get 'em all out."

"How many do you think we can move?" Chuck asked.

"As many as we can, and when and as things get crazier the security situation will hamper us. Frankly, the north is moving so fast that we'll be lucky to move half of them. The only names on our ad-hoc list are the high-risk folks—we're not even talking about the family members."

The men were glued to Bob Frailey.

"Gentlemen, I fully understand that taking any action in direct defiance of Ambassador Martin could impact your career. We could be looking at legal investigations, maybe even prison time. That's why I'm not *directing* you to do anything. This is *your* choice. But it's important, and the moves we make today could keep people alive. If you choose not to take part, that's fine—I will make no issue of it. My hope, though, is that you decide to help us keep this thing moving."

Bob Frailey was taking a huge risk. What if one of these men he was talking to was loyal to Graham Martin?

"It's an unpredictable environment, and this is pretty ad-hoc."

On one hand, Chuck was frustrated that he and his peers and coworkers seemed to be the last to know what was going on, which potentially put a lot of people at risk. On the other, he fully appreciated Bob Frailey's situation. It took a lot of backbone to take on an ambassador, who was an executive appointee—a proxy for the President of the United States in-country. He stood to lose a lot.

"You guys need to keep your shit packed and be ready to move in short order. Chuck, you've got Vietnamese friends who ought to know at least a little about what's happening, and if I'm not mistaken, one of them is an air force pilot, right?"

"Yes."

"Remind him that he possesses skills that can help some of his countrymen."

"There'll be a lot of people who won't want to go."

"That's on *them*," Frailey answered strongly, "but by God we're gonna give them the opportunity."

It was indeed grave. Ho Chi Minh's birthday was a month

away, but Chuck knew Bob Frailey was right—that the communists wouldn't wait to "unify" their country, and they'd want blood in the process.

American blood, too, if they could get it.

6

April 16th, 1975
DOWNTOWN SAIGON
12:30 PM

Chau and Vinh weren't hungry. In fact, neither of them had slept much the night before and both felt ill, especially Vinh. The worry about the recent threats to him and his family were taking their toll. Chau tried to feel bad that his friend had been targeted, but he knew he and his family were in similar danger themselves, so any sympathy that might have existed hardly made a difference. He knew weaving like a madman through the busy streets of Saigon wasn't making things much better for his co-pilot either. It always struck Chau as morbidly funny that Vinh was a command military pilot with over three thousand hours in a C-130 (better than half of them in combat), yet the guy still regularly got motion sick in a moving vehicle.

Chau drove his Jeep through the choked Saigon thoroughfare towards his home under the guise of a 'lunch break.' In reality, they were going to try and meet with Chuck Sterrett to discuss Vinh's letter. He knew his neighbor was the most logical person to go to, based on what they assumed, which was mostly based on feelings and very little fact.

As Chau navigated the busy street, he glanced over at his dazed friend sitting next to him. A large truck went by, rumbling the ground under their floorboards, even over the Jeep's engine.

"It will be OK, Vinh."

Chau knew his co-pilot like he did his own brother. They went back years, and he was aware his good friend's angst could get the best of him sometimes. However, this time, it was probably well-founded.

"I think Chuck will be able to tell us something."

Vinh pulled the threatening communist letter out of his left breast zipper pocket and scanned it again, thinking of his three young daughters.

"You know, when we first talked about leaving Vietnam, it sounded crazy to me, even with everything going on."

Chau could sense Vinh's dread.

"I know we have to leave," Vinh continued. "but it is hard for me to believe it has come to this."

"Of course we have to leave," Chau responded reassuringly, doing his best to hide his nervousness about his own family. "The difficult thing for me will be convincing Mai's father that it is time to go. I have already tried, and it has been exhausting."

"My family will not need persuading. The minute I tell my wife, she will want to be on the next plane out of town."

A 737 hurled itself skyward and banked overhead as Chau approached the family home and CIA offices. He quickly looked up and saw the blue "ANA" logo of All Nippon Airways, Japan's largest commercial carrier, taking off to who knew where. Just as a large tree blocked his view of the low-flying aircraft, Chau silently hoped every one of its seats were full.

He passed a series of short buildings along the asphalt and dust-covered street, dodging several bicycles in the process. He was in such a hurry that he had to brake quickly to avoid hitting a small boy and his waif-like mother, who were crossing the street as he turned into the small alleyway that led to his home. Splashing through a stagnant puddle from a brief shower late the evening before, Chau came to the long plaster wall that separated their house from the alley. He stopped at the gate, then got out and opened it with a rousing metallic squeal that announced his presence to everyone inside. Pulling the drab Jeep into the hard-tiled courtyard, he looked up to see Mai and her mother emerging from the house with baby Trung. She approached his vehicle as he switched the ignition off, its cylinders coughing and sputtering as the power petered out.

"I did not expect you," she said with concern.

"Ba!"

Just then, Truc came bounding out the front door and jumped on her father, embracing him and planting a giant kiss on his greasy cheek.

"Hello, con gái."

Daughter.

Chau was doing his best to put on a façade of confidence and normalcy in order to keep his family calm. He looked back at Mai.

"Vinh and I have come home to get something small to eat," he said calmly, trying to keep his persistent feeling of anxiety at bay as he held his young daughter.

Here was his beautiful wife. She was the woman he loved—the one he couldn't hide his feelings from very well the one he'd been thinking about all morning. She was clearly nervous and wore a worried look on her face. Mai knew him, and Chau knew she probably thought he didn't look much better than he did when he came to bed the night before. Sweat had been pouring down his face and neck, staining the chest of his flight suit. He quickly wiped what felt like a snatch of dried blood from his lower lip before she could notice, but he wasn't sure if he'd done it in time.

"Chau," Mai's mother said, sounding puzzled, "you are not usually home for lunch ... ?"

"It is ok. Would one of you mind fixing us something to eat? We want to go say hello to the neighbors."

Chau could tell Mai was suspicious. He rarely came home during the day, and today he had showed up 'for lunch' to 'talk to the neighbors.' He had been a workaholic his whole life and couldn't help but stay at the office until every task was complete. Sometimes that meant missing lunch, and more than a few late nights. Today was unusual.

"We will be back shortly," he said, as he put Truc back down onto the tile of the courtyard. Lowering his gaze toward her, he said, "Vinh and I will be over in a minute to eat lunch with you!"

"OK!" she responded, with a small leap.

Mai and Dat both looked sideways at the two men. Chau and Vinh made their way under Hong's queen flower tree into the corner of the courtyard, then proceeded outside where the front door to Chuck Sterrett's residence was located. After knocking for what seemed like forever, his wife Lien came to the door with their baby boy on her hip wearing an unusually twisted expression of worry.

"Chào bà Lien."

Hello Mrs. Lien.

"Is everything OK in here?"

"Yes."

"Is your husband home?"

"Yes, come in. Chuck came back a short time ago. I will tell him you are here."

"Thank you."

Chau and Vinh removed their sweaty flight caps and entered the house. They noticed Lien's mother in the kitchen washing in the sink, but she didn't acknowledge or even look up at them. Lien left the two military pilots in a small vestibule area while she went to retrieve her husband. In short order, Chuck appeared from the darkness at the back of their living space near a set of stairs.

"Hello, Chau," Chuck said.

Chau and Vinh were fairly skilled English-speakers—they had to be. During the height of the Vietnam War, they received an extensive battery of training from US Air Force personnel and spent a great deal of time at Sheppard Air Force Base, Texas for proficiency instruction on T-38s. Moreover, all the manuals and controls of their American C-130 aircraft were in English, air traffic control personnel the world over used English, and in order to fly the plane, a reasonable command of the language was an absolute necessity.

Chau and Vinh each bowed and shook Chuck's outstretched hand. He regarded them as quizzically as Mai and Dat had, and Chau figured he was probably wondering why they were there. It wasn't typical for them to interact with each other too much inside their respective homes.

"What can I do for you guys?"

"Chuck, I am so sorry to interrupt you. We have something we would like to discuss with you privately."

"Of course," Chuck answered. "Come with me."

Chuck led them to a small bedroom on the second floor that was used by Lien's teenage younger brother when he wasn't carousing with his friends, which was most of the time. It wasn't exactly tidy—the small bed was unmade, and the floor could have used a broom. Chuck took a seat on the corner of the mattress.

"What's going on?"

"It is difficult for me to be so forward, but I feel I must," Chau started. "Out of respect, we have never asked you what you do for the American Embassy. We do not expect you to say, but Vinh and I believe you might be in a position to help us."

It was an implied admission that the two men had their suspicions about what Chuck did for a living. If it surprised him, Chau couldn't tell.

"I received this in the mail," Vinh explained, handing the threatening letter he'd received to Chuck.

He did his best to read through it, but his Vietnamese wasn't good enough to ascertain the message.

"I only recognize a few words," Chuck explained.

"I will interpret."

Vinh translated the words into simple English with a very shaky voice. By the end, Chuck was staring into space, clearly speechless.

All he could manage was a weak, *"Damn."*

"That is not all," Chau cut in. "We also found a banner near the base earlier this week."

"What did it say?"

"It talked about the corruptness of the Thieu government, that we should quit our jobs, and join the enemy before it is too late."

Chuck was silent for a moment, then opened his mouth to say something but stopped before looking up at the two pilots with a strange expression. He was holding something back—Chau could see it.

What is it? Chau wondered. *What does he know?*

"Our leadership has said nothing," Chau continued, "but there are rumors of leaflets and communists approaching from the north. Our intelligence has indicated to us that there is nothing to worry about, but we do not believe it is true."

"Does your leadership know about the letter, Vinh?" Chuck asked.

"No," Vinh answered. "We have only shown it to you."

Chuck suspected Vinh's letter wasn't the only one that had been sent to southern military members.

"Vinh, I have to ask you a question."

"Yes?"

"Are you thinking about defecting?"

Chau's and Vinh's eyes widened, and they shot surprised looks at each other before turning back to Chuck. It wasn't the reaction Chau expected.

"*No!*"

"OK, good."

"Chuck," Chau started again, "is there anything you are able to tell us?"

Chuck put his hands on his knees and then stood up.

"Chau?" he began, his eyes drilling holes into Chau's. "You guys need to start thinking about getting out of town."

"Are the rumors true?"

"Which ones?"

"That the communists are coming."

Chuck hesitated.

"I can't say much."

He was proceeding carefully.

"I just know you should leave, Chau," he affirmed cautiously. "You have access to airlift, and you could help others get out too. I shouldn't say much more."

Chuck had now told them *twice* that they should leave in the space of fifteen seconds, and suggested they use an aircraft to do it. It was enough of a confirmation of what they already suspected was true that Chau felt it validated the basic plan he and Vinh had discussed the day before.

"How much time do we have?"

"Don't wait," Chuck said. "I can help you and your families with diplomatic paperwork if you need it."

April 16th, 1975
NGUYEN HOME
1:00 PM

Mai and her mother served bánh canh chả cá for Chau and Vinh, which consisted of a heaping bowl of tofu and fish cakes. All was fairly quiet until Hong walked in with a distressed look on his face. In his hand was a ragged white envelope with a red and blue border and several postmarks. Several lines of beautiful handwriting appeared in blue ink on the front and the top of it was frayed where it had been opened.

"We have received a letter from Nga," Hong announced.

His words sounded weak, but foreboding. Chau, who had regained some of his appetite since talking to Chuck, casually shoveled a bit of fish cake into his mouth as he looked up at Mai's father. Hong took a few minutes to read Nga's words, and from the start was unable to hide his alarm. He didn't scare easily, but he was clearly disturbed by something. He gave the letter to his wife, who unfolded it and took a moment to skim through it. As she reached the end, her hands began to tremble, and she couldn't hold the letter still.

"It is a warning," she said distantly as the folded paper escaped her fingers and fell to the table.

Chau and Vinh stopped chewing.

"A warning about what?" Chau asked.

"It says the Australian news is reporting the enemy is pushing towards Saigon. She is worried," Dat went on, "Da Nang and Hue are now under communist control. She says there is fighting, and many have died. Hong, why would this not be on the radio?"

Mai dropped her utensil and swallowed hard.

"It is like I said, Hong," Chau responded.

He was indignant and threw his napkin on top of his bowl in frustration. What appetite he'd briefly gotten back was gone again. He'd been down this road once with Hong, but it was risky to essentially tell him '*I told you so*,'" especially in front of Vinh.

"It cannot be," Hong said in confusion, ignoring Chau. "I cannot believe it."

"Hong," Chau said irritably, "I am certain that Nga sees news in Australia that is very different than it is here."

"OK, mommy?" Truc chimed in innocently.

"Yes, sweetheart. Eat your lunch."

There was a heavy quiet in the room, punctuated by the sounds of Trung's messy eating and toddler noises.

"What do we do, Ba?" Mai asked her father.

"We do *nothing*. If there was a problem, we would *know*."

Dat handed the letter to Mai. As her daughter began reading it, the heavy quiet returned. Hong went to the stove and silently served himself some lunch from the cookware that rested on the kitchen counter.

"I am *not* leaving Vietnam," he said resentfully under his breath. "The plantation is our livelihood, and we are *safe* here."

Chau thought it sounded like he was trying to convince himself. He stood up from the table.

"Please step out here with me, Hong."

Mai's father dropped the serving spoon and marched with Chau out the kitchen door into the next room. He hoped it was far enough that the family couldn't hear.

"Do you not see what is going on here, Hong?" Chau said quietly. "We need to get the hell *out* of Saigon!"

"NO!" Hong whispered angrily before stepping away from him.

As Hong turned around, Chau could see him wince, then reach up his back to rub where he'd been kicked. Chau sighed and ran his fingers through his hair. Daylight poured through the slats outside the windows, throwing shadows of parallel lines across the worn rug that covered the tile floor.

"I do not know the whole story," Chau said, "but something is going on. How can you not see this?"

"We are NOT leaving!" Hong retorted, shaking his finger at Chau.

"We *must* leave!"

Chau pressed harder.

"If we stay here, we could be killed! *All* of us. You, me, Dat, and your children and grandchildren. It is not worth the risk!"

"I *cannot* leave my business, Chau! *I will not start again with nothing in a place that is not my home!*"

"Nga's letter matches what I have heard at the air base. A

bomb blew up at the presidential palace, and you and Dzung are still bruised. What will it take for you to do the right thing? Your plantation will be burned to the ground, and you will start with nothing anyway, if you survive at all. Your home will be gone, and you could be *dead!*"

Hong only glared at his son-in-law, the sores on his face from the kidnapping scabbed over and yellow, and his hands trembling slightly as he wrung them together. Chau had seen the man upset before, but unless it had something to do with Mai's brothers, it was rare.

"For God's sake, Hong…" Chau said, lowering his voice.

A bead of sweat traced itself down his forehead and soaked into his greasy brow. How could this man be so damned rigid?

"Vinh and I are planning to escape," Chau finally admitted. "We have an airplane I can use."

Hong's anger turned to surprise.

"What?"

"I have kept it quiet," he continued.

"Have you said this to Mai?"

"Yes.

Hong's sudden hush indicated to Chau that he might be getting through.

"And Hong," Chau went on, "Vinh received some mail. From the communists, and it told him to throw down his arms and defect. *Defect*, Hong."

Mai's father took a deep breath and looked away as if he could no longer deny the truth, but Chau knew there was still some fight left in him. Hong could be quite contrary when he wanted to, especially when he was convinced he was right.

"They threatened his family. He has three young girls at home."

Hong turned his eyes back to Chau.

Is he hearing me? Chau wondered.

"I showed it to the Americans. You and I both know they do something secret."

"What did they say?" Hong asked.

"Chuck was very troubled, and he said we should leave as soon as we are able."

Chau stared eye to eye with his father-in-law, his look one of determination, concern, and fear.

"He said it to me twice."

"Hong?"

Dat was standing next to Mai at the kitchen entrance. Slightly startled, the two men turned, unsure how much of their conversation the women had heard.

"What is going on?"

"We are just talking," Hong answered.

"It sounds like an argument."

The brassy ringing of the phone suddenly stabbed the heated atmosphere and Mai disengaged to answer.

"Nga!" she said excitedly from the kitchen. "I did not think you could call from Australia!"

Distracted by an apparent call from Mai's older sister, Dat rushed to join Mai at their home's sole telephone. At first thrilled to hear her sister's voice, Mai's manner rapidly changed back to one of trepidation.

"How are you?" she asked. "Yes, Ba is here."

Hong walked back into the kitchen with Chau close on his heels, nearly bowling over his wife in the process.

"It is Nga," Mai whispered to her father. "She is using Australia's new international phone service to call. She sounds scared."

Hong jerked the receiver from his daughter and took a deep breath.

"Hello, Nga. Are you there?" he asked loudly.

Chau thought it looked like his father-in-law believed speaking at a higher volume might improve their connection.

"Ba?"

Hong tipped the receiver so the others could hear. There was a slight delay in the line, causing uncomfortable pauses. Chau presumed it was due to the multiple connection nodes in between the two distant locations.

"Yes, I am here."

"Ba," Nga said, "I am so glad we have this new phone service. I have been very worried about you."

"We are fine, my dear," her father answered.

A short pause followed.

"Ba, did you get my letter?"

"Yes," her father continued. "This morning."

"I have been watching the Australian news reports," Nga continued, her voice cracking. "You must get out of Vietnam."

The family members all looked at each other worriedly as they stood around

Hong, listening intently to Nga's words coming through the small earpiece. After a pause, Hong said:

"There is nothing wrong here, Nga."

"That is not what the news says here," came the belated, muddled reply.

A sob could be heard over the phone line.

"Please do not cry, Nga."

"Ba," she wept, "please! It is no longer safe!"

"It is OK, Nga," Hong tried to reassure her. "We are all fine. There is no danger in Saigon."

"But there *is* danger! *They are coming to Saigon!*" came Nga's delayed cries. "There are tanks! People died in Da Nang! If you do not leave, you could die, too!"

Dat, Mai, Vinh, and Chau looked on, hanging on every word they could hear.

"It is OK, I promise—"

"I am trying to get you to Australia," Nga interrupted abruptly.

"Please do not do that," her father answered.

What? Nga was trying to bring the family into Australia? What did that statement mean? What exactly was Nga seeing in the news?

"We will stay here. Saigon is very peaceful—it is quieter here now than it has been in years."

It was a deliberate white lie. Mai shot her father a disapproving glare.

There was another pause.

"Ba," Nga started again, "please don't –"

Then the line went silent.

"Nga?" Hong called into the dead air. "Hello?"

Hong turned and looked at his wife, removing the receiver from his ear.

"Disconnected."

April 17th, 1975
CIA OFFICES AT THE NGUYEN HOME
9:00AM

Rusty McClay was in his early thirties and didn't have any children (much less a wife or even a girlfriend), but he loved kids, nonetheless. His older brother and sister-in-law back home in Fort Worth had two boys that Rusty doted on whenever he could. At four and six years old, they were into the rodeo and all things cowboy—boots, Stetsons, over-sized belt buckles, and the works. Rusty had left an assignment at Langley before leaving for Vietnam and visited them before shipping out. The things they said cracked him up—he found it so amazing that a kid's view of the world was so literal, honest…often brutal, and how they could really appreciate the simple things in life.

Chuck's child was small, and Rusty thought he was great, but he wasn't as much fun as young Truc Nguyen, who at three years old was the closest thing he'd get in Vietnam to his nephews. She was so dang sweet in the little dresses Mai put her in, and when her smooth, jet black hair was put up in pig tails, it just melted his heart. Yup, Rusty McClay was a big, fat, stupid sap.

On this sultry morning, he stepped outside on the small balcony of the third-floor CIA office and noticed Truc playing on the adjacent one at her home next door. The two verandas were built on the same concrete slab and were only separated by a thin iron rail, so Rusty went over to say hello.

"Good morning, Truc!"

She only looked at him, unable to understand his English.

"Do you think your mom would mind if I gave you some candy?" he whispered, playfully making sure nobody of any authority was watching.

Rusty produced a small, dark brown paper package of M&M candies from his baggy pants pocket and waved it at her. Truc, sitting on the concrete, straightened her back as her mouth exploded into a toothy grin. Every kid spoke the language of *sugar*, regardless of their nationality and linguistics. She said something in Vietnamese that Rusty couldn't understand, but based on her excited facial expression, he knew it had to be positive. It wasn't the first time he'd snuck sweets to Chau and Mai's kid through the metal porch rails. He kneeled down into a squat and tore the top of the small bag open.

"Here ya go, honey."

A light morning breeze tousled her hair as a mound of colorful candies, each emblazoned with a small white '*m*,' poured into Truc's tiny, outstretched hand. She picked a few up with her fingers and quickly shoved them into her mouth, her little molars crunching the outer sugary shells.

"Rusty."

It was Chuck Sterrett, who had emerged from the glass porch door behind him.

"Hope you cleared those M&M's with Mai," he said in a faux-ominous tone. "She'll get pretty pissed if she finds out you're feeding chocolate to her kids for breakfast."

Rusty shrugged off his boss with a playfully exaggerated eye-roll.

"Oh, whatever."

"Hey, come inside. There are a few things the three of us need to talk about."

Rusty motioned to Truc with the small M&M bag as if to say, '*you want some more?*' No English required. Her open palm shot out like a lightning bolt through the vertical rungs towards Rusty. He poured another vibrantly-colored bunch into her hand.

"I'll see you later, OK?"

Truc flashed him a big chocolatey smile. It was all the thanks he needed.

Rusty followed close behind Chuck as they entered the main office area and shut the door.

"Close the windows and shutters, guys."

'Closing the shutters' didn't happen often, but when it did, it meant they were about to discuss some extremely sobering stuff—things that could be so uber-sensitive that they couldn't risk being heard from outside and they had to take every precaution. Rusty knew it also meant it was gonna get hot as hell in their already stifling, cigarette-smoky workspace.

Chuck sat on the edge of his desk as his agents closed off the outside world.

"Something serious up, boss?" Rusty asked as he made his way over to his desk.

"You could say that."

Jesse closed the last shutter with a wooden 'smack,' locked the window, and moved to his desk. The chair squeaked as he fished a Camel out of his flowing shirt's breast pocket.

"What's going on?" he asked.

The fresh cigarette moved up and down in his lips as he spoke.

"Well," Chuck started. "I'll be blunt, guys. Things are bad. Worse than we thought."

"Oh," Jesse said. "Well, great!"

"Has Martin finally made a call?" Rusty asked.

"Not exactly."

"Bob Frailey knows more than we do, doesn't he," Jesse asked. "Told ya."

"He's between a rock and a hard place, Jess," Chuck answered sounding slightly agitated. "He's under direct orders to keep his mouth shut, which is keeping him from doing what's right. What would you do?"

Rusty thought Chuck was toeing the line a little by defending his boss. He knew damn well Chuck was as frustrated as he and Jesse were.

"Is this why you were at the Embassy?"

"Uh-huh," he answered. "The long and short of it is the ambassador hasn't made *any* call about a full evac. Preparation for a few things? Yes, but that's all, and *only* because he's being directed by the higher-ups. He's got muster locations confirmed and supplies stockpiled. You know the non-essentials are leaving, and you know about the helicopter LZs. The US government is evacuating kids—you know that too. But there probably won't be a call made any time soon for full evacuation for the rest of us. If it happens at all, it probably won't be until after things have gotten pretty hazardous."

"I don't get this at all, Chuck," Rusty wondered aloud.

"Well, you've heard me talking to the Embassy on the phone, right? Martin's denying reality, Rusty. Thing is there's been more infiltrations, defections, leaflets, and other stuff than we've been privy to. There are thousands of Americans that live here, and rumors are flying—they have families in the States who are seeing news reports and have told them what's up—people like your mom, Jesse. So folks are scared and they're getting out. A lot of Vietnamese too, who've caught wind of the whole Da Nang thing through their own networks."

His agents only stared, absorbing it.

"And, oh by the way," Chuck said, "Chau Nguyen showed up on my doorstep yesterday and showed me a letter that came in the mail to his co-pilot. It was communist, and it was threatening…basically a message of 'join us or die.'"

Jesse exhaled a cloud of smoke across the room in a giant

sigh, then leaned back in his chair and put his hands behind his head.

"So now they're individually targeting southern military personnel," he said.

"I'm sure his letter probably wasn't the first."

"Oh, no shit?" Jesse responded sarcastically.

"Well, here's the rest. The commies might as well be at the gates of Saigon."

That changed Rusty's attitude.

"How close?" he asked.

"Fighting at Xuan Loc."

"*Sheez...*"

"Yeah, about sixty miles from us. And they're moving fast along the coast, border areas near Cambodia, and to the south uncomfortably close to us."

"Shit," Jesse said. "The *south?*"

"Why aren't we getting out?" Rusty asked.

"Like I said, man. Dunno."

The agents' mouths hung open.

"Martin just can't seem to swallow the fact that there's a real danger here, and Frailey's tired of trying to convince him," Chuck went on. "It's falling on deaf ears and he's taken too many hard knocks for asking too many times. So, there's a small group of guys at the mission who have decided to take matters into their own hands."

"They're gonna do something under Martin's nose?" Rusty asked. "What?"

"Move the high-risk folks. You know, South Vietnamese guys who've worked with us, senior military and government officials, do-da, do-da, day. It's quiet, so keep your mouths shut about it."

"How in the hell is that gonna work, Chuck?"

"It's already happening. People like the Nguyens and others—they don't have a real solid list of names, so Frailey and Mosey Copenhaver have compiled their own and some guys are already moving them—all of it under the radar. Frailey's asked us to identify who we know and add names to the list. If we wait 'til the last minute to try and get 'em outta town, you know what might happen."

"None of 'em go," Jesse answered.

"That's right. He needs all-hands-on-deck and he's asked us to assist with helping facilitate things, but because this is basically 'illegal,' it isn't an order. You don't have to do it."

"Don't have to do it?" Rusty asked incredulously. "So we can just say 'no' and not participate, then sit here with our 'essential' thumbs up our asses?"

"If you want to," Chuck responded. "I can tell you I'm gonna help. It's the right thing to do."

"Chuck," Jesse began, "we have our jobs to think abou –"

"I know, I know. It's no small thing what he's asking—it's my job too."

Chuck trailed off and the room filled with silence.

"OK, boss," Rusty finally said with steely-eyed seriousness, "so what's your plan?"

"They'll get us some vehicles and radios. We'll add names to the list, and we get to it. Start ferrying people to the port and airport."

Rusty pondered their position—much like Bob Frailey, the three agents were between a rock and a hard place. Defy the ambassador, do the right thing, and risk their careers? Or do nothing and sit on the big secret while everyone else jumps in feet first?

"Guys, it's your call. But whatever you decide, we're 'essential' personnel and we're staying here for now."

"Hmph," Rusty grumbled.

"As for us getting out," Chuck continued, "if Martin doesn't decide that the rest of us leave, we could get caught up in it all when the bad guys break through. And we face a very real risk of capture if they get into the city. You know what that means, right?"

"Escape and evade," Jesse answered coolly, looking off into space as he exhaled a stream of R.J. Reynolds' finest tobacco into the stolid air inside the office.

Rusty thought back to his escape and evasion training. It was something all CIA agents were instructed on — how to survive in non-permissive or semi-permissive environments…which meant, in a word, 'unfriendly.' The idea was to avoid contact with enemy forces or their agents and get the hell outta Dodge to friendly people using whatever means available. The idea wasn't unfamiliar, but neither Rusty, nor Jesse, nor Chuck had ever done it for real, and the thought that their 'just-in-case' training might have to be put into practical use was very disquieting, to say the least.

"You got it. Evading doesn't excite me, and it isn't something I want for my family. They're high-risk, being attached to a guy like me."

"Why don't you put 'em on a plane?" Jesse asked.

"Because they also won't leave without me. If it gets bad enough I will, but for now it isn't a battle worth fighting. I'll get their paperwork together, we'll get our bags packed and all that, but for now they're high-risk and they're staying."

"What about the Nguyens?" Rusty asked.

"Already talked to Chau and I'll keep working on them. Obviously, his being a pilot 'll help since he might have the means to move people too. Here's what I want you to do right now: decide whether you're gonna participate in our black op. Then get your personal gear organized, put anything in the office you don't need into burn bags and get rid of it. Each of us needs to be able to move out quickly in case the call comes. Or when the northern tanks start rolling down the city streets, whichever comes first."

Chuck's agents were motionless.

"How do we know if the call to evacuate is made?" Rusty asked.

"Keep it on American radio and listen for '*White Christmas.*' That's the signal to get to the Embassy."

"Couldn't they have picked a better song?"

"Be smart guys. We have to be methodical. It's a serious situation, but it isn't a race. We don't have much time, but we do have *some*. The goal here is to accelerate movement out-of-country."

"OK."

"Any questions?"

Stillness.

The KY-3 broke the silence with a buzz that might as well have been a bolt of electricity. It startled the three men, who reflexively jumped in their seats. Jesse made his way over to it in order to kill the sound, his heart racing.

"Flounders."

A pause.

"Going secure."

He fumbled with the switches on the large gray-metal piece of equipment and within fifteen seconds, a light came on.

"Showing you secret on this end. Standby one."

He shot a look at Chuck, covering the lower end of the receiver handle with the palm of his hand.

"It's Frailey."

Rusty felt a drop of sweat go down his back, pass his waist line, and continue down the crack between his glutes as he handed the phone to his boss.

"Sterrett."

It wasn't clear what Bob Frailey had to say, but it sure took a long time for him to explain it to Chuck from the other end.

"Can Tho…*shit*, Bob. That's almost as close as Xuan Loc!"

Rusty felt a brief flash of alarm ripple across his body like a power surge. Can Tho was roughly a hundred miles southwest of Saigon.

"Yeah, but this is closer than we thought," Chuck said into the phone.

More silence as Frailey responded.

"Right, OK," Chuck said. "Out."

He hung up the phone.

"Can Tho?" Jesse asked.

"We knew they were to the south of us, Jesse. But not this close. We got a lot of shelling, tanks, and even some air strikes. Center of town is ugly. Dead bodies — not just soldiers but civilians — old ladies and kids."

"Let me guess, the ARVN is caving and everyone's defecting?" Rusty asked.

"How'd you know?"

April 19th, 1975
SAIGON
11:00AM

Rusty and Jesse made their way back to their offices through Saigon's busy streets after leaving the Embassy in their detachment's clunky Citroën. Loaded scooters and lorries droned noisily by through dense traffic around the lushly decorated square that they were passing through, surrounded by French-European architecture and a dry marble fountain in the center. The frantic nature of southeast Asian traffic—the kind that a driver had to take on an air of aggressiveness to penetrate—was ever-present, especially now, given the information known to be circulating amongst populace about the violence to their north.

Because of the media stranglehold on information, Jesse knew that most people around him weren't aware of a lot of the details unless they'd been exposed to refugees from cities and towns seized by the communists. This was possible and even likely. That message trickled into homes, offices, and markets and contributed to the simmering panic that threatened to turn to a boil. It was more than enough for many to decide to leave.

His mind went back to the last time he was in the States with his mother—she had commented on his crazy driving, and how she knew his father had not taught him that way. Jesse shrugged it off and told his mom that he'd been perfecting his driving skills in foreign cities ... and in those places if you didn't take on some boldness behind the wheel, you'd never get anywhere. There were main drags in Saigon that had two or three lanes of traffic painted on the asphalt, but to many locals, that meant five car widths when trying to get through. It was utter insanity *without* the security threat, and it was hard not to take that driving style home.

Car horns, small buzzing motorbikes, and frustrated Vietnamese curse words peppered the late morning air. The day before, Rusty and Jesse organized their personal effects to make a quick exit in line with Chuck's direction. Once complete, they placed most of the sensitive paperwork and cryptologic materials they'd kept in their offices into brown paper 'burn bags,' which if not for the red and white stripes printed on their sides would have looked like the grocery bags Jesse's mother hauled home from the supermarket when he was a kid.

Any time classified materials had to be destroyed, Chuck insisted the bags be brought to the incinerator in a first-floor room of the Embassy facility so they could be burned to ashes. Shredders, while available, just weren't as secure — shredded paperwork could be pieced back together by a bad guy with a few rolls of scotch tape and a lot of time, and Chuck wasn't willing to take the risk. Ashes couldn't be taped together. Jesse didn't relish the idea of hauling classified through the streets of Saigon to be destroyed, but they couldn't inconspicuously burn it at the detachment without people knowing either.

At the wheel, he noted another jetliner taking to the air from Tan Son Nhut as he wove through the traffic-choked street. It had to have been the tenth one he'd noticed since about nine that morning.

"There goes another one," he said casually, putting his elbow up on the bottom of the opened driver's side window frame.

"Yup."

"Air traffic's definitely up."

"For sure," Rusty replied. "I think locals are more clued in than we give them credit for, and they want the hell out of here."

"Ya think?"

"All you gotta do's look at the street—it's busier than normal, every vehicle's loaded, and drivers look worried. I'm tellin' ya—I've been feeling it for a while, but up until now I couldn't put my finger on it."

Chuck and his agents were highly trained to pick up on subtle nuances of people and their surroundings. Jesse and Rusty, despite having less than twenty years' experience between them, had spent enough time in their careers in a variety of cultures and situations to be able to notice slight differences that most people might not be attuned to. Jesse took a turn on to the long, narrow street that led to their offices and suddenly slammed on the brakes, leaning on the French automobile's tinny horn as he scarcely missed a moped skirting past, stacked high with packages and one or two suitcases.

"Where do these people learn how to drive?"

Rusty, his mind in another place, didn't seem to notice the near-collision.

"I'm just glad we got rid of those bags," Jesse said with relief. "I hate taking those damn things out of the office. Always makes me nervous to have that stuff in the car when I'm driving through town, especially right now with all this shit going on."

He didn't get an immediate response, and although he was a little worried, he knew they'd get out of there somehow. Jesse had been in plenty of scrapes before that made him more nervous than *this*. Compared to Tet '68, this didn't seem as big of a deal to him. But there was *definitely* an odd and nagging urgency behind it all.

"You nervous?"

"Yeah," Rusty answered quickly.

After a brief silence, he chimed back in.

"Shit's been eating away at me for a little while," he continued. "Just a vibe, you know? Like something's just...*off*. It's spooky."

"Right."

A small, worn out-looking bus filled to the brim with people passed to their right, filling the passenger window with choking diesel smoke that reminded Jesse of the tanks he and his Marines sat atop when they convoyed out of Hue seven years before—the same Hue he and his buddies fought and died for that was now back in enemy hands...this time, probably forever.

What a waste, he thought.

"So you sure you're OK with this plan, Jess?" Rusty asked inquisitively, coughing away the smoke as it dissipated in the breeze that passed through the vehicle's open windows. "Moving people?"

The two young agents had met with Mosey Copenhaver while they were on their 'burn-classified-info' mission at the Embassy.

"I guess," Jesse replied after a brief pause, "I mean, what's our option? Might as well do the right thing and not be a pansy."

It *was* the right thing to do.

"What about you?"

"Well, if I was a South Vietnamese guy that worked with Americans, knowing the commies were coming and that I might get executed right along with my family when they got here, I'm pretty sure I'd wanna get out. Wouldn't you?"

Jesse got off the main thoroughfare and snaked his way through a couple small alleyways, then parked in a narrow space next to the CIA offices attached to the Nguyen residence at 69 Vinh Mang in the Phu Nhuan district of the city. The sun beat down on the hot, cracked asphalt next to the large white stucco structure.

"I need a shot of coffee," Jesse said as they made their way out of the car and into the building and up the stairs.

The air inside the small stairwell was cooler than it was outside, but only because it was shielded from the sun. It was momentary relief for the two CIA agents before they emerged into the office area. Hearing them come up, Chuck, who had been downstairs in his family's small residence area, could be heard thundering up the steps.

He must have been waiting.

"How's the family, Chuck?" Rusty asked as Jesse poured himself a stale cup of Folgers.

Chuck fell into his chair and leaned back with an exasperated sigh.

"Well, I think we've got most of our important stuff together," he explained. "I'm gonna head to the Embassy to finish the paperwork. Turns out it can be done pretty quickly when your family members are about to become refugees."

"Where are the bad guys this morning?" Jesse asked.

"As of early this morning, the ARVN is still getting their asses kicked up at Xuan Loc. No real update on what's changed to the south of us. We don't have a lot of time, but most of the intel I've heard indicates we have a little. Maybe a week. Maybe a little less. I don't know."

"You trust that intel, Chuck?" Jesse replied. "Ain't like we've been exactly kept in the loop over the last month or so."

"Well, *hell* Jesse. This is what we've got," he retorted. "You guys make any decisions?"

"Yuh," he answered. "We met with Copenhaver, and we'll hook up again later today. He needs some locals to be smuggled down to the port. We'll knock that out and keep going until we can't go any more."

"You got bags packed?" Chuck asked.

"Got a couple things in the van in case we need to make a quick withdrawal."

"Good. I think I'm gonna see if I can track down Hong Nguyen before I go downtown. We'll pull some strings to get their papers in order if we can. I figure if I'm going in anyway, maybe I can get their stuff moving too."

"I guess," Jesse trailed off.

"Any issues getting the bags burned?" Chuck asked. "You didn't shred 'em, right?"

"Nah," Rusty answered. "Pretty routine. We've got the office cleared out of everything classified except for the crypto inside the phone. Figured we might need it for a few days if we're all still gonna be here."

"Right," Chuck responded.

"We can pocket it when we leave for good and burn it up later."

Chuck sat silently, leaning back on his chair with his hand on his chin, as if in deep thought.

"That's fine," he said without looking directly at Rusty.

"Chuck," Rusty began, "I know you said your wife's sticking with you until the end. You really don't think there's a way to get them on a plane sooner?"

He gently rocked on his chair.

"No, Lien was pretty adamant. Grandma's pretty unhappy too. Doesn't wanna go. I had to level with her and make sure she understood that if she stayed, she might be killed because of her son-in-law. You can probably imagine how well that went over."

"Didn't convince her, huh?"

"I give it a day or two. We'll see where we end up," Chuck explained. "The good news is we've been talking about trying to get reassigned to the States for a long time. Lien's been wanting to get her citizenship. This is all a shock to her of course, but the end result is that is if we can get outta here she'll be where she wants to be. Better life for the kid and all that."

It was no small thing to take a family out of their home, even if it was the right move.

"Her mom'll end up coming, what with her husband being gone and all," Chuck said. "She doesn't have to like it, and she may even resent me, or resent Lien for marrying me ... but she'll still come. She'd have nothing left here."

Jesse remembered the story Chuck told him once over beers about a year before. His father-in-law had been an ARVN translator for the US Seventh Cavalry in the mid-sixties and was killed fighting alongside them in the Ia Drang Valley. Lien was their only child. It all happened well before Chuck came on the scene.

"Well," Chuck said, "I'm gonna go find Hong. Chau's down there, I saw his Jeep, so it'll be a good time do get some help with the whole language thing."

"What'll ya say?" Jesse asked. "I'm bettin you won't convince him to leave. Not with that plantation."

"Maybe not," Chuck answered, rising from his seat, "but I think the rest of 'em wanna go. He knows that, so who knows? He may just go for it."

"Well ... good luck."

Chuck descended the stairs and entered Saigon's heat, hopeful he might be able to convince Hong to leave. Chuck and the Nguyens were friends, though they didn't interact very often—mainly because of work and family—but with a Vietnamese family of his own, Chuck had a connection to the culture and always felt accepted by them. The barriers of tradition, language, and family often made it tough to make friends with locals in places like Vietnam. At least that was Chuck's experience in other locations he'd served in across the globe, but he never had a problem with the Nguyens.

With Chau around, Chuck knew he might be able to communicate a little better, too. Hong's English was limited—not even conversational—and having Chau there would make it far easier to get his point across. It was a good thing too because Chuck's Vietnamese was rudimentary at best. He walked around the outer wall of the home and entered the Nguyens' courtyard at the large metal gate, which screeched as he pulled it open. After making his way across the tiled surface of the small enclosure, he knocked on the worn, wood-slatted door.

"Hello, Chuck."

It was Mai, who bowed respectfully and used some of her simple English.

"Chào Mai, tôi mong Châu và Ba của cô có ở nhà," Chuck said in his best, heavily-accented Vietnamese.

Hello Mai, I hope Chau and your father are home.

"Dạ có, mời ông vô nhà."

Yes, please come in.

Mai led Chuck to the kitchen area where Hong sat with Chau over a modest lunch. Both men immediately stood and bowed slightly toward him.

"Hello, Hong. Chau," Chuck said, bowing respectfully in return, then reaching out for a handshake.

He shook Chau's hand, nodding slightly and taking note of

the unusual bags under his eyes. He also noticed the disheveled flight suit, sleeves rolled up, sweat-stained, with unit patches on his shoulders. Chau bowed again shakily. It was clear this was a man who was under stress. Family, nation, service. It had to be a lot to bear.

"Would you like some tea?" Chau asked.

It was always a good idea to take a Vietnamese host up on their offers of hospitality, and besides, Chuck thought, tea sounded good.

"Yes, thank you."

"Please sit down," Chau said welcomingly, gesturing towards an empty chair, as Mai went to prepare a cup of tea for Chuck.

"I'm sorry to bother you gentlemen," Chuck began, "but there's something urgent I need to talk to you about."

Chau looked up suddenly. He'd recently shared his own concerns with Chuck only days before and social calls were rare. Chuck knew the man could probably predict what their conversation would be about.

"Yes, of course."

Chau turned to his father-in-law and quickly told him in Vietnamese what was said. Upon hearing it, Hong appeared to grow interested as well, but Chuck sensed a touch of defensiveness. Mai returned to the table with a piping hot cup of green tea and a small bowl of sugar. Chuck didn't see her face, but knew she'd heard her husband's translation of Chuck's words for her father.

"Chau, I was a little secretive with you the other day because I don't know how much I'm allowed to share, but you know things are not looking good for Saigon right now. I am sure you have discussed this with your family."

"Yes," Chau responded.

Chau then translated for Hong.

"I have already told you that I think you should leave town, but things have worsened," Chuck said. "Some of the people I work with have become concerned that there may not be much time left to get out of the country before things turn bad for all of us. There are a lot of Americans leaving. Some of my co-workers will be departing within the next few days."

Chau froze. A small noodle fell from the end of his chopsticks and back into his bowl in what felt like slow motion, and Chuck thought he saw some color leave his face. Hong could see his son-in-law's shock and said something to him impatiently in Vietnamese (as if to say, *what?*). It broke Chau's brief catatonic gaze and after a short pause, he translated.

A long and concerned-sounding *"Ohhhh"* was all that came from Hong.

"Chau," Chuck continued, "I am very worried about you and your family. You are in danger, and when the northern army makes it to Saigon, you could be captured. If that happens, they will *kill* you and your children too."

Chau laid the chopsticks in his bowl and wiped his mouth with a small cloth napkin, never once turning his gaze away. Chuck thought he would already have put these pieces together for himself, but the look on Chau's face made him uncertain. It might have been that hearing it from an American—who he had already tried to get answers from—served as validation, and likely added tremendous weight.

"I want to stress to you again that I think you and your family should leave the country. I've come to offer help with paperwork and any transportation you might need."

Chau absorbed the words from his American neighbor and paused for a moment, nodding in acknowledgement.

Chuck was silent.

After a brief pause, Chau translated Chuck's words for Hong. His father-in-law nodded quietly.

"I'm sorry," Chuck said. "I hate to be so forward."

To a Vietnamese host, it was unusual—even offensive—for a guest to use such directness so early in a conversation, but Chuck didn't know how else to do it. He knew the Nguyens. They were exactly the kind of 'high-risk' Vietnamese that Frailey and Copenhaver were trying to get out under the ambassador's nose.

As Chau completed his translation, his father-in-law suddenly looked frustrated at Chuck Sterrett's words. Mai was in the periphery, standing motionless just a few feet away near the kitchen sink, listening. Hong said something in Vietnamese that Chuck thought sounded like irritation, but he wasn't sure. All he picked up was 'we will,' but he couldn't understand the rest. He secretly hoped it was, *"we will... leave Vietnam."*

But that wasn't it. Not even close.

"My father-in-law says he will *not* leave Vietnam," Chau stated, unable to look Chuck in the eye.

Chuck was dismayed, but calm and sympathetic. He had to be—he was a human being. These were *people*. No matter the language barrier, cultural barrier, or suspicions about his work, they had accommodated him, respected him, and treated him and his family with nothing but hospitality. Humanity was humanity.

"I understand he has a strong business here, and that Saigon is your home. But staying here is very, very risky. I have friends at the Embassy who can prepare diplomatic paperwork very quickly that will help you escape."

Chau translated as Chuck took a sip of tea, slightly burning the tip of his tongue. Hong, his facial bruises still visible, tarried for a moment and then looked directly at him, leaned forward and emphatically said *"NO"* in the best English Chuck had ever heard come out of his mouth.

This was a stubborn man, and Chuck could feel Chau's frustration. He also understood there was a family obligation to honor his father-in-law.

"Hong does not want to lose his business," Chau explained regretfully. It almost seemed like he was embarrassed. "We have discussed this before, and he insists that there is nothing in our news about any danger. That there *is no danger.*"

"I understand, Chau," Chuck said, letting out an exasperated sigh. "But your government doesn't want people to panic. That's why you aren't hearing anything in the press."

Chau didn't translate.

"Chau," Chuck spoke under his breath as if to emphasize the weight of his words, "There is fighting to the north of us, the west, and the south, and it is getting closer. Saigon is surrounded and it is only a matter of time before the enemy is here. I can get paperwork for you and your family as early as tonight. Enemy forces *will reach the city* and you will not be able to get out. Please make sure Hong understands the danger."

Chuck hoped both men understood that he wouldn't say anything at all if it weren't such a serious situation. He also hoped they grasped that the information he was sharing was sensitive, maybe even classified. The risk was immense.

"I think he does," Chau answered. "I am still trying to convince him too … my friend. I believe you, but this is very difficult for my family."

Chuck put his tea down on the table with a clink. Maybe Chau would take his family and leave without Hong.

"I can *help* you."

Chuck furrowed his brow as Chau met his eyes.

"You do not have to. I have acquired a plane."

7

April 21st, 1975
TAN SON NHUT AIR BASE
3:00PM

"Vinh!" Chau called through an open port in the cockpit windscreen and across the hangar.

The two men had been doing initial preparations on the down-for-parts C-130 since that morning. Without the forward door, the plane wasn't perfect, but it would do.

A large jet liner lifted off the runway, engines noisily rotating overhead, briefly drowning the echo of Chau's voice across the small, but cavernous facility. It had to have been the ten thousandth one that had launched since about 7am that morning. He'd begun to think that his beloved Vietnam was not unlike the Titanic—not enough lifeboats to save every soul aboard. He could only hope that, unlike that ill-fated vessel, the lifeboat that had just hurled itself into the wild blue over their heads was at capacity.

The large rolling doors were closed at his insistence in order to keep any curious eyes from noticing anything marginally unusual. Known as a 'nose dock,' the shallow building wasn't designed to fit an entire aircraft inside it, so a relatively small padded hole in the large doors allowed the rear tail and stabilizers to protrude from the facility when they were shut. Normally, when maintenance was being performed (unless the weather was bad), they remained open to allow airflow into the un-air-conditioned environment inside. In this case, Chau and Vinh thought it was worth bearing the exceedingly hot temperatures inside to avoid calling attention to themselves.

It was precautionary—most of those who had access to the base and hadn't yet departed weren't paying much attention to hangar doors. In addition, plenty of American airlifters were providing as organized a lift as possible, and most people who'd come on to Tan Son Nhut from outside were being shuttled directly to those planes. Chau's plane, by contrast, was located in a relatively obscure area where it wasn't as obvious. Also, besides Chau, those who might pilot a C-130 were already in-the-know that this one was not flyable, and if they were going to hijack anything, it was more likely to be one that wasn't broken.

The situation in Saigon was quickly becoming 'every man for himself,' and the notion that communists were nearly at the gates had made its rounds through the informal Vietnamese communication networks over and over. While things hadn't yet reached full panic mode, the sense of urgency had become quite palpable. In fact, Vinh told Chau he'd heard the Port of Saigon was becoming as busy as the airport, if not more.

His co-pilot looked up from the floor at the cockpit as Chau's head poked out.

"I thought you said we were getting a loadmaster today?" he asked.

"The majority of available crewmen are leaving or already

gone," Vinh explained, turning his palms upward. "Chau—you know this."

He bit his lip again.

"I talked to one this morning," Vinh continued. "He said he was prepared to bring his family and depart Vietnam with us. We will see if he comes."

"Only one?"

"That is all I could find."

"Come up here."

In moments, Vinh's tanned, sweating body arrived at the top of the steep steps and onto the flight deck.

Chau spoke from the left seat without looking at him.

"I am worried about the door," he stated, referring to the plane's missing hatch.

It was an abrupt subject change—one that they'd already discussed several times.

"Why are you worried about the door when we know we can fly without it?"

"Technically, it is not airworthy," he mumbled.

"Yes, but that is under normal circumstances. These are not normal circumstances."

Chau was silent.

"All we have to do is stay below ten thousand feet," Vinh said, "just like you said. Even if we aim for Thailand, we can still cross the mountains and stay below that."

Chau *had* said these things. Why was he suddenly feeling such apprehension? Hercules aircraft like this one were designed to fly at low levels and had done it since the 1950s for all manner of airdrops. Cabin pressure wasn't a problem. Getting out of Vietnam—practically speaking—was a non-issue with the plane in its current state. In fact, low-level flying might be smart anyway in order to avoid enemy radar that might originate from occupied territory they could be flying over. The greater danger was of someone falling out once they were airborne.

Maybe it was stress. Chau knew the replacement door wasn't coming, and Vinh's inbound crewman wasn't going to fix the problem with chicken wire and duct tape.

He sighed as he shoved a small cloth bag into an area next to the pilot's seat. Chau had been stocking the crew compartment in the cockpit with provisions that he'd brought to the base from home that morning—stowing them in any small cubby or cranny that he could find. He ran his fingers through his sweaty black hair, then sat heavily in the left seat and leaned his left elbow on the arm rest.

"I am sorry, Vinh," he said. "I know."

Of course he knew. This was their plane—the one Chau had selected. The one that would be most unassuming, and the one that would get them to freedom.

Vinh reached over and put his hand on Chau's left deltoid, gently shook him, and the men stared at each other. Military rank was important in the South Vietnamese Air Force. Crucial, in fact. Chau was a lieutenant colonel, and Vinh was a major. In any other situation, someone of Vinh's rank would have fallen in line with Chau's orders unquestioningly, whether he liked them or not, even if it meant certain death. There was no calling each other by first names, no familiarity, no family interaction, no mercy. But the South Vietnamese military was in its death throes, and these were two men who had seen years of hell together, lost friends and witnessed blood spilled for the country they loved…knowing that the next crimson drop could be their own. It was different. They were—for all intents and purposes—brothers.

"Hey," Vinh said with a slightly disarming grin, "Chau."

His old friend managed a half-hearted, if somewhat bloody, half-grin in return.

"We will be OK."

Even if his stubborn father-in-law was unwilling to leave, Chau had decided he had to do *something* to save his wife and kids. He swore the bad guys *would not* menace his family if he had anything to say about it. He and Mai had talked about it the evening before. He respected his wife…greatly, in fact. She was the mother of his children. But he was about done with her father. He loved and respected the man—Hong had built his fortune and provided for his family for years with business sense and good, hard work. But to Chau, this was becoming more about Trung and Truc. Mai was uneasy about it all—she was torn between two worlds: her father who had raised her, loved her, provided for her as a child; and her husband, who she loved madly, cherished, and trusted to keep them safe from harm. In the end, Chau felt he had won her over, but it had taken effort.

"What about your family, Vinh?"

"They are ready to move—all I have to do is say the word. Vietnam will survive without us," he continued.

Chau recognized good sense when he heard it.

"We need to leave all this behind and find something better where we can *live*. We owe it to our children, and you and I both know it will not happen here."

Chau soaked in Vinh's wisdom. It was a moment of clarity that seemed to make it all so obvious. They *would* survive.

April 21st, 1975
TAN SON NHUT AIR BASE
3:30PM

Chau was unpacking a box of small unperishable foodstuffs into a small space between two ribs in the forward area of the cargo bay when he thought he heard the sound of a vehicle motor near the concrete apron outside the hangar doors. He stopped and listened. Was it a small truck? He couldn't be sure.

"Chau!" Vinh called from somewhere behind and outside their plane.

Chau jogged across the C-130's yawning hold towards the rear. Vinh stood frozen near the bottom of the open ramp as Chau traversed its aluminum floor, which was covered in a worn layout of rough, no-slip tape.

"Listen," he said quietly.

Vinh was frozen in place, screwdriver in his left hand. He'd been back and forth between a small toolbox outside the craft and the starboard side of its bay making minor repairs to a lever on the tiny rear latrine. It wasn't normal for pilots to fix their own airplanes—that was typically a job for maintenance personnel—but the two men were trying to keep their activities quiet, so they improvised. Besides, many of the maintenance personnel had already disappeared.

Vinh's eyes looked upward, and his ears perked, straining to hear outside the building. A vehicle was indeed approaching, hopefully their crew chief.

"Go look," Chau directed.

Vinh snuck to a small personnel door set into the larger hangar door, cracked it open, and peeked out before opening it wider. He glanced back at Chau with an expression of relief on his face.

"Come meet our loadmaster."

Chau could hear the vehicle's engine shut off to the side of the building. He looked out through the door and immediately recognized the young man who would be their third crewman.

"*Quan* is who you chose?"

Quan Lac was a young sergeant who Vinh and Chau had worked with before. He was about 28 years old and had seen more than his fair share of violence in the last few years. But he was also known as a bit of a problem child, mainly due to his affection for intoxicating liquors.

"He is the only one left," Vinh said, "and he can fix anything, including that damned rear latrine. He will do his job."

Chau was skeptical.

"Vinh," he whispered, "this is the young man who brought back all that Soju from Seoul two years ago, got drunk, and vomited on the ramp the morning of a mission."

"Yes. You are correct."

"I am not sure about this," Chau said shaking his head.

"We are all desperate right now, Chau. He might like his Soju, but he has a wife and three young children. He wants to go as bad as we do … and we need him."

Quan's reputation preceded him. It was true he could fix about anything, but alcohol was a pretty big weakness. Under the circumstances, Chau knew there probably wasn't much choice. After all, when he wasn't drunk, rumor had it, he did OK.

"I hope he is sober," Chau said.

"Me too."

Vinh and Chau cautiously stepped out the door. Quan

was impressive in his flight suit, as if he'd dressed for the occasion—patches straight, and not a wrinkle to be found. He popped a sharp salute, which Chau quickly batted down.

"Do *not* salute me out here!"

Quan, with the smell of toothpaste on his breath—not liquor—looked confused.

"If there are any enemy watching, you could endanger us!"

"Yes, sir. Sorry."

"What did you bring with you?"

"Sir—I have a few bags of clothing and some food for my family."

"Is your family in a safe place?"

"Yes. I was not sure when we would be departing, and I brought as much as I could so we could make a cleaner escape later."

"You see, Chau?" Vinh said with a grin. "He thinks."

"Hmph."

"We should unload your vehicle quickly, Quan," Vinh said. "Let's get your things."

In moments, Quan was tossing bags to Vinh from the bed of the small pickup truck Quan had been driving.

"When we are finished," Chau called to him as he caught a small sack, "help the major fix the rear latrine."

"Yes, sir."

The three men brought Quan's bags into the hangar and dropped them just inside. Vinh walked ahead towards the rear of their aircraft with one in each hand as Chau pulled the personnel door shut behind him.

"Quan?"

"Yes, sir?" he turned.

Chau's big-brother instinct had kicked in. Vinh was

right—this was a guy that was probably desperate to get out of town with his family, same as them. Booze or not, Quan likely just wanted to do what was right, and God knew what rumors *he* had heard. No doubt he was scared too.

"Are you OK?" he asked softly.

Quan looked at Chau inquisitively.

"OK?" he asked.

"Yes," Chau answered. "Take your rank off and speak to me man-to-man."

Quan exhaled.

"My family is very conflicted," he said, turning his glance downward. "My father has heard about the communists approaching, and we have also heard the rumors about Da Nang. I have also heard rumors and many people we know are leaving Saigon. I feel we must go too."

Quan, it seemed, was human too. He turned his black eyes toward Chau.

"I am scared, Colonel."

Chau could sympathize.

"How old are your children?"

"My two sons are three and six. My daughter is only a baby."

"Will your mother and father be traveling with us?"

"Yes, sir," he answered. "And my brothers and a few aunts and uncles too."

"OK. Well, we are getting out of here," Chau reassured him, "and your family will be safe."

Quan didn't say anything, but his eyes became watery. Chau put his hand on the young man's shoulder. He was as concerned as the young crew chief, but felt it was important to keep an air of calm, even if it was a shaky act.

"Sir..." he said. "I am not a perfect man. I know I have done some stupid things. But I will do whatever is necessary to get my wife and children to safety. Tell me what I need to do, and it will be done."

"You are safe with us."

"Thank you."

"Where is your family now?"

"They are at my father's house in the city."

"Well, secure your things, then help the major with that toilet. We will need all our facilities to work if we plan to put people in there. Otherwise it will be a very uncomfortable flight."

"Yes, sir."

Quan began moving toward the C-130 with one of his small canvas bags.

"Oh, and Quan?" Chau called after him.

The young sergeant stopped and quickly wheeled around.

"Yes, Colonel?"

"I must ask," Chau continued cautiously. "Is there liquor in any of your bags?"

Quan turned his head towards the ground guiltily.

"We need to put our problems aside today."

The young man couldn't look Chau in the eye.

"Let me have it, please."

Without a word, Quan opened his small bag, then reached inside and pulled out a small balled-up towel. Unfolding it revealed an unopened 250-milliliter bottle of Crown Royal. Quan handed it to Chau.

"I am sorry, sir."

"It is OK," Chau answered. "How about if I hold on to this for you."

Quan nodded in reluctant agreement and continued to the aircraft with his empty bag in search of Vinh. Chau slowly followed and placed the small bottle in a pant leg zipper pocket of his flight suit.

April 21st, 1975
TAN SON NHUT AIR BASE
3:50PM

The cockpit smelled like leather and jet fuel; a scent Chau had become so accustomed to that he rarely noticed it anymore. But today, he savored it, knowing the flight they were preparing to embark on might be the last in his beloved Hercules. If he and his family were leaving the country, it would mean the end of flying for him. As he sat in the aircraft commander's left seat, he ran and re-ran his departure checklists. The aromas of flight filled his nostrils and lit his senses on fire.

It was sad, but it was also a reckoning—despite an untold number of harrowing combat experiences he'd had over the years, he loved flying. There was nothing like being airborne, looking down at the ground, and thinking that a hundred years ago, nobody would have believed that humans would be plying the skies the way he was. It was something that had thrilled and excited him since the first time he sat in a pilot seat. Now, with his country collapsing, he found it quite appropriate that his final mission would be the one that would save his family. What better way to retire?

Yes. It was magnificently appropriate.

He heard the sound of heavy boots coming up the steps, and Vinh emerged from the rear of the cockpit, plopping himself in the right seat—the co-pilot's chair.

"Latrine is fixed. I told you Quan could fix anything."

"Great," Chau answered. "Now I can piss. How is he doing?"

"Oh, he is fine," Vinh answered casually. "I think he is embarrassed."

"Why?"

"He told me you took his whiskey."

"Oh, yes," Chau replied somewhat absent-mindedly.

He reached into a cranny next to the pilot's seat and produced the still-sealed glass bottle of Crown Royal.

"Here," he said, handing it to Vinh. "Do something with this."

Vinh took the bottle and without hesitation, cracked it open and waved it under his nose.

"Have you ever tasted Crown Royal?"

Chau couldn't help but huff at his co-pilot.

"It is one of the best whiskies," Vinh continued, "or so I have been told."

"Do not let Quan find out it is opened," Chau directed. "We need him to have a clear head."

"Oh, do not worry, Chau," Vinh answered with some jest in his voice. "He will not find it."

"What are you going to do?"

Vinh cracked a mischievous half-smile.

"Drink it, of course."

Vinh tipped the bottle and took a good hard shot of the amber liquid, swallowing it deeply, without even the slightest wince.

"Great," Chau said disdainfully.

Just what he needed! A co-pilot with a buzz.

After lowering it from his lips, Vinh tipped the open top towards Chau as if to offer him some.

"No, thank you."

With Chau's response, Vinh took another pull from the bottle, lowering his chin with a wince, followed by a pronounced 'aaahh.'

"It is good, Chau," he said, smacking his lips.

"I am so glad," Chau responded. "Please, enjoy."

"Later."

Vinh replaced the screw-on aluminum cap and stowed the liquor in his own pant leg zipper pocket.

"I had an interesting conversation with Quan," Vinh said, changing the subject.

"About what?"

"It appears our commander, Colonel Giang has not been heard from in several days. Have you seen him?"

"No."

"The rumor is that he has departed Vietnam."

"Is that so?"

"Yes. Evidently Quan is friends with one of Giang's administrative NCOs," Vinh continued. "The colonel has not reported to work in three or four days."

Chau found it interesting that it hadn't even been a week since Giang had been in their office space looking at the communist banner Vinh had found, denying that it had meant anything. It was a prank, he'd said. Now it appeared he was gone to who-knew-where. Perhaps Giang was clued in on something Chau and Vinh were not.

"You know?" Chau exhaled. "I never liked him."

"Me neither."

"Well. What do you think happened to him?"

Vinh didn't answer right away. He just stared at the console of his airplane, his olive skin taking on a tinge of red around his cheeks and earlobes as the alcohol quickly began flowing through his blood vessels.

"I do not know. Perhaps he defected?"

The two old friends quietly chuckled, and then Vinh's mood changed to one of somber reflection as he stared off into nothingness.

A C-141 taxied in the distance. *Full of orphans, maybe,* Chau thought derisively.

"Chau, we need to pick a date to fly out of here," he said quietly.

He turned to look at his boss...his pilot and friend...his brother.

"How much time do you think we have?"

"I do not know," Chau pondered. "Perhaps a week. It is hard to say."

"My wife will go whenever I ask her," Vinh said. "We are ready to board at a moment's notice."

Chau continued to listen.

"I am not interested in being captured. Or killed. I am not interested in my wife being raped, or my children re-educated in a camp. We have neighbors who left from the port yesterday, Chau. They heard the American Navy is somewhere offshore."

"What?"

Chau was shocked, but also not shocked. This was how news traveled these days in South Vietnam. Was it true? Was it a rumor? All they had was the underground.

"Do you think it is true?"

"I do not know, but I know they are gone."

Chau bit and tasted a tinge of fresh blood from his bottom lip.

"We need a date, Chau. I've also heard there is fighting at

Xuan Loc, and our brothers in the Army are not faring well, and if it falls—"

"—yes, then Saigon is next. I know"

Chau paused, gathering a thought.

"I need time."

"For what?"

"To try and get my father-in-law to agree with me."

"I thought you gave up on him?"

"He is family, Vinh," Chau said. "It is complicated."

While he *had* decided to give up on Hong, the pain and consternation caused a gut-wrenching thought process in Chau's mind at times.

"Time is ticking, Chau. We need to move faster! Do you not agree?" Vinh asked, throwing his hands up slightly in irritation.

Was it the alcohol?

"Who will come with you, Chau?"

"Mai and her brothers probably."

"Will Mai's mother stay here with her husband?"

"I do not know."

"Well," Vinh said, "make a decision and let us get moving."

He pulled Quan's whiskey from his pants pocket, unscrewed the cap, and took another tug.

"This whole thing is enough to drive a man to drink," Vinh mumbled as he replaced the cap and stowed it back in his pocket.

"Today is Monday the 21st," Chau said. "We should try to leave in a week or so."

"Do you think we have that long?"

"I hope so," Chau answered. "There are a few more things I need to get together at home. Besides, we have a large airplane, Vinh. A week will allow us to fill it."

"Who?"

"Talk to who you know. Be quiet about it."

Chau didn't say anything else. A South Vietnamese F-5 two-ship soared off the runway and the two men could feel the roar of their engines vibrating their chests.

"Do you hear that, Chau?"

"Hear what?"

"Fighters," his co-pilot answered. "If there is fighting at Xuan Loc, those fighters are flying combat missions to support it. You have seen their empty rails yourself."

"Yes. I know."

Vinh continued. "The enemy is close."

Chau nodded, his troubled gaze unable to look at his co-pilot and friend.

"Chau," Vinh continued, his cheeks flushed, "this C-130 could be the last aircraft on the ramp if we wait much longer."

His words penetrated Chau like a six-inch blade.

"Let us go while we still can. Before the city turns into chaos."

"One week, Vinh," Chau insisted. "Quan will make sure we have enough fuel in the tanks as we get closer. Forget the rules about takeoff weight. We will go heavy."

"Do you think that much fuel will be left on the base if we wait a week?"

"Order him to get it now and fill our tanks."

"Have you thought about where we might go?"

"What about Utapau?" Chau suggested.

They'd been there before. Utapau Air Base was a Thai installation about eighty miles from Bangkok, used extensively by the US Air Force during the height of combat operations over Hanoi in the late sixties and early seventies.

"I suppose," Vinh responded.

"Maybe there are Americans or Australians there. We can claim refugee status."

"*Trời đất ơi!*," Chau cursed.

"I cannot believe this is happening either," Vinh said, "but Chau—this is it. We go to Utapau, we talk to the Americans…or the Australians…or whoever. From there, we move our families forward and get on with our lives. But we will be *alive.*"

Hong…Mai…Trung…Truc, Chau thought.

"We aim for April 28th."

8

April 22nd, 1975
THE PORT OF SAIGON
3:00PM

Rusty McClay carefully wound the Embassy's Ford Econoline van through a swarm of people moving hastily towards Saigon's port facilities, but it was slow-going. This was their third day trying to inconspicuously move people to the port and airport, and this run had to be their sixth or seventh of the day. He had simply lost count.

Unlike the subtle tension he and Jesse had felt amongst the public on their way to destroy classified materials just a few days prior, the growing anarchy they'd witnessed in the last forty-eight hours was impossible to deny. Ever-growing crowds of people moved frantically to get themselves out before the looming communist threat arrived—on foot, by car, truck, bus, bicycle, cyclo, scooter, or moped. All were trying to haphazardly squeeze themselves towards Saigon's tumultuous riverfront that led to open sea and freedom. The din of the mob, it's shouts and screams, the panicked cries of women and children, and the drone of motors was nearly deafening. Diesel engine exhaust clouded the air like a thick fog. There had to be at least five thousand people within their immediate environs, and the atmosphere was one of near panic.

"This is insane," Jesse exclaimed.

His cigarette smoke slowly exited through a 2-inch crack in the partially-opened passenger side window of their van.

The two young agents were carrying seventeen South Vietnamese souls in their twelve-passenger vehicle—women, children, a few elderly, and one thirties-ish man with a military haircut and grievous scar on his face—to a port area where they hoped to board a ship. It was all part of Bob Frailey and Mosey Copenhaver's covert "underground railroad" operation to help high-risk people escape their country. Rusty thought it wasn't unlike the American Civil War when abolitionists risked life and property to assist escaped slaves barely a hundred years before. And also like the 1860s, their current situation was one of America's own dubious creation.

Rusty said nothing but took his right hand momentarily off the wheel to make sure his .45 pistol was still securely mounted on his belt on his right hip. This wasn't exactly a safe environment—he was acutely aware that during societal collapse, rule of law was out the window, and it became 'every man for himself.' Almost anything could happen. The crowd was desperate, and there was no telling what they might do when they saw two white guys driving an American van packed to the roof with Vietnamese citizens. Not to mention the potential presence of communist agents.

The gun was ready—its single stack magazine 8-rounds-full, with one in the chamber. Its .45 ACP+P cartridges were man killers. A single .225-grain slug to someone's head would quickly turn it into a pulpy mess and clear a crowd from the immediate area. He clicked the safety off, then moved his hand to the van's horn, leaning on it to open a small path to his front, but he found that the crowd only became denser and denser.

"We're not gonna get much closer," he muttered, honking again.

"Try," Jesse answered, his blue eyes and blocky jowl pointed sharply forward.

Rusty wondered if the bedlam that surrounded them was causing Jesse to feel jittery from his war experience.

"Look up there," he said, pointing over the short hood towards the port's massive loading equipment permanently affixed to the piers. "You can see the handling cranes just ahead. We're close."

"OK."

"Find a place to off-load these guys. We'll go get another group after that. Still gotta get back out through all this."

Rusty nodded.

He slowly tried to work his way leftward toward an area roughly fifty yards off with tall shrubbery and fewer people. He leaned on the horn again as panicked people hustled past him. There was a large military-style truck about thirty yards to his right, its high-railed bed crammed with people and personal items—arms and heads could be seen above the truck's cab, which was also packed beyond its capacity. A small white scooter, loaded impossibly high with faded gold, hot pink, and pea-green suitcases, revved its engine and slipped into a small gap to the agents' immediate right as people near it shouted angrily at the riders. A whiff of sweat-soaked body odor wafted across their noses. Rusty glanced at his passengers in the rear-view mirror and saw red, perspiring faces, emblazoned with anxiety.

Three days prior, Copenhaver had distributed radios set to

an obscure frequency to a small number of Americans and distributed a haphazard list of over two thousand souls who fit the bill. They began moving people soon afterward.

Vehicles from the Embassy fleet and a number of commandeered civilian cars were immediately pressed into service to transport from muster locations to Tanh Son Nhut's airport and the seaport under the nose of Ambassador Martin. Rusty didn't see how the unauthorized evacuation would put much of a dent in the numbers, but at least they'd be able to evacuate a few.

In the short term, keeping the operation quiet wouldn't be that difficult—at least that was the thought—since most of the movement to embarkation sites at the airport and seaport would be conducted from places all around the city. Movements at the Embassy itself were designed to be quite limited, and so far that's what they'd been.

"OK," Rusty pointed breathlessly, "right over here."

Rusty approached his targeted drop-off point. Looking past the trees and trucks, a medium-sized cargo vessel could be seen, its decks brimming with people. Bare legs hung from the edges of every deck, every portal featured worried Asian faces, and gangways intended for single-file lines bowed grotesquely under the weight of people moving up them two and three abreast. A motorcycle could even be seen being hoisted up the side. At last, he reached the tall hedge he'd selected, set the brake, and turned to his rear.

"Đến lúc phải ra đi!"

Time to go.

The nervous people in the seats behind him began to gather the few personal belongings they were able to scrounge together.

"That didn't sound like what you said to the last load," Jesse said. "How much Vietnamese do you know, anyway?"

Rusty ignored him, his hands still grasping the steering wheel in a death grip.

"Come on, help 'em out, Jess!"

Jesse took a last drag on his cigarette and opened his door, pitched the butt on the ground, and was quickly at the side doors. The first person to exit was an elderly woman pushing ninety who he had to help gently down from the van's high step.

My God, he thought to himself, *how in the hell is she gonna make it?*

The single adult male passenger handed Jesse an infant wrapped in white and pastel yellow blankets before climbing out. The baby began to cry and Jesse, apparently unsure of exactly what to do, began to bounce her slightly to calm her down, uttering soft words under his breath. The baby's scarred father began to help his young wife out of the van before taking the child from him and turning to leave with barely a word.

The last one out was a young girl who couldn't have been older than ten. After exiting, she abruptly stopped, then whimpered next to the passenger's side door and stared at Jesse.

"Thank you," she cried with a quivering lower lip in heavily accented English, before the older woman she was with hollered after her. They quickly disappeared into the mob.

The gravity of the personal risk these people were taking didn't hit Rusty until that moment. It was impossible not to feel the intense emotion of this little girl who had been heaved against her will into this hellish madness. At such a young age, she *knew* what was at stake — this ten-year-old child, who should have been playing hula-hoops with her girlfriends in the schoolyard, was now running for her life from all that she knew into the oblivious unknown. It made him altogether angry and profoundly sad.

Jesse climbed back into the van and reached for a fresh smoke.

"What the hell was that all about?" Rusty asked.

"Nothing. Let's get the hell outta here."

April 22nd, 1975
CIA OFFICES AT THE NGUYEN HOME
7:00PM

"Xuan Loc's gone, Chuck."

Bob Frailey was seated at Chuck's desk.

"Did you already hear?"

Chuck had just walked into his work area covered in sweat and carried a bowl of noodles in his hand. With the uber-secret evacuation now in full swing, Frailey had opted to keep clear of his Embassy office and try to lay low. Being visible was a risk—if the ambassador found out what was going on, it could cause a major problem, so he had relocated to Chuck's detachment at the Nguyens' home for what he told the compound's staff was 'field work.'

Well, it wasn't exactly a lie.

"No," Chuck answered nervously as he put his bowl down.

He sloughed into a rickety chair, surrounded by the dimming light barely making it through the window slats.

"I've spent half the day getting my family's affairs in order and the other driving people to the airport. Figured it was a matter of time, though."

"It's been totally flattened," Frailey continued, "and now the north's got it under their control. Resistance isn't completely gone, but what's left of the ARVN's Eighteenth Infantry is in full retreat and not putting up much of a rear defense."

"What about Can Tho?"

"Not much new at the moment, but Xuan Loc's obviously the more immediate threat."

With resupply and even basic provisions for the south moving at barely a trickle, Chuck knew it wouldn't be long before the communists were able to squash whatever opposition remained, whether at Xuan Loc, or Can Tho, or anywhere else. Now that the town was in enemy hands, it was all but assured the communists would mop up what was left between them and Saigon, including Tan Son Nhut's sister installation, Bien Hoa Air Base to the northeast. Chuck reckoned the South Vietnamese capital would be lucky to hold out for much more than five or six more days. What was worse is that he knew that the word about Xuan Loc would make its way at lightning speed through the underground civilian networks, meaning the tenor in Saigon would become even more panicked.

"How many dead?" Chuck asked.

"Don't know, but it'll be a lot," his boss answered with concern, "and it isn't only ARVN. A lot of civilians too."

Chuck sighed. Saigon was firmly in check-mate, and it was anyone's guess how long they had to get as many people out of town as they could. It could be two days, or it could be a week.

"So what's next?"

"Well, from what I understand, the fifteen divisions that have been moving this direction since the beginning of the month haven't really diminished much in strength. They've got tanks, triple-A, and all kinds of other goodies for us. Probably more than ten thousand troops from the Xuan Loc fight alone will be on their way here in pretty short order. The remaining elements of the Eighteenth that are trying to stand in between them and us won't last long."

"Great," Chuck replied, turning his gaze to his noodle bowl.

"And with the anti-aircraft weapons, the bad guys could shoot jet liners full of refugees out of the sky if they really wanted to."

Chuck suddenly lost what little was left of his appetite.

"Wanna hear some more?"

"No."

"Remember that whole thing about Ford asking Congress for $700 million?"

"You mean his request that everyone knows won't fly?"

"That's the one," Frailey retorted. "Well, it's officially dead as of late yesterday."

"Hmph."

"Oh, right…" Frailey went on, "and you probably heard President Thieu resigned last night. Announced it on state TV. The Vietnamese media is finally reporting truth."

Chuck felt a jumble of nerves growing in his gut, punctuated by uncomfortable gas bubbles in his intestines.

"I heard he didn't have a lot of nice things to say about Uncle Sam. I know a lot of his government buddies haven't been real happy with how he's handled the commies."

"Well, he took the fall," Frailey answered. "We didn't really help the ARVN either. Even if Ford's military aid package was pushed through today, it would have been too little too late. Those guys needed resupply months ago."

"So Vice President Huong is in charge now, I guess."

"Yup. But who knows how long he'll stay there?"

"He's gonna try to negotiate, isn't he?"

"Probably."

"Won't go anywhere, will it?"

"Nope."

No strangers to shaky situations, the men paused to consider their roles in this one.

"Chuck, you need to get your family the hell out of here. And I mean *yesterday*."

Chuck nodded. His family and the Nguyens had been on his mind ever since he heard about Thieu's resignation.

"I know."

"I pulled the trigger this morning on enough seats for you and your family to get on a jet tomorrow out of Tan Son Nhut. You, Lien, and her mother and brother. Your wife will have to hold the kid in her lap—it was the best I could do."

"Wait...we're leaving tomorrow?"

"Yup."

"Well, how's that work if I'm considered essential? I don't –"

"You're getting the *essential hell* out of here. Quit worrying about who's supposed to be here and who's not. Go and live to be a father to your kid."

"What are you gonna do, just throw me on to a plane and not worry about what the Agency or State thinks about it?"

"That's about the size of it. I don't give a shit about 'essential.'"

"OK, so let me get this straight, boss. I'm in a mission-essential Central Intelligence Agency position and you're *ordering* me to leave?"

Frailey nodded.

"We're doing all this other stuff without permission," his boss told him, "so I'm not asking for it in this case either. They can forgive me later. You and your family are outta here."

It was a real surprise for Chuck, and he knew it could have potential ripple effects. What would his agents think? He'd be leaving them behind, high and dry. At the same time, he felt a twinge of relief that he'd be able to go safely with his family, but it was a grain of sand on a beach full of guilt.

"I wouldn't feel right leaving."

"I don't care about your feelings," Frailey answered. "Your family needs you, and I'm putting you on a plane tomorrow."

"What are the details?"

"Thirteen hundred. Can you guys be ready to go?"

"Diplomatic papers are done, and the basic stuff is packed. Where's it headed?"

"Clark."

Chuck had been through Clark Air Base before. It was a sprawling US Air Force installation that was situated north of Manila in the Philippines, and it had been used extensively as a hub for military cargo movement at the height of the war.

"Then Hawaii. The agency can get you reassigned from there."

"How's that gonna happen if I'm essential and I show up on their doorstep before a full evac is announced?"

"Stick it out at Clark until this place collapses. Nobody will bat an eye."

It was official. Chuck was receiving orders to permanently depart his post.

"You've done good here. It's OK."

"I don't like running."

"I know. That's why I booked your seats. I knew your wife wouldn't leave without you, so I did it for you. I appreciate your sense of duty, Chuck, but frankly *to hell with it*. You know damn well if you stay it'll be ugly for all of you. Can you imagine escaping and evading with a kid barely walking, a young wife and her middle-aged mother, along with a rebellious Vietnamese teenager?"

Just then, a door slammed, followed by the sound of people stomping up the steps. Jesse and Rusty charged in through the door.

"What's the word?" Jesse asked, slightly out of breath, as they emerged from the dim doorway and into the low light of the large wood-paneled office area.

"What's *your* word?" Bob Frailey countered.

"Well," Rusty began as he and Jesse fell into their desk chairs, "we've been up since 3am, got a bunch of loads to the port and the air base, got cried at by a ten-year-old girl, and nearly ran over a few people in the process. In all it's been a productive day."

Jesse lit a cigarette, then picked up where his partner left off.

"My ass hurts from sitting in that damn van."

"Well, sorry for your ass. How are the crowds at the port?"

"Crazy. It's chaos," Jesse answered. "It doesn't feel like we're making a dent, especially with all the people trying to get out, and the word on the street is that crowds are growing outside the Embassy."

Jesse's smoke cast a gray-blue fog over the four men.

"You been keeping radio silence?"

"For the most part," Rusty answered, "but we ran into Mosey. He said Martin might've gotten wise a couple hours ago to what we're doing."

"How's that?" Frailey asked, not hiding his surprise well. It was obvious this was the first he'd heard it.

"Evidently he got a call from some guys at Clark saying

a few passenger planes full of South Vietnamese brass and their families came in late last night with a few of our State guys aboard. So they asked him how many more they should expect."

Chuck was afraid of this — he knew it wouldn't be long before Martin discovered what was happening.

"I guess he found out it was some guy at the DAO. Martin fired him."

Usually confident, Bob Frailey was clearly a little shaken. Jesse pulled on his Camel, the orange glow slowly creeping its way towards its filter.

"Fortunately," Rusty began, "it doesn't sound like anyone gave up any other names, so for the moment, it might look like an isolated case to him. I'd say we're probably OK, at least for now."

"Well, you're gonna have one less driver." Frailey said flatly.

"Whaddya mean?" Jesse asked.

"I'm moving out with my family tomorrow," Chuck said, his head hanging. "Bob got Lien and me on a plane that leaves after lunch tomorrow."

Jesse and Rusty appeared to take it better than he had hoped, but it didn't make him feel any better.

"Well…you should," Rusty replied as he cleared his sweaty red bangs from his eyebrows. "Get your wife and that kid outta here."

"Damned if I feel good about it."

"Something tells me we won't be far behind you," Jesse answered. "Our shit's packed and already in the van. We can get on a plane or a boat with any one of the groups if we have to. But I'm sticking around as long as I need to."

"Me too," Rusty proclaimed.

His body's stench from long hours in the heat was beginning to comingle with Jesse's smoke.

"What about you, Bob?" he asked. "What're you gonna do if Martin finds out you're behind a lot of this?"

"Me?" he said with a bit of bravado. "Hell, I ain't afraid o' no Graham Martin. I'm gonna do what I gotta do, even if I gotta die doing it."

Chuck respected Bob Frailey and knew he was well-respected by the rest of his agents. It wasn't only because he had a sharp mind and good sense of things, but because he'd served in so many capacities all his life. People in the spy business esteemed him for his World War II experience—especially Jesse, who felt a particular sense of connection to him that was not uncommon with veterans, regardless of which conflict they served in. The man had seen death right in front of him, stared it in the face in the cold and snowy forests of the Ardennes, and hocked a big loogie in its face.

"Hey Chuck," Rusty said, "what are the Nguyens doing?"

"Chau's still fighting Mai's dad."

"Sounds to me like ol' Chau just needs to take his kids and go on without him."

"He'll go—he's got some kinda plan," Chuck said. "I offered help with paperwork, but so far he's been reluctant to take it."

The room got silent for a moment.

"Well," Rusty said, "when you're ready to leave, Jesse and I will take you."

"OK. But for now, get a few hours of rest, then get your asses back in that van and get some more people to safety. You're obviously gonna want to avoid the Embassy, at least for right now. And Rusty?"

"Yeah?"

"Please get a shower."

With a look of sudden concern, Rusty raised his right arm and buried his nose in his armpit.

"What?" he asked, frowning back at Chuck. "Is it that bad?"

"How much time you think we got?" Jesse asked.

"Well, Xuan Loc went dark a little while ago," Frailey replied, "and there's a division of more than ten thousand troops coming in our direction."

"*Dammit,*" Jesse mumbled, wiping a drop of sweat from his brow.

"The only thing holding them back is leftovers of the Eighteenth ARVN, and most of those guys are shot full of holes or out of ammo or both."

"OK, so they're what…sixty miles out?" Jesse asked. "What about the defenses around the city?"

"You know as well as the rest of us that they're weak, Jesse."

"Still, I bet things hold for a while."

"Maybe," Frailey answered cautiously. "Maybe not. Chances are they won't be here tonight…but I give 'em a few days before there's a commie tank parked in front of the Presidential Palace."

Another aircraft tore overhead, its jets whining into the distance, headed for freedom.

April 23rd, 1975
NGUYEN HOME, SAIGON
8:30AM

Chuck didn't have a lot of time, but he was very concerned about the Nguyens. These were good people who he held great respect for—especially Chau, who had been putting his life on the line for years in the interest of keeping his country free from the dark red shadow of communism. He'd survived literally thousands of flight hours on combat missions over the last decade, many of them extremely dangerous, and in the process saved not only his and his crews' lives, but the lives of untold numbers of his countrymen. He was one of the most honorable men Chuck had ever met, and now that twilight was descending on Chau's war, he felt it was his duty to give it one last-ditch attempt to offer assistance. With the remaining time before he and his family were to depart town, Chuck focused on that final attempt.

He, Lien, and her mother and brother were as ready as they were going to be. Much of what they kept at the house would have to remain there, which was something Lien's mother had a hard time with. When her husband died, she became melancholy and nostalgic, and it was a very sensitive and complex struggle to induce her to abandon the vast majority of her household items and things of sentimental value. But they simply couldn't take it all. She resigned to a single suitcase with a large manila envelope packed tightly with wedding items and dog-eared black and white photographs. In his haste, Chuck kept having to remind himself what it might have been like if he'd have had to leave his West Virginia home behind, with little hope of ever returning. No doubt it might be the hardest thing he'd ever have to do. He was as patient as he could be with his mother-in-law, but it was a chore. There wasn't much time to waste.

He'd been up since four in the morning and was now sitting in the detachment office alone in the unnerving morning quiet. Jesse, Rusty, and Bob Frailey had already flung themselves to points far and wide across Saigon to find more high-risk locals and get them to their points of embarkation. Chuck expected them back some time around ten o'clock to help him and his family get out of town. He was in the thick of the calm before the storm and it was a very surreal feeling. The electric fan blithely rotated in the corner of the room, and he could just detect the vestiges of the last cigarette Jesse had smoked before he went back out to the passenger van earlier. The alley below the building was fairly silent, save for the odd scooter that went by, while the main road about a half-block away seemed to be supporting some minor vehicle traffic. How many people had already left Saigon? A city this big? Couldn't be *that* many. There'd be scores that stuck behind, most of them probably choosing to hole up in their homes until all the madness blew over.

He'd come to the office to extract the crypto from the KY-3 phone then destroy it with the rest of the comm equipment, but for the moment stayed slumped in his chair, reflecting and taking stock of his time in Vietnam. When it came to evacuation planning, Chuck's experience at other embassies across the globe was to follow the standard practice for any foreign State-Department-activity: make sure all the secrets were shredded, burned, or otherwise obliterated lest they fall into enemy hands, trash the equipment, then get the hell out.

He held the inch-wide, waxy-paper roll of crypto tape in his hands and spun it between his fingers. Of all the places he'd been in the world since he'd graduated college at West Virginia the better part of two decades before, he thought this one had been the most interesting. It had also been the most nerve-wracking—more so than the three jaunts into Sub-Saharan Africa he had in the late sixties that he couldn't talk about, or the boring two years he spent in Belgrade before coming to Saigon. He'd arrived in early 1972 while the war wound down as a result of the soon-to-be-signed Paris Peace Accords—a murky and frustrating effort for Nixon to say the least. The very next year, the president negotiated a cease-fire and gave the order to withdraw American troops from the country. Chuck believed he was there to help close the bloody and arguably fruitless chapter for the United States once and for all.

Maybe it was less a belief and more of a cautious hope.

He knew at the time there was no guarantee Hanoi would stick to whatever was agreed to. Since then, they clearly hadn't ... and here was Uncle Sam again, doing little to nothing productive to address it. As an American, he found it frustrating and embarrassing, especially when he had to face his family or the Nguyens. After all, if not for the United States, would this even be happening? Maybe, but it was discomforting nonetheless, and he wondered how people like Hong and Chau couldn't be a little pissed off at Americans like him.

He did have something to show for it though—a beautiful wife and a child. Without Vietnam, he might never have been a husband and father. It was easy to think about the what-ifs. Leaving Vietnam behind would be hard on them, but he had to admit to himself that he was excited to show them the United States.

His thoughts drifted to Rusty and Jesse. Chuck had a ticket out—mainly because Bob Frailey was insistent and had pulled some strings. For his agents—both 'essential' personnel and single guys with no kids—it wouldn't be as easy. With Ambassador Martin as obstinate as ever, there was no telling whether any full evac order would ever come. The possibility of Bob, Jesse, and Rusty getting caught up in an imminent and violent coup because their own nation's in-country leadership refused to face reality was a real danger.

Chuck was sure the communists wouldn't be nice if they were apprehended. Much like the POW situation during the war, there were many who would go missing. What if his guys did? There were few good options, but the best one would be if Graham Martin did the right thing in the end and got them all out before things got really bad. But for now, his guys were trapped.

He rocked on his clunky, government chair, causing it to mutely squeak under him, and gathered his thoughts. Chau had told him he had some sort of plan that involved an airplane. What was it? Chuck hadn't asked any questions, but having a plan was good.

He was acutely aware that the pull of family in Vietnam was strong. Hong's concurrence would be sticky, but Chuck was still optimistic that he'd agree to get to a safe place with his son-in-law before the inevitable collapse. It was obvious the man was not interested in listening to a tall, pale American. Chuck had seen Chau's Jeep downstairs—he was home. Besides, he'd gotten some US dollars at the Embassy. The rent was due, and he wouldn't feel right leaving town without paying the Nguyens.

Chuck got up from his chair and pocketed the crypto tape, then went over to the small bathroom just outside the office. Behind the door and leaning against an inside wall laid a large, red fire axe. Time to destroy the KY-3. Chuck grasped the handle, then walked back in to the work area. He opened the large cabinet door on the front of the unit, then forcefully ripped the receiver from the front panel. Backing up a couple feet, he held the axe in front of his body with both hands, huffed once or twice, then raised it. Its head crashed with a noisy crunch into the top panel of the KY-3, slinging bits of hard plastic into the air.

He dislodged his tool and took another mammoth swing, followed by another one, and then another. Small switches dangled by their wires from the gaping holes he'd created, as pieces of the phone's inner components fell to the floor. Was that enough? Chuck wanted to make sure, so for good measure he gave it three more overhead and sideways swings, crushing the bowels of the antiquated communication device. Twisted metal hung garishly from the frame, and bits of wiring and dust ejected toward him as his axe met its target. It was oddly satisfying.

That oughtta do it, Chuck thought to himself.

But he swung again. One last crushing blow to the phone.

No, THAT oughtta do it.

He dropped the axe to the floor, then descended the stairs as Lien and his mother-in-law were clearing the kitchen.

"I'm going next door for a minute."

He walked into the alley, then into the Nguyens' cool, tiled courtyard. The small gate swung shut behind him with a clap and Chuck emerged under Hong's queen flower tree, which had begun to shed some of its blooms on to the hard surface of the piazza. As he made his way to the front entrance of the home, Chau emerged carrying two small bags of baby items and food in his left hand. Thankfully, there was no sign of Hong.

"Oh," Chau said, not expecting to see Chuck. "Good morning, Chuck."

"Hello, Chau."

Chuck reached out to shake and as Chau took his hand, he politely bowed. He still looked as fatigued as the last time Chuck had seen him.

"Would you like to come inside for some tea?"

"Uh, no. Thank you, I don't have very much time."

Chau nodded and walked toward his worn, OD green American Jeep to put the bags in the back seat. Chuck followed him.

"Chau, I wanted to come by and let you know that Lien and I are leaving."

Chau's expression turned to one of apparent surprise. Americans leaving town wasn't new to him, but this was the first one he knew personally.

"Oh," he said as he plunked the bags into the back of the Jeep. "When?"

"A few hours. We fly out this afternoon."

The self-imposed shame Chuck felt leaving his agents and his duty extended to the Nguyens.

"Chau, you don't have much time left. Maybe less than you think."

Chau didn't look at him, just kept loading his Jeep.

"Did you see Thieu on television?"

"Yes," Chau said. "I think this has been due for a long time."

He stopped for a moment and scratched his head before turning to Chuck.

"Chuck, you have always been very honest with me, and it is out of respect that I never ask about your work," Chau began in his heavy accent. "Mai's sister called from Australia. I have heard what is on television there. You told Vinh and I we should leave, and that you could help with papers and transport. Now *you* are leaving."

It was uncharacteristic for a Vietnamese man to pry.

"It is not my business," he continued, "and normally I would not ask you. But *what do you know?* What is your job in Saigon?"

Although Chuck had prepared for the eventuality that he

might be asked what he did for a living, he still felt a little un-comfortable when the question finally came.

"I trust you, Chau," he answered. After a long pause, he add-ed, "I work for the Central Intelligence Agency."

Chau didn't show any demonstrable reaction to Chuck's words.

"There are some things I want tell you, because—"

"—how much time do we have?" Chau interrupted.

"Four, maybe five days at most."

The seasoned pilot didn't respond.

"Chau, I could get in real trouble for telling you this, but I don't guess your intelligence services have notified you that communist forces are surrounding Saigon. Vice President Huong will not be in charge for long. There is fighting at Can Tho and the last of what stood between North Vietnam and a free city was destroyed yesterday at Xuan Loc. You may have heard there's been violence there all week. The remaining friendly forces are fighting a retreat now towards the perimeter of Saigon."

Chau bit his lip hard.

"If you could be sent to jail, why are you telling me this?"

"Because you deserve to know. My family is Vietnamese. I'm a father too, and I believe our kids deserve to grow up in a place where they don't have to worry about getting shot."

The two men stared wordlessly at each other. Chuck realized this would probably be the last time they'd ever see each other and share a conversation.

"Chau, I know family is very important. But you should leave Vietnam even if some of them refuse to go. You said you have a plane. What is your plan?"

Chau looked away and walked towards the front entrance to

the house without answering, grabbing two more small bags to put into the Jeep. He pulled the door shut as he wandered back in Chuck's direction.

"Chau, when are you going to leave?" Chuck asked again.

"Mai and I and the children will fly out on Monday."

Chuck couldn't help but feel a small sense of relief at Chau's words, but Monday was five days away—an eternity under the circumstances.

"How did you get a plane?"

"There is one C-130 we have been preparing. It is grounded for maintenance but can still be flown. We will load it with as many people as we can find and fly out."

"Chau," Chuck pleaded, "I told you I can arrange to have the right paperwork prepared for you and your family. The Embassy has done it for hundreds of people in the last forty-eight hours. I could make it happen fast."

"No, thank you. It is too much to ask. Besides, we can get into Thailand or Malaysia very easily and trying to get my father-in-law to agree to prepare any papers is more than I want to worry about."

"I'm glad you are planning to go…*but please do not wait long.*"

"Thank you, Chuck," he said abruptly, extending his hand to shake. "I am very grateful for your help."

Chuck firmly shook hands with Chau as he bowed.

"I don't feel like I've done anything."

"You are a good man. I wish we had more time to talk over some beer."

"Me too."

Chuck reached into his pocket and pulled out a thick roll of hundred-dollar bills.

"I didn't want to leave without paying the rent."

He grabbed Chau's hand and placed the wad of cash in it.

"Please take this. I hope it helps you wherever you and your family are going."

Chau grasped the money, then shot Chuck a curious look as if he was about to say something. Then without a word, he zipped it into the left breast pocket of his flight suit.

"If it's OK, I'd like my agents to be able to use the apartment for a few more days as they prepare to get out themselves."

Chau nodded, turning his eyes sadly to the courtyard tile.

"Yes, of course."

"Thank you."

Chuck struggled to hold his guilt at bay, but it was painful.

"I wish you and your family the best of luck and safe travels."

Chau nodded, looking away so he couldn't see his face.

Chuck turned to leave as the sound of a vehicle motor and brakes emanated from the alleyway. Jesse and Rusty had arrived. It was time to go.

"Chau," Chuck said, "I will be in Hawaii for a little while. If by some chance you end up there, you can find me through the main FBI facility in Honolulu. Maybe I can help you get to the continental United States."

"Thank you."

April 23rd, 1975
TAN SON NHUT AIR BASE MAIN GATE
10:00AM

Rusty and Jesse had made so many trips to the port and airport that they'd lost count, and they'd become callously used to the crowds. Now it was Chuck's turn to be the passenger in his agents' van, along with Lien, their son, and her mother and brother. Most of their airport runs had been to the civilian side of the runway, with only a handful to the military side for non-essential Americans leaving town via chartered jet and C-141.

The approach to Tan Son Nhut's main gate was busy, and they found themselves waiting in a line of cars and trucks for nearly an hour to be processed through security. The ARVN sentries who stood guard had been handling a steady, but not overwhelming stream of people destined for any plane that could be found sitting on the ramp.

"Not too bad here," Rusty said as he stared out the window from behind the driver's seat.

"It'll get a lot crazier before it's all said and done," Frailey replied.

They sat idly behind a pale blue Italian-made Fiat 850—a small vehicle which would normally only seat four people, however Chuck noted this one was packed to the rafters with what looked like six or seven passengers and one westerner at the wheel. Their Econoline van was positioned about three cars back from the guards, who despite the growing chaotic feeling in Saigon, were successfully handling a fairly orderly procession of vehicles without much that looked like pandemonium. Like his boss, Chuck didn't think that would hold up for long as more and more people tried to get out of the city over the coming hours and days.

"This is nothing compared to the civilian side," Rusty added casually. "I don't know which is busier. The airport or the port."

The security gate at the military side was somewhat of a deterrent to a casual citizen who wanted to make his way to an airplane to leave the country, for the simple reason that it was 'military.' Most seemed to be choosing to brave the commercial side to try and find their flights out. Besides, most of those at the main gate fell within some category of passenger that was allowed out on American airlift—children of US citizens and their families, some Vietnamese workers, and others. There were also untold numbers of European workers and diplomats still trying to get free of the threat—many of them lined up in front of the guard building.

The base's gate complex consisted of an open area surrounded by power lines, a chain link and barbed wire perimeter fence, and a small, unimpressive concrete and glass guard shack flanked by a larger building across the exit lane to its left. A tall, pagoda-like building with a red roof stood to the right side of the road, just outside the fence.

"This gate was a much harder target when I came through it on the way back from Hue," Jesse commented. "I remember a lot of M-60s, sandbags, and concrete."

They slowly advanced toward the guards, and as they pulled up to one of the young soldiers, Rusty flashed his Embassy ID card. The young South Vietnamese guard couldn't have been a day older than eighteen, and as he adjusted the M-16 slung over his shoulder, he indifferently checked the front and back of the small laminated badge and waved them through.

"We should be able to drive right on to the ramp," Rusty said. "There'll be a couple guys out on the tarmac who'll process you guys to get on the bird, Chuck."

Chuck and Lien's young son whimpered a little as they pulled through the perimeter. Lien's mother and brother sat numbly, saying little, and taking in the scene—the last they'd see of their home country…maybe forever.

Chuck took in the stark ugliness of the once sprawling American base and thought that for a tropical location like Vietnam, there didn't seem to be much in the way of trees or vegetation. Mostly one-story, light-colored cinder block buildings were prolific, and the installation's red and white-checkered communications tower showed its age with visible rust and corrosion. They followed a small line of traffic down a long street, on the edges of which stood several empty and dilapidated two-story barracks facilities once used by American service members during the war. After about three years without any occupants, vines had crept up the sides and had begun covering doors and windows. In some cases, parts of the structures were collapsing and in substantial disrepair.

A US C-141 lifted off the runway as they passed a vacant and boarded red brick building with large lettering on the side that read "Airmens' Open Mess." In the last day or so, it was apparent that military traffic had picked up even more than it had been only days before—and it was already busy. Perhaps Xuan Loc's collapse and Thieu throwing in the towel had sent the message to the Air Force that it was time to ramp up flying ops. Chuck wondered what the ambassador might have to say about that as Rusty drove slowly towards the aircraft support area. Hardened concrete fighter shelters came into view, surrounded by a thick corrugated wall which served to protect expensive airplanes from incoming shells and shrapnel. Chuck noticed two of them housed South Vietnamese F-5E's which had been flying support missions over Xuan Loc but were now being used to support the retreating ARVN as they were pursued by the communists toward Saigon.

"T-tails," Jesse said under his breath, referring to a quintet of two-toned gray and white C-141 cargo jets that appeared on the tarmac as they rounded a block building. "One of those is your ride, Chuck."

The black-striped flash on the rear stabilizer of the plane sported a 'MAC' in yellow text, with the tail number right under it. A stark "US Air Force" was visible on the fuselage. The sight of the long, pencil-thin airplane sent a spasm of remorse through Chuck Sterrett. He'd been a public servant his whole adult life, and it wasn't easy to leave his comrades behind. Never an overtly religious guy, he whispered a silent prayer that his agents would be able to find their way to safety before things got *really* bad.

"You OK?"

Bob Frailey, sitting to Chuck's left, noticed his anguished look. He grabbed Chuck's shoulder, shaking it in a playful way to try and lighten the heavy mood that blanketed the inside of their vehicle.

"I guess," Chuck answered sullenly. "Just torn about all this."

"We'll be right behind you," Frailey answered with confidence. "Won't be more than a few days and we'll see you on Waikiki. Beaches, bikinis, and mai tais."

The line of vehicles pulled through an opening in a second chain link fence toward two ARVN soldiers who directed Rusty to an area where he could shut the van off and unload.

"OK, Chuck," he said as he shifted into park and set the brake.

Jesse wordlessly exited the passenger side and opened the doors so Chuck and his family could get out. Chuck slid off the vinyl seat and stood outside to help his mother-in-law. Lien's brother followed and went with Jesse to the back to unload what little luggage they had.

Once Lien and her mother were out, Chuck walked behind

the van. The noisy hum of aircraft ground generators traveled across the breezy air.

"Thanks, Jesse."

"No problem, boss," he said coolly.

Rusty, now positioned at the back of the van with the rest, looked out on to the ramp and waved at an American dressed in baggy khakis with a clipboard, a black shirt, and teardrop aviator sunglasses. Chuck saw the man wave back and thought for a moment that he looked like a caricature of Douglas MacArthur, minus the bus driver hat and corn cob pipe.

"The guy over there in the shades will tell you where you need to go," Rusty said. "There'll be another guy at the jet who'll take your paperwork and get you manifested."

"I don't wanna spend a lot of time saying goodbye to you guys," Chuck said. "I suck at it."

Chuck half-smiled at Rusty, who's sweat rings under his arms had begun to creep towards his shoulders.

"Rusty, I –"

"Shut up, Chuck."

He did as he was told.

"I'm not gonna hug you," Rusty joked.

"You soulless bastard."

Rusty chuckled as he shook his boss' hand firmly. Chuck turned to Jesse.

"I ain't hugging you either," Jesse stated with a grizzled look that could kill a man standing.

"Don't worry. I wasn't gonna hug you anyway."

Jesse, usually the serious one, displayed a very slight half-smile.

"Be smart, Jess. When they tell you it's time to go, you get the hell gone, you hear me?"

"Yes, sir," Jesse responded, nodding and shaking Chuck's hand.

"OK, Chuck," Frailey interrupted. "Get your pretty wife and your kid outta here."

Bob Frailey was giving him a direct order.

"Bob," Chuck said, "thank you."

"Have fun in fuckin' Hawaii."

It was hard for Chuck to keep a straight face and he laughed out loud.

"Lien," Bob said to Chuck's wife, "you take care of Chuck and that baby."

With her baby on her hip, Lien, a sublimely beautiful mother who learned basic English and French in her formative years, approached Bob Frailey as the moving air blew her jet-black hair. She looked like she'd just leaped off the cover of Redbook.

"I will," she answered appreciatively, then stood on her tip toes to lay a light kiss on his cheek.

Lien extended her hand and squeezed Frailey's upper arm. Uncharacteristically, he gave her an awkward but brief embrace.

"Thank you," she whispered.

Chuck thought it might have been the only time he'd ever seen Bob Frailey get misty.

"I'll have those mai tais waiting for you," Chuck called as he walked off.

With his final words, he turned to his wife and her family and said, "OK, đi bây giờ."

Let's go now.

He turned for one last look at Bob, Jesse, and Rusty, who stood three abreast, each standing silently with their hands in their pockets watching him leave. Bob gave Chuck one last nod. With that, Chuck Sterrett and his family turned proudly towards the ramp, and left Vietnam in their rear-view mirror.

9

April 24th, 1975

NGUYEN HOME, SAIGON

1:00PM

Mai stopped sweeping the main entrance of the family home and froze.

What was that noise?

The thunder of a large truck hitting a pothole on the nearby street? Or was it something else? She stood still, looked skyward and listened raptly to see if she could hear it again. Was it her brothers playing in their upstairs bedroom? What were they doing, wrestling? It certainly couldn't have been *her* kids — Truc rarely got very rowdy, and Trung was barely walking.

What does artillery sound like anyway?

There it was again. A dull and deep thud in the distance. She shook it off and went back to sweeping. It was a truck. Had to be.

Then it came again. Another thud, and this time it was unmistakable.

Mai propped the long, red-handled broom against the doorframe and went inside.

"Má ơi?" she called for her mother.

"Upstairs!" came Dat's answer.

Mai climbed the steps to the second floor and found her way to her mother and father's bedroom where she was folding laundry. Truc sat quietly on the floor playing with wooden blocks as Trung sat next to her with a single drool-covered toy block.

"Did you hear a strange noise?" she asked inquisitively.

The family had been on edge for several days now, and her mother's nerves were a little frayed.

"*What* noise?" she asked, somewhat annoyed.

"It sounded like a boom. I am not sure."

"No. I did not hear anything. Maybe check on your brothers. They are probably destroying a bedroom again."

Mai turned into the hall and looked at the boys' bedroom door, which sat open.

"Dzung!" she called while simultaneously walking towards their room. "What are you boys doing?"

As she peeked her head inside, she found the three of them laying down on the floor, each reading a book. Dzung propped himself on his elbows and looked up, scabs from his near-miss with the North Vietnamese fading, but still visible on his face.

"We are reading."

"Are you jumping on the beds again?"

"No."

Mai stared back authoritatively.

"Why is it always *me*?" Dzung asked.

Mai walked out without comment and thought it might be a good idea to go to the roof where she could hear better.

She climbed to the third floor and on her way up the narrow steps to the square hatch in the ceiling, she began to think maybe she didn't want to know what the thuds were. Could it have been something at the airfield? She convinced herself that her imagination was running away with her as she lifted the squeaky door. The breeze hit her face and the sun caused her to squint her eyes, bathing her in a warm blanket of light. She climbed up a few more steps, then paused and stood in the open port, listening.

Other than the normal city noises of traffic and a distant siren or two, she heard nothing out of the ordinary. She decided to climb the rest of the way to the rooftop and look out over the city. The Nguyens occupied the tallest home in the area, and it boasted a commanding view of the low Saigon skyline. She walked past several small puddles and stood with her hands on her hips to look around, perking her ears to see if she could hear the sound again. There was nothing. But looking to the northeast, she thought she could see what appeared to be a faint, and very distant, pillar of light gray smoke.

What is that? she thought to herself.

She held her open palm over her eyebrows and strained to try and figure out what it could be. It was such a hazy day that it was hard to tell if it was smoke or some kind of optical illusion. But when she used her peripheral vision, she knew *something* was there.

Probably just a fire of some kind. Nothing to worry about.

Mai turned and made her way back to the roof hatch, then climbed down.

As she descended the stairs that led back to the first floor, she reflected nervously on what the thuds could have been, briefly pondering what Chau had told her about the threat the city faced. She was on her way to the family kitchen but was interrupted by distinct knocking on the large metal gate that separated their courtyard from the small street next to the house. She went to the front door and opened it to listen for it again.

Bang, bang, bang!

More persistent this time. Someone was at the courtyard gate.

"Á-lô?"

It was a man's voice speaking softly as if trying not to be heard, and he sounded young. Mai walked across the courtyard to the secured entry and positioned herself next to the bolt.

"Who is there?"

"My name is Binh," came the reply. "Will you open the gate?"

It was a rare thing for anyone to knock on the Nguyens' gate, but these were strange times in Saigon. Against her better judgment, Mai slid the lock open and pulled inward on the gate to open it, but only an inch or two. She stared out and found a short, young man with a dirty white shirt and disheveled hair standing outside looking in at her. The dark bags under his eyes made him appear exhausted.

"I am Binh," he repeated, flashing a large government-issued ID card at her.

"What do you want?" Mai asked with an abundance of caution.

"I understand someone named Chau lives here," he continued meekly, "and that he is a pilot. Is he home?"

Mai couldn't fathom what someone would want from her husband in the middle of the day. With the tension in the air throughout the city and in their own home, she didn't quite know what to make of this strange individual who simply showed up at the house unannounced.

"What is it that you want, Mr. Binh?"

"I am trying to get my family out of Vietnam," he answered,

sounding desperate. "Please. I hope Mr. Chau can fly us. Are you his wife?"

A wave of anxiety rippled through Mai's body like an electric shock. There'd been a lot of talk in the house about escape, much of it fairly blunt. Images of the diminished crowds at the market came flooding back, and now there was a man she didn't know at their gate asking for help flying his family out of the country.

"What are you talking about?"

"I have money. Five hundred thousand dong."

Binh reached into his right pants pocket and produced a wad of large reddish bills, urgently flashing it at her. It appeared to be a sizable chunk of currency, although Mai thought if South Vietnam really was facing imminent collapse, it wouldn't be worth much for long.

"My mother is sick," he pleaded, "and we are afraid of the communists. We want to get out of Vietnam!"

Mai could only stare, motionless.

"Please," he implored again. "This is a lot of money."

The few seconds she waited to provide him an answer seemed like an eternity. Her gut was screaming at her that something wasn't right.

"I am sorry. I cannot help you."

With that, she closed the gate, slid the lock into place and began to walk back towards the house.

"Wait!" the man begged, calling louder and beating hard on the gate. "Please!"

Bang! Bang! BANG!

The incessant blows on the gate echoed through the courtyard like a cymbal being smashed with a sledge hammer.

"Please *open the gate!*"

More repeated bangs.

"GO AWAY!" Mai commanded.

As she entered the front door, Dat appeared on the steps to the second floor.

"What is going on out there?" she asked with unease.

"Why will you not help!" came the call from the alley. *"I know Chau lives here!"*

"Why does he want Chau?"

"Stay inside," Mai nervously replied to her mother as she walked through the door, then closed and locked it.

"Who is that, Mai?"

The banging continued for another minute or so until the man finally gave up.

"What is going on?"

"He wanted Chau to fly him and his family out of Vietnam."

"What?"

"He offered me five hundred thousand dong."

"Why?"

"I do not know."

But she did know and so did her mother—it just went unsaid. People were becoming desperate. The information about the danger that they'd been hearing was true.

April 25th, 1975
THE NGUYEN RESIDENCE
1:00AM

Mai laid awake in bed under the mosquito net, missing her husband. It had been about six hours since he'd called to inform her he'd be having a late night at work.

I will be home late, Chau had said. *Go ahead to bed.*

But Mai couldn't sleep. She was becoming more and more scared. On two separate occasions since a man named Binh had pounded on their gate, she heard the mysterious 'thud' sounds again in the distance, and her mind had run wild with fear. She'd been trying to convince herself that it wasn't the sound of shelling. Objectively, she figured she was just over-worrying. The sounds were far away from where she was, and maybe it *was* trucks. Her father had told her not to be afraid. Subjectively though, her imagination was in overdrive.

Overcome by her nerves, Mai shed a tear, worried that she and her children might not get out in time. She decided to get up — what was the sense in lying in bed sleepless? She hoisted herself off the sheets and walked into the hallway to the back of the home where Truc and Trung's bedroom was. Cracking the door, she peeked in. Such sweet babies, especially while they were asleep. She was so supremely in love with them. They didn't have a care in the world about any of the madness mounting around them. How wonderful it must have felt to them to be blissfully ignorant. Why couldn't it just be the same for her? Would Chau be able to keep them safe from harm? Mai was petrified that her kids would become another sad statistic in the lengthy conflict the Americans had called the 'Vietnam War.' Too many children had died already.

Her thoughts turned to Chau. What was he doing at the air base so late?

She had done as he'd asked and had begun to organize some small items and clothing for their kids for Chau to squirrel away in his plane.

Mai shut the door to the children's room. As she walked down the hall, she heard a vehicle stop in the alley, then the audible crack of the metal lock on the gate, followed by the familiar squeak as it opened. Rushing to the front door, she opened it to see Chau's headlights pulling into the courtyard. She ran out to him as he dismounted from the Jeep's driver's seat, then grabbed his cheeks and kissed his mouth.

"I have been worried, Chau. You have not called," she said in a low voice, her hands still pressing on his greasy face. "Is everything OK?"

"I am OK, Mai."

Chau left her brief embrace to close the gate, trying to keep as quiet as possible to avoid waking anyone inside, but it was probably impossible.

"We have been making some minor repairs and preparing the plane."

"Come inside and get cleaned up."

Then Mai heard it again—that deep *thud* in the distance. She stopped dead in her tracks and Chau nearly ran into her backside. There was no way it was a truck hitting a pot hole at one o'clock in the morning.

"Did you hear that?"

She stopped and listened.

Thud.

Another one.

"We must leave soon, Mai."

"What was that noise?""I think you might guess it if you try."

"Is it bombs?"

"No," Chau answered. "It is artillery."

Her face went cold.

"Whose artillery?"

"Theirs."

Mai nearly fainted. She reached for the door frame to support herself as Chau grabbed her shoulders, then she slid her silk nightwear-covered body downward until she was seated on the floor.

"Where ...?" she asked numbly.

"Close," came Chau's answer as he squatted to talk to her. "Chuck told me. There is also fighting to the south. We are surrounded, Mai."

"*Mon Dieu.*"

"They will be at Bien Hoa soon, and I believe some units must be already probing the defenses around Saigon."

Mai suddenly felt as if an elephant was sitting on her chest.

"Come on," Chau said. "We should go inside."

He helped her up and they gingerly walked into the bedroom and shut the door.

"A man came to the house today looking for you."

"Who was it?"

Mai slowly opened the mosquito netting on their bed and slowly lowered herself on to the mattress.

"He said his name was 'Binh.' He offered me money for you to fly him and his family out of Vietnam. Chau, what is happening?"

"People are scared."

"Of course they are scared!" Mai replied with frustration. "You just told me the communists are shelling the perimeter around the city!"

"It is good that you did not let him in."

"Why? Do you think we will see more of this?"

"Maybe," Chau nodded silently.

"We have the airplane almost ready and we have started quietly gathering passengers," he continued. "There are already a few families waiting in the hangar. Vinh and one crew chief are finishing some minor repairs and it should be fully prepared to leave on Monday."

They were really leaving.

"I need a few days. I want to talk to your father again."

"You *know* he will not go. You have heard him say it a hundred times!"

"I will try again. I want to talk to a few more people too."

"What should I do if someone else comes to the house looking for you?"

"Do *not* let them into the courtyard. Some people have guns, and it is dangerous."

Mai felt dread creeping back in.

"What about the artillery? They will soon be here!"

"We still have some time."

Mai was barely able to hold herself upright. Chau squatted and held her hands.

"They still have to get past Bien Hoa. They will not try to come into the city until they are at full strength, and for right now, there is too much in front of them."

Mai was not reassured.

"What did Chuck tell you? How does he even know anything?" she asked, but she suspected she knew the answer.

"They are CIA," her husband answered, looking away momentarily. "I should not even be telling you this."

"*CIA?*"

"Yes, Mai. He has already departed Saigon with his family."

"They left? Then who is still over there?"

Chau stroked her hands.

"And why did Lien not say goodbye to me!" she added, sounding a little hurt.

"They were in a hurry to leave, Mai," Chau responded. "There are a few men left who are still using the office on the upper floor."

"Will they leave too?"

"Yes, I am sure they will."

"Where did Chuck go? Will we see them again?"

"Hawaii, I think. I doubt we will see them again."

"Chau, I do not *like* this. I am scared."

"I kno—"

"I do *not* want to leave Vietnam! Why does this have to happen to us?"

Mai sobbed.

"I wish it was different. It is beyond our control, but you *know* we have to leave."

All Mai could do was cry, trying to be as quiet as she could. "It will be OK."

Chau sat next to her on the bed and embraced her. The tears flowed, but Mai felt a momentary sense of security in his sweaty, smelly arms. He pulled away and looked her in the eyes in the dim light coming through their window slats.

"I am going to keep us safe," he said. "I promise."

She knew he would.

"What can I do?"

Mai felt she had to do something. Even if it was small, she had to occupy her mind with some kind of task. If she sat around waiting for something to happen, she thought she might go crazy.

"We will leave on Monday," he answered coolly. "Make sure some things are packed for you and me and the children. Some changes of clothes, baby items, and a little food. Talk to your mother and ask her to do the same for herself and the boys."

"Yes...OK."

"And Mai?"

"Yes?"

"I need you to get your good jewelry together. Get the gold coins and the money we have. Your mother should do the same with hers and your father's valuables. We may never be back. What stays behind will stay here forever."

"I understand."

"Your mother and father have American dollars. A lot of them—from when Chuck paid the final rent bill. I gave it to them myself. When it is all organized in the morning, I will secure it in my uniform until we can find a safer place for it."

"OK. I will."

"And if we can, we need to talk to some of the people we trust. Neighbors, friends. I can fly them out if they are able to go. But we *must* do it quietly."

"Who should I ask?"

"Perhaps you can start with the Thams. Your father often uses their bakery," Chau answered. "They have always been good to us. We can also talk to the two families next door. I trust them. Do you?"

"Yes, but…what about Vinh?"

"Vinh is putting a similar plan together for his family," Chau answered. "Several agents are still next door. If you find people who want to leave, they will coordinate to get them a ride to the air base. The sooner we can get passengers over there, the better. They can sleep in the hangar; it is safer there."

It was a lot to take in, but Mai felt a sudden resolve and was ready to get started.

"We must get some sleep now, Mai."

"I do not know if I can. I have been awake since ten thirty worried about *you!*"

"I know," he said with a slight sense of shame. "I am sorry. But there will be a few more nights like this. It has to be this way, or we will not be able to get free from here."

Mai stared at her husband's swollen lip, visible even in the low light, and slowly brushed her thumb across it.

"Chau, are we really leaving?"

"I am afraid so."

April 25th, 1975
TIEM BANH BAKERY, SAIGON
9:30AM

Mai entered the Nguyens' favorite bakery on duong Le Tu Tai, not far from the family home. On a typical morning, it would be bustling with people and the delectable aromas of fresh bread would fill the air.

But not today.

Mai was somewhat shocked to find the establishment nearly deserted, its glass cases scattered with only the odd bread loaves and pastries… and most appeared quite stale. The somewhat disorganized wall shelving and ceiling hooks would normally be stacked with all manner of wares, but today those wares appeared picked over and half gone. The wafting scent of baking food, normally detectable from the street, was noticeably absent and the business was largely devoid of patrons. Besides Mai, there was only one other customer, seated alone at a small table near the front window, staring blankly out of it with an untouched hot drink in front of him. The counter and serving areas were completely vacant of anyone that appeared to be a proprietor.

"Have you seen Mrs. Tham this morning?" Mai asked, turning to the lone client.

"In the back," he answered.

Mai turned back towards the near-empty display cases and walked between them towards a door that led to the rear kitchen areas.

"Á-lô?" Mai called through the door. "Mrs. Tham?"

Mrs. Tham's suspicious face emerged on the other side of the humid and dirty kitchen from behind a doorway. When she saw it was Mai, her expression changed to mild relief and she smiled slightly before walking toward her.

"Hello, Mai," she said before giving Mai a polite bow.

The short, pear-shaped mid-fifties woman looked sullen, and it was clear something was weighing on her. Mai could tell—though she and her family didn't know the Thams well, they *were* familiar, having used their bakery for years.

"No fresh bread today?" Mai asked.

Mrs. Tham wasn't the chipper woman she usually was when Mai came into her bakery.

"My mind is racing, Mai. My husband is upstairs getting some things in order," she answered worriedly. "Customers have been declining for the last few days."

"Mrs. Tham, I –"

"Mai, we are closing the shop this afternoon and going to the port," she interrupted. "We have decided to leave Vietnam if we can get on to a boat."

Mai was afraid she might hear something like that, and it didn't sound like a very solid plan. '… *if we can get on to a boat.*'

"Are you and your family leaving too?"

"Mrs. Tham," Mai started, a little nervously, "I need to talk to you privately."

"Yes, of course," she responded. "Come back here with me."

The two women walked through the kitchen area past several ovens and a large butcher-block table. A yeasty smell hung on the air. There was a small table and chairs in the cramped kitchen storage area, which sat next to an opened screen door that led directly to an alley behind the building. Mai noticed a black cat with white feet amble past the door on the concrete landing; its green eyes momentarily looked into the bakery as if searching for a scrap of food.

"Please have a seat. I am sorry I have run out of tea."

"Oh, it is no problem," Mai answered. "Mrs. Tham, my husband asked me to come talk to you today."

She leaned in and listened as Mai scooted her chair closer to the small table.

"Are you leaving Saigon?" she asked again.

"Yes. We want you to come with us, but we must keep this silent."

Mrs. Tham seemed a bit taken aback and didn't immediately respond.

"You may remember, my husband is an Air Force pilot. He has a plane at the air base, and we are leaving Monday."

"A plane?" she asked skeptically. "Where are you going?"

"I do not know for sure. Maybe Thailand…or Malaysia or the Philippines."

Mrs. Tham hesitated for a moment.

"What will it cost us?"

It was not a question Mai had expected. She and Chau had never talked about charging anyone money to take them away from danger.

"Cost?"

"Yes, Mai. How much will it cost my family?"

The image of the man at their gate the day before — Binh — suddenly popped back into her mind. He had offered Mai a lot of money for Chau's services. She hadn't thought much about it, even after Binh's visit to their home. But she supposed she and Chau *could* make some money offering spaces on their flight to freedom.

"You see, one of our customers was here three days ago and he offered my husband some space on a boat for my family for one hundred thousand dong. We had already been thinking about leaving but could not figure out how to do it. Taking advantage of the boat seemed like a good idea because our seats were guaranteed. We gave him the money and a list of the names of our family members, and he promised to be back the next day to pick us up in his truck. That day came and went … then the next day, and the next one after that."

"I see."

"I am sure you understand what happened," Mrs. Tham replied. "All he wanted was our money. Perhaps he used it to get his own family out of the country."

Mai felt pity. How many other unscrupulous individuals would take advantage of good people like this? It was, after all, a desperate time. Chau had warned her that there were many who had guns and suddenly she began to see the cold, hard reality of it all. Humans were capable of horrible things when they were backed into corners. They would do whatever it took to survive.

"Mai," Mrs. Tham said, "we want to leave Vietnam before Ho Chi Minh gets here, and in the last week, we have sold much of what we own. Furniture, clothing, even my daughter's Vespa, and we took almost nothing for it. We were waiting to see if we could sell the bakery, but nobody wants to buy something that might trap them here, only to find that if they stayed, it could be taken by the communists."

"Mrs. Tham," Mai responded nervously, "it will not cost you anything to come."

"Nothing?" she asked.

"N-no," Mai answered as she shook her head.

She could see that Mrs. Tham didn't believe her.

"Mai, you and your family have been good customers for years. But Saigon has gone crazy. Do you expect me to trust that we will not have to pay you for passage out?"

Mai wasn't quite sure how to respond but supposed she would feel similarly guarded if she'd already been burned once.

"We run a business and, in my experience, everybody wants *something*. We have already been played for fools. I will not let that happen again. This is about the survival of my family."

"There is no cost," Mai said firmly. "Mrs. Tham — my husband is a good man, and I am not a liar. You have been very good to us and we want you to come with us. We know some Americans who can ensure you get to the air base as early as this afternoon. You can see the plane for yourself."

The middle-aged woman was silent and appeared to ponder the offer.

"If the rumors are true, you know that the port and airport must be very busy," Mai added matter-of-factly. "Desperate crowds do desperate things. Do you not think it would be safer for you and your family to come to the air base to get out? There are fewer people, and you are more likely to get on board there than you are anywhere else."

"One minute," she said, and with that rose quickly from her seat. "Wait here."

"But –"

"I will be right back."

Against instructions, Mai followed her toward the front of the empty establishment. Even the lone patron who had been there a few minutes before had gone. Mrs. Tham shut the front door and locked it, then turned the lights out to make it appear to the outside world that she had closed. She turned and walked past Mai, making her way to a small staircase behind the check-out counter that led upstairs into a residence.

"Wait here, Mai."

She reached the top of the steps and walked into a door, slamming it behind her. Mai could hear muffled voices talking but couldn't make out what was being said. It went on for a few minutes, got heated at several points, then grew quiet. The doorknob soon turned and out walked Mrs. Tham, followed by her frowning husband.

"You remember Mai," she said to him when they'd reached the bottom step. "Like I have said to you, she says she can get us out of Vietnam at no cost."

Her husband was plainly unconvinced.

"How can you do this at no cost?" he asked.

"My husband is a pilot," Mai answered, "and he has a plane at the base."

Mr. Tham shook his head suspiciously.

"Nothing is free."

"We are leaving Monday. If your things are in order, I can have you brought to the base as early as today."

Mr. Tham sighed deeply and ran his fingers through his thinning hair.

"I do not know..." he started.

"Mr. Tham, I am offering you and your family a free flight out of Vietnam. Would you rather try to board a ship? I already know you have sold much of what you own, and that you would sell this business too, if only you could. What will become of you if you risk the port and are forced to remain here? If you do not take this offer, you could be trapped in Saigon at the mercy of the communists."

Mr. Tham looked at his wife, then lowered his head and turned away as if deep in thought. He threw up his right hand in desperation, as if unsure of the right thing to do.

"Come with us," Mai implored.

Mrs. Tham grabbed her husband's hand and shot an expression at him as if to say, *trust her*. Mai thought she might have gotten through. Outside, a truck rumbled by, followed by a small motorbike that buzzed along right behind it.

Mr. Tham turned back to Mai.

"How many people can you accommodate?" he asked.

"How many do you have?"

April 25th, 1975
NEAR TAN SON NHUT AIRPORT'S CIVILIAN TERMINAL
10:30PM

"Kinda dark out here," Rusty said to Jesse in an effort to break the awkward silence that hung in the van. It was filled to capacity.

"Yup."

They were in a less populated area close to the edge of the city, about a mile and a half from the civilian terminal at the airfield. The low buildings and homes along the right side of the road were darkened, and only a few lonely streetlights provided light to see by. Smack in the middle of a long line of cars, the people in the vehicles surrounding them were no doubt headed to the same place they were. Fortunately, at least for the moment, it was moving along steadily at about twenty-five miles per hour. Both men knew it was temporary, though. On nearly every one of their earlier passenger runs, they found themselves letting people out of their van a good distance from the airport's main entrance—refugees would just have to go the rest of the way on foot. It was impossible to get very close without being caught in a snarl of traffic, which would have slowed them from maximizing the movement of as many high-risk Vietnamese officials and business people as they could.

In front of them was an old and battered, dark-blue Volkswagen Beetle, sporting a roof rack piled high with suitcases and bags tied down haphazardly with tattered lengths of rope. The interior was packed like a can of human sardines. Behind them, a small pickup truck followed with even more civilians crammed in its cab and bed.

A steady parade of people walked the road as well, carrying luggage in their hands, in wagons, and even in wheelbarrows. To their left was the vast open space of Tan Son Nhut's airfield, which with only a little bit of light around, created an inky black void in the sky above. Other than the sparse streetlights and headlights, the only illumination that could be seen came from the approach strobes that periodically went off like a thousand flashbulbs from behind the long and decaying perimeter fence. Jesse thought they made the base a pretty easy target.

Rusty was at the wheel of one of the Embassy's white Econoline passenger vans which on this run, was solidly packed with more than twenty Vietnamese citizens. They'd been transporting people to the port and airport since five o'clock that morning.

"How many you think we've moved today?" Rusty asked inquisitively.

"Hell, I don't know," Jesse replied, "this is probably our fifteenth trip of the day. If we average about fifteen on each one, that's a little over two hundred people."

It was something, Jesse thought, but so many would be still left behind. He hoped his peers from the Embassy and the other detachments had been able to keep the flow as steady as possible.

"Let's make this our last one for the day, Jess," Rusty said. "We can get up and do more in a few hours, but I gotta get some sleep."

"Right."

The passengers in the rear were eerily quiet, as most had been while the two agents drove each group to a place where their lives would change dramatically from what they'd known. It was a profound thing, leaving behind a place that was familiar—your home, your family—because it had become too dangerous to stay.

The van had just passed a ragged road sign that read 'Tan Son Nhut—Saigon,' which indicated they were getting closer to the terminal, when traffic began to slow. Three scooters putted by on their left and cars in the long procession began to take up both lanes in the road, honking incessantly.

"Probably gonna have to let them out up here somewhere," Jesse said. "We won't get much farther up the road than this."

"Man, crowds must be growing ahead," Rusty commented with a bit of surprise, "It's never gotten slow this far out."

Rusty decelerated to about fifteen miles per hour and within a quarter mile, the long line of vehicles came to a dead stop. People several cars ahead of them began to get out with babies, young children, and elderly. He reached to his side and unclicked the safety on his pistol.

"Well, I guess this is the best we're gonna do."

Rusty pulled into the left lane, threw the transmission into park, and called to the passengers.

"Đến lúc phải ra khỏi đây!"

Time to get out.

Jesse climbed out and opened the side doors to begin helping people disembark. Rusty exited as well, coming around to help three aging women and a senior government official to step down from the van's high floor. The low murmur of scores of idling vehicle engines drowned out much of the other ambient noise, but as Jesse was letting go of another elderly passenger's arm, angry voices and screaming suddenly pierced the relative calm from somewhere ahead of them. At first it didn't seem too worrisome, but the shouting continued unabated.

"What the hell's going on up there?" Jesse said with slight alarm as he helped a 12-ish year-old boy out.

Out of nowhere, the sharp reports of two gunshots rang out close by. Women screamed in terror as the two agents and their charges hit the ground in a split second.

"*What the hell!*" Jesse called out with shock.

Adrenaline kicked into high gear. A third sharp report was followed by more screams.

"What's happening up there?" Rusty yelled before reaching down to his belt and drawing his pistol. "Let's get these people behind something!"

Hue flashed vividly through Jesse's mind and his heart

pounded at a thousand miles per hour, as people came frantically running by them to get away from the commotion. He and Rusty instinctively got up to avoid being trampled but remained hunkered low as they helped the others to their feet.

"Over there!"

Rusty pointed toward two vacated buildings about twenty feet off the side of the road and the two agents began shepherding their passengers in its general direction.

"Come on!" Jesse called, motioning to one of the men who'd been in their van only moments before. *"Move!"*

It was unlikely his words were understood, especially over the now-raised dissonance of humans around him, but Jesse was certain his body language made it pretty clear what the intent was. Nobody had to tell anyone what to do as their natural fight-or-flight instincts took over. He did his best to guide the three old women towards safety, but they were hysterically crying and shouting. They were finally able to get their small group away from the van, joining several other people who'd crouched down behind a block and stucco wall near the empty buildings.

"We need to get away from here, Rusty. This ain't good."

Jesse was on high alert and it was like he was right back in combat. He surveyed the street and the behavior of the crowd.

"The van's boxed in, Russ," he said shakily. "We need to sit here for a second—people are still moving away from it."

The strobes from the airfield approach flashed in the darkness, intermittently highlighting the alarm on Rusty's face. He sat crouched on his knees with his pistol at the ready. After a few minutes that passed as slow as hours, the terrified Vietnamese crowds that had been running away started to slow. There was a sense that whatever danger may have existed might have begun to subside.

Jesse panted.

"Hang on…hang on," he said quietly. "I think people are stopping."

A larger crowd of individuals had formed and was looking from a distance towards the location of the gunshots.

"Just give it a second."

"Is it over?" Rusty asked, wiping away a drop of sweat from his temple.

Jesse was still for another moment, then looked back at their passengers.

"These folks are fine," he said. "We can leave them here. They'll be all right."

"Do you think it's safe to get back into the van and try to move it?"

"Still risky, maybe," Jesse answered, "but we need to roll the dice and move out."

Jesse turned his attention towards two Vietnamese men in their mid-thirties who'd been among the last to disembark their vehicle before the shooting started.

"OK?" he asked with a nod, looking at both of them and hoping they understood what he was trying to say: *Are you OK now? We have to go.*

"Yes, yes," one answered, probably using the few words of English that he knew.

"OK, OK. Thank you," the other said in a thick accent, while putting his hands together like he was praying, then bowing several times. "Thank you. Thank you."

Jesse nodded. That was it. They'd accomplished their mission and it was time to egress in any way they could.

"We good, Jess?" Rusty called to his partner as he turned in his direction.

"Probably as good as we're gonna get," Jesse answered. "People are moving slow, but they're still moving."

"Uh-huh, I think it's over," Rusty said as if trying to convince himself.

"Yeah," Jesse answered as he slowly emerged from their position. "Think so."

"There's a drainage ditch on the opposite side of the road, but it's real shallow," Rusty said as he came up next to Jesse, walking forward cautiously and deliberately with his pistol still in his hand. "I think there may be enough room to get turned around without having to scrape against the perimeter fence. Might be a ten-point turn is all."

As Rusty and Jesse moved cautiously in the direction of the road, they noticed others emerging from positions they'd taken between buildings and behind low walls to continue advancing in the direction of the airfield entrance, which stood nearly a mile in front of them.

"Just move slow," Jesse warned.

They reached the road. Jesse noticed Rusty death-gripping his weapon, his index finger positioned at the ready above its trigger housing.

"Go easy, Russ."

It was hard to tell what had happened, but he did notice a small crowd about three vehicles in front of their van and could hear a woman crying hysterically.

"I'm gonna go see," Rusty said as he walked ahead of Jesse.

"*No!*" Jesse commanded. "Leave it alone, Rusty. We need to go."

Rusty glared at him defiantly.

"We need to stay together," Jesse continued. "Leave it."

"Come on—it'll be quick," Rusty said as he turned forward again and began moving in the direction of the crying.

"*RUSS!*"

The crowd parted slightly and Rusty froze in his tracks as three middle-aged men carried the body of a young man past the beam of a set of headlights about thirty feet in front of them. His arms and neck were limp and three distinct bullet holes could be seen in his blood-soaked shirt.

"Rusty. Let's go."

10

"It's getting real, guys," Bob Frailey said as he pushed his fingers through his perfectly combed salt-and-pepper hair. The only evident sign of stress was some slight perspiration bleeding through his shirt.

Jesse and Rusty had just returned to the offices next to the Nguyens after what seemed like endless hours of ferrying threatened civilians to the crowded and dangerous port and airport and they were surprised to see Frailey there. They'd spent the previous night sleeping in Chuck's semi-vacated quarters with the intent of getting up early and moving more bodies, and that's how it went down too. Although after the excitement of the night before, neither of them had gotten a whole lot of sleep. Jesse had an especially hard time, tossing and turning as he tried to suppress the invasive violent mental images from his time in combat. They replayed through his head on a never-ending loop.

The worst one was from Hue. Jesse kept remembering how

he'd instructed his Marines to crouch low behind a cinder block wall under heavy machine gun fire. It rained in like a deadly hailstorm, taking out a Jeep and a Navy corpsman with its massive 108-millimeter rounds. Each impact sent horrendous eruptions of masonry, soil, and dust into the air. Up to that point Jesse had never lost a man under his supervision, but that day, one of his charges who'd been hunkered down next to him, a kid with the last name of 'Black' (even though he was a white guy from Pittsburgh), raised his eyes a little too high during a brief lull in the onslaught. In an instant, a huge caliber round obliterated his head as it tore past, leaving nothing but a gristly mess of ruined bone and muscle protruding from between his shoulders. Jesse was looking right at him when it happened and ended up with bits of the young man's brain matter all over his face and neck. What was left of Private Black's lifeless body slumped onto the dirty street as dark crimson blood poured from the gaping wound.

His and Rusty's last movement from the night before — the man's bleeding and limp corpse, the screaming of the crowd, the panic — had stirred everything all back up.

"I've been laying low," Frailey continued coolly, "but I've been stopping into the dets here and there, monitoring the radios, and keeping loose contact with some guys inside the compound downtown."

"How you doing that without a KY-3?" Jesse asked.

Frailey shrugged with an evasiveness they'd become accustomed to.

"Don't worry about it," he said. "All you need to know is that things are real, real bad. Bien Hoa is gone."

"Hell..." Rusty muttered.

It wasn't unexpected. It was the next target in line after Xuan Loc.

"Overrun."

"How much time do you think we have?" Jesse asked.

"Not long."

Jesse was annoyed. Why were they still in-country? He didn't ask. He and Rusty knew Frailey felt the same, and that he was doing his best to try and remain cool.

"We need to keep the people movement rolling forward. Focus on any remaining Americans and their families, the high-value local nationals, and after that, take anyone you can get who doesn't have a gun."

"Haven't seen many Americans," Rusty commented. "I'm starting to think they're all gone except for us."

"There's some non-essentials left, plus the locals still on our list."

"Lots of them left," Jesse commented under his breath.

Jesse and Rusty had been working their way down their assigned portion of the list of high-risk Vietnamese that Mosey Copenhaver had provided several days prior. They'd show up on short notice to a house, high-rise apartment, or unassuming collection point for the next run — sometimes they'd find people, and sometimes they were already gone. When warm bodies were found, they'd pat down the men, then search all the baggage and women's purses. If a weapon was found, they'd stash it somewhere innocuous and leave it behind. It seemed like they never got all the names, but they took almost everyone anyway. They knew it was a hazard — after all, it was known that there were enemy agents around town, and any one of the passengers they took could be one, but they kept their weapons close and took their chances.

Despite Frailey's admitting he'd been stopping into the detachment offices at the Nguyens' home, it remained somewhat of a mystery what *else* he had been doing while his agents unceasingly delivered civilian after civilian to their ever more-crowded ports of embarkation. Maybe he was getting his personal affairs in order? Or maybe he was quietly coordinating something else. Neither Jesse nor Rusty knew for certain, and Jesse for one wasn't sure he *wanted* to know. Frailey wasn't saying anyway. The guy had been a spook for almost three decades. Frankly, Jesse didn't even expect to see him at the Nguyens' rental property at all—he and Rusty had just come by to pick up a couple cold drinks from what was left of their miniscule fridge stash that Chuck had kept in a small room nearby.

"…by the way, you oughta know the Navy is mission-complete positioning their ships here," Frailey said.

"How many?" Jesse asked.

"Fifty or so vessels about twenty miles off-shore. Ready to go for helo ops."

"That's a lot of boats."

"Bet that's going over well with Martin," Rusty said contemptuously.

"Like a fart in church. But the Ambassador understands embassies aren't the only ones with a role with evac plans. Just because he's being cautious about executing his part of it doesn't mean the president and the military can't lean forward, and truthfully, it's wise and pretty normal for this type of thing. With that said, the final decision to get everyone out is basically still his."

"How long you think it's been since PACOM pulled their Vietnam plan out?"

"I don't know. Probably not long after Da Nang, but I don't work in the SCIF at Camp Smith, so I don't have much detail."

"Martin's still cold on it, huh?"

"Far as I know, yeah," Frailey explained. "But this is their action, not State's, and not the Agency's. Graham Martin doesn't get a vote."

"I don't remember hearing anything about fifty ships when they read *me* into the plan," Jesse snapped, "but OK."

"It's because you didn't. PACOM updates the plans based on the in-country scenario. They gave it to the ambassador the other day."

Jesse began fishing for a cigarette in his left breast pocket.

"So, I guess even if the Navy's here it doesn't necessarily mean Martin's gonna engage the helicopter evac?"

"No."

"Is the Navy a 'question of prudence' too?" Rusty teased, using words that Graham Martin often repeated about the ongoing non-essential evacuation.

"The Navy's here to provide medical care and transpo and is available in case we go full-helo-ops. Until then, the Port of Saigon and the air base and airport are still the main APOE and SPOE — they'll use civilian aircraft and cargo jets of every kind until they can't anymore. Choppers are only for when it gets really bad."

"Only when it gets really bad?" Jesse fired back. "Why aren't we doing *both?*"

"Because we don't need rotary yet. Airplanes carry two or three hundred people at a pop, so we need to maximize their use as much as we can, *while* we can. If Tan Son Nhut goes down, we use helicopters and take small groups out to sea," he explained. "And it *will* go down, guys."

"Ya think?"

"Well, whatever. The airfield's still available so the helos are on standby," Frailey went on. "Even if the ambassador's living in an alternate reality, it's still his call and right now the powers that be—including him—all agree that keeping the airfield open as long as possible is the best-case scenario. All I can tell you is keep your radio on and don't use it unless you have to. We're all listening twenty-four-seven. Keep the van tuned into the right station. You know what to do if you hear Bing Crosby. With any luck we'll have some time to hop something out of here from the base."

"OK, Bob," Rusty said, "but I gotta tell ya, things are pretty spooky—Jess and I got mixed up in a shooting last night."

"What?"

"By the airport—late last night on our last run," Jesse replied. "Some guy took a few rounds to the chest. Not sure what happened because we got the hell outta there, but probably some kind of dispute or a robbery or something."

"Damn."

Jesse exhaled smoke.

"Full panic feels close, Bob," he continued. "Isn't that what Martin was trying to avoid with his tap dancing around about a full evac? Hell, how many other embassies have already closed?"

"Well, we may not have twenty-four hours left of this. Before long, you guys are gonna need to hole up on the compound because all this madness will turn into something you can't fend off with a pistol. You still got your stuff packed and in the van, right?"

"Yup."

"Good," Frailey went on, "because here's something else: the commies are already probing defenses around the city."

"Man," Jesse said, appearing slightly gray, "those Navy racks are sounding more and more comfortable all the time."

"It's a big city," Rusty said. "There's a lot they'd have to get through and it would take some time for them to mobilize to do it…right, Bob?"

"Probably," Frailey answered. "They're still mopping up after Xuan Loc. They didn't exactly roll through there unhurt—the fight lasted a week. I don't guess they'd throw themselves at us until they're full-up on all sides. But hell, maybe I'm wrong."

"We even gonna be able to get to the Embassy?" Jesse asked.

"Yeah, at least for now," he affirmed. "Which is not to say it's looking exactly peachy down there."

"What do you mean?"

"As of this morning, the crowds have grown a lot bigger. Same thing at the Presidential Palace. People want out, and they remember what Nixon said—that we wouldn't abandon them. So some of 'em are getting pretty pissed."

"Great job avoiding panic, Mr. Ambassador," Rusty mumbled.

"What about the South Vietnamese government?" Jesse asked. "What the hell are they doing? They gonna pack up and leave too?"

"There's been talk that they'd try and engage with the north."

"Negotiations," Rusty commented.

"I guess they wanna see if the bad guys will agree to make Saigon a free republic. The idea is the north leaves the city alone and then 'live and let live.' It's a pipe dream, though. It'll never happen."

"What's next, then?" Jesse asked.

"We keep on keepin' on. Get as many more folks as you can and let's meet back here tomorrow morning at nine. That's when we'll make a judgement on the next move."

Suddenly, a burst of what sounded like machine gun fire roared through the Nguyens' courtyard downstairs, echoing off the high plaster walls and into the slatted windows of the CIA offices.

"DOWN!" Frailey shouted.

The three men hit the floor.

"Aw, you gotta be KIDDING me!" Jesse cried out, his lit cigarette tumbling from his mouth and landing smoldering on the dusty brown and green linoleum.

He was surprised at how much all this gunfire stuff was beginning to bother him.

April 26th, 1975
NGUYEN COURTYARD
1:45PM

Hong Nguyen quickly made for his front door.

I hope that was not what I think it was.

He slowly cracked it open to find Dzung and his brothers tossing a strip of firecrackers from the side of the courtyard into its center, exploding and popping with a fury, and sending bits of black and red paper and debris into the air. Hong flung the door open angrily as the sounds echoed off the interior walls

"DZUNG!"

The boys dropped everything and ran for the tall metal gate that opened to the street.

"STOP!"

The boys immediately stopped, knowing they couldn't escape, and Hong's normally passive expression was a contorted mix of fury and fear. He knew he must have been flushed. He grabbed Dzung's shirt collar with one hand and Son's with the other, sparing Tuan, but shaking the two older brothers angrily.

"Do you *know* what you are *doing?!*" he half-whispered, trying to avoid being heard by anyone who might be listening besides his sons. He ripped the lighter from Dzung's hand.

"Sorry, Ba," Tuan said timidly, wincing and bracing himself for a beating.

"*Get to your rooms,*" he eked out through clenched teeth. "I do not want to see you or hear you."

They skulked into the house. Hong was incensed, but fear had a grip on him that clung tighter than his anger—people were already spooked and all he needed was his boys getting into mischief that involved something that could be mistaken for automatic gunfire. The family had been doing their best to remain calm around the boys. They all knew they could feel the tension too—especially Dzung—but Hong wasn't sure they understood the enormity of what was happening in Saigon.

The truth was that Hong was terrified, and it was all he could do to hide it from his wife, Mai, and Chau. If the American next door was right, it might only be a matter of days before he would have to make the agonizing decision to leave or stay.

Hong had been hearing the sporadic thumps and thuds of what he knew must be incoming artillery on the outskirts of Saigon, and he was acutely aware that anything remotely resembling the sound of gunshots could be a huge danger. He figured it was best to lay low and not draw attention to yourself. Perhaps it was time for the boys to remain sequestered in the home to keep them from getting into any more trouble.

The late middle-aged father stood quietly for a moment, breathing deeply as the sun beat down on the tile floor of his courtyard, causing a faint sheen of sweat to begin to cover his brow. He removed a handkerchief from his pocket and wiped it, then unceremoniously stuffed it back and went inside. Dat and Mai were waiting at the door.

"It was Dzung, wasn't it?" Dat asked with suspicion.

Hong stopped. "It is always Dzung."

"I think he would tell you Son and Tuan are just as guilty."

Perhaps, he thought to himself, but said nothing.

"Hong," Dat said, "the boys know something is happening. They can sense it."

He remained quiet as he walked through the door, passed by the front room, then into the kitchen area at the back of the home, followed by the two women.

"I know."

Hong paused next to the kitchen sink and reached into a small cupboard for a cup. Maybe tea would be a nice diversion.

"Hong, I —"

"I have not decided we are leaving yet, Dat," he interrupted.

Mai didn't dare speak.

Hong stood with the two women at his back. Dat strode toward her husband and placed her hand on his shoulder as he hung his head in thought. She knew their days in Vietnam were numbered and Hong was aware she wanted to go.

"Hong," Dat spoke, "there is cannon fire. I know that is what I hear at night."

Hong remained silent and motionless, lost in his own contemplations.

"You *know* this. They are coming, and they will be here soon. What will you do when they get here?"

She squeezed his shoulder.

"This is difficult," she went on. "But we must get our family to safety. Your things are already set aside. It is Saturday. We can leave with Chau on Monday."

Hong only nodded.

"Please," she whispered. "We *must* do the right thing."

A heavy silence slowly penetrated the kitchen for what seemed like several minutes but was shattered by the sound of strident thumping above them as Mai's brothers bounded down the stairs with reckless abandon. Son, Dzung, and Tuan, who hadn't been gone long, appeared abruptly at the archway into the kitchen, gray as the dead. Only Mai, who'd been standing some distance behind her parents, had noticed.

"What are you doing down here!" she whispered to them impatiently, trying to shoo them out of the room. "Ba said to get upstairs! Now *go!*"

They refused to be moved and stood firm like three stone pillars, staring at their sister with grave expressions. Hong was suddenly aware that something had happened—the three brothers *never* looked this serious. In the distance, an aircraft could be heard taking off from the base.

Son slowly handed his older sister a small piece of crinkled paper that looked like large-font typed text. She took a moment to read it, then all the color drained from her face. The paper slumped out of her hand and drifted lightly to the floor on the thick air before landing noiselessly on the cold kitchen tiles. Looking faint, she placed her hand on her sternum.

"What?" Hong asked.

Tuan quickly navigated around his sister, frozen in place where she stood, and picked the leaflet off the floor.

"Give me that!" their father demanded.

Tuan did as he was told. His parents took a moment to read it as the four siblings stared at them, looking for a reaction, or some direction, or anything remotely parent-ish that might replace the impending sense of doom they clearly felt.

Brothers and sisters in Saigon,

The great Ho Chi Minh begs you to join the final resistance against the corrupt enemy government. Soldiers from the People's Army will soon join you in Saigon. Honest citizens will be generously rewarded for the turnover of traitorous collaborators. Turncoats and spies will be dealt with harshly. The day of victory is at hand! Prepare yourself.

Next to the ominous text was a grainy, newspaper-like photo of Ho himself.

Dat gasped and grabbed the edge of the countertop behind her as her husband slowly turned to his children. Their mother regained a scrap of balance, breathed deeply, and became angry at her indecisive husband.

"Do you think it is time to leave *now?*"

He ignored her.

"Where did you get this?" Hong asked his children.

Tuan began to whimper. Even a nine-year-old understood what the ominous message meant.

"*WHERE?*" Hong appealed with anger and dread, crumpling and shaking the leaflet, his eyes becoming wet.

"On the roof," Son answered pitifully, not taking his eyes off the floor.

"Why were you on the roof?!"

"We were going to swim," he admitted, "instead of going to our rooms. We found it when we opened the hatch."

The room hung heavy with undeniable horror. It was an awful thing for a child—even a grown one like Mai—to witness their parents frightened and helpless.

In the distance, two unmistakable thuds could be heard.

April 26th, 1975
TAN SON NHUT AIR BASE
3:45PM

"How many more times will you be reorganizing in here, Chau?" Vinh asked with exasperation.

The cockpit smelled like leather with notes of jet fuel, exhaust, and body odor. He'd brought a few more armfuls of items from the house and had been packing and re-packing them into any spare nook or cranny he could find on the flight deck.

"I brought more from home," he replied, failing to make eye contact with his co-pilot and longtime friend. "It must go somewhere."

"You have really brought more from home?" Vinh asked skeptically. "I do not believe you, Chau. Why have you have been up here for three hours...?"

He didn't respond and only removed items from one location and placed them back into other holes.

"...doing nothing?"

Maybe he was trying to keep busy passing the time, so he wouldn't go nuts. The day before, Quan had brought his children, young wife, and extended family to the hangar and into a space that he thought would be a little more secure than their home. When it came time to leave, they'd be ready to board. His little group joined numerous other groups, including Vinh's wife and family, who had left the tension of the city and were spending nights sleeping on the facility's ever-more-crowded floor, anxiously awaiting their ultimate departure. There were already easily over a hundred civilians inside.

"Chau," Vinh said gently, trying unsuccessfully to capture

his full attention, "we should probably fuel the plane while we can if you want to leave on Monday."

It was one of the last things they had to do to prepare for their escape. Thus far they'd avoided it in order to keep things low-profile, but the longer they waited, the riskier it might be to obtain fuel.

In the distance, the thuds of two distinct artillery shell impacts could be heard. "*whump…*"

"*whump…*"

"Do you hear that? We should not wait any longer," he continued. "It will take some time to fill the wing tanks, especially if we are forced to use drums."

Chau could hardly bear to dwell on the atrociousness of what was happening.

"*Chau!*"

Vinh shook his friend's shoulder, as if to snap him out of some witchy trance. Another series of dull thuds could be heard in the distance.

"When will you bring your family here?" Vinh asked candidly. "Do you not hear the artillery?"

Chau finally turned to his friend, revealing a dazed sweaty appearance accentuated by bloodshot eyes.

Vinh only stared at him.

"My family?"

"Yes. When are you bringing Mai here, Chau?"

He looked away.

Fuel?

The heat of the cabin penetrated his flight suit.

"*Trời ơi!*" Vinh bellowed at him.

For God's sake!

"Snap *out* of this!" Vinh said with authority, almost punching Chau in the shoulder. "*Chau!* Collect yourself! We need fuel. *Come back to reality!*"

Chau paused, slowly coming to his senses from a bizarre state of fugue-like semi-consciousness. Vinh's words were heard, and he knew they were right. His sweaty, and very unsteady fingers reached into his hair, smoothing it backward as he shook his head, as if to shake off a blow to the temple. Outside the hangar, the sound of an aircraft launching into the sky drowned everything else out.

Vinh leaned in.

"Listen!" he said under his breath. "It is another American plane taking off. The population of Saigon is shrinking, and we are not yet ready to be part of it!"

"Is the rear latrine repaired?" Chau asked as he began to sense reality again.

"What?"

"The latrine."

"It was repaired days ago!" Vinh replied with frustration. "Are you hearing a word I am saying to you?"

Faced with imminent danger and the shame of failing to provide for the defense of Mai and his kids across his years of seemingly wasted service, Chau had been overcome by his racing mind. He'd been almost obsessed with the disgrace of being unable to win a place for them to stay in their home country. Now, at the end, he struggled to concede to the truth that there was nothing left, no matter how anyone sliced it.

He slumped into the pilot's seat.

"Okay," he uttered, appearing to finally put himself back into full-reality mode.

"Okay, what?"

"Tell Quan to go find us fuel."

Relieved, Vinh nodded, then stood firm before turning to leave the cockpit.

"Are you with me now?"

"Yes."

"Time is short, Chau." Vinh placed his hand on Chau's shoulder. "We will get through this. But we need you present."

"I am sorry."

Neither of the men said anything else. As Vinh turned to go find their crew chief, Chau sighed, tempted to go back to what he was doing but instead, he too turned to leave the cockpit. It was getting stuffy in there and he felt like he had to get out and move around. To do *something*. Anything. He slowly crept down the steep stairs and emerged into the C-130's mostly-empty bay, save for a few people that had set up small encampments inside to await their escape. Scattered in a few locations, he saw some randomly-placed bags and personal belongings of people who would become his passengers in a few short days. Near the rear latrine, there were two pillow cases—one stained a dingy white, and the other a striped grimy pea-green. Its opening hung wide, revealing a box of dried seaweed and a small stuffed toy elephant.

The detritus of daily life. What a surreal thing to see something so normal—just like his own children's toys—against a backdrop of such expanding chaos. Chau decided it might be a good idea to visit with some of the passengers. Maybe it would make him feel better, and perhaps it might be a good idea for them to see who would be flying them to their ultimate freedom. He forced himself across the scruffy strips of black no-slip tape on the bay floor, then down the rear cargo ramp into the cavernous nose dock. Parking himself at the foot of the wide ramp, he gawked into the large space, noting the group of families waiting for movement like a small bivouac of refugees. Indeed, that's what they were now.

He and Vinh, as well as Mai had been discreetly letting close friends and relatives know that they'd be getting out of town, but Chau knew if too many showed up, they could have a crowd control issue on their hands—it was a balancing act. A quick look around indicated there were quite a few people whom he didn't know. With much of the city's population having access to small arms, he'd confided with Mai that things stood a good chance of getting contentious at the hangar…especially if there were more would-be passengers than there was room on board his Hercules.

In the rear of the building near a door to the outer office and shop areas, Chau saw Vinh's young wife, Khanh, with their daughters. Thinking she'd smartly placed herself in a good location near a restroom for her kids, he thought it was nice to see a familiar face and he reckoned he would go say hello and make some small talk. Though bursting inside, he walked confidently across the smooth and expansive concrete floor.

Before he could get to Vinh's family however, he came upon an elderly man sitting on a small quilt with an older woman. His gnarled hand grabbed Chau's leg.

"Excuse me," the man muttered in a frail voice, tugging on the baggy leg of Chau's flight suit. "Colonel?"

Chau halted mid-stride, not expecting to be stopped.

"Yes, sir?" he responded, turning slightly off-balance to look back at the aging gentleman, who wore a long and thin white beard peppered with flecks of black.

"Tell me," the old man said almost inaudibly in his hoarse and craggy voice. "Are you our pilot?"

Chau squatted to the floor—partly to hear better, and partly to get close to the man, who he wanted to make sure heard him back.

"I am, sir."

"Hmm," the elderly man responded, nodding his balding head in understanding.

"Can you tell me when we will be leaving Saigon?"

"Well, sir," Chau started, "we will be fueling the plane short-ly. We need to wait until we have some more passengers, so we can–"

"*I was at Dien Bien Phu!*" the man shouted suddenly and angrily. His milky, cataract-covered eyes frowned in a contorted look of wrath and fear.

The old woman he sat with, presumably his wife, tried to in-terrupt her husband to stop him from verbally accosting Chau, placing her hands on his shoulder.

"*SHHH!*" he commanded her, brushing her hand away.

Chau was a bit shocked at the man's sudden attack but didn't react.

"I was *THERE!*" he said loudly. "Do you *know* what is com-ing to Saigon?"

Chau didn't quite know what to say.

"Yes, sir."

"I was a French interpreter," he continued, trying to sound authoritative, but his voice was so fragile it didn't work very well. "Castries was a *fool!*"

Every Vietnamese school kid knew Christian Marie Ferdi-nand de la Croix de Castries as the blundering French general from the 1954 Dien Bien Phu bloodbath. It was his colonial forces who fought and were ultimately crushed by the commu-nist Viet Minh.

"Do you know," he went on, this time much calmer but with

a persistent death grip on Chau's ankle, "I was captured. They marched us north. Three of my friends and one of my sons died of cholera on the way."

Chau remembered hearing the stories when he was younger—communist soldiers forced ten thousand prisoners to camps more than six hundred miles away to points in the north and east—a distance that put the Bataan Death March to shame. Of the captives, only a little over three thousand were repatriated four months later. Many were unaccounted for. Apparently, this man was a witness to it.

"My *son*, colonel!" he stated vehemently, shaking Chau's leg again as his eyes filled with tears.

"Yes, sir, I am sorry."

Chau did his best to keep the situation calm, but it was hard to tell where the man was going. He had no doubt it was difficult for a father to lose a child—something that had crossed his mind often, especially in the last few months.

"The communists," he went on, his voice cracking with emotion, "do not care about *you!* They do not care about me, or our families! Now they are coming *here!*"

"Sir, I—"

"*No!* You do NOT understand! We need to leave *now!*"

"I appreciate your concern, sir, but—"

"*They will kill us all!*"

"Sir, we are all scared," Chau responded calmly. "I have a wife and two young children. My co-pilot has small daughters. We all want to get our families to safety."

"We cannot wait!" the man implored. "THAT is why I have THIS!"

Reaching from his baggy clothing, the man produced a small snub-nosed Smith and Wesson .38-caliber revolver and began waving it in front of Chau. Fortunately, most of the other passengers weren't close enough to see what was happening, but his shocked wife gasped and grabbed at him to stop her husband from doing something stupid. Not expecting to have a weapon brandished in his face, Chau reeled back on his squatted feet, catching his rearward fall by placing his hand on the even concrete of the hangar floor. Gaining his balance, he rose to his feet, grabbed the elderly man's wrist and squeezed hard to seize the pistol from his grip.

"You will not need that weapon on my aircraft!"

The aged man's wife was angry and tearful at the exchange, obviously shaken by her husband's unwise behavior. Chau's heart pounded as he did his best to stifle his disbelief at what had just happened. The man rambled on about the Viet Minh and prison camps, but Chau ignored him and stuffed the gun into a zipper pocket near his hip. After taking a deep breath, he wiped a bead of sweat from his forehead and looked around the hangar as the old soldier incoherently went on.

"Madam," Chau said, turning to the man's wife, "I will hold this and return it to you after we arrive at our destination."

The tearful woman nodded in understanding.

"I am sorry, Colonel," she whimpered with shame while letting her husband continue to spout off, "he has bad memories!"

Chau thought his heart would explode out of his chest.

"He gets very upset and . . ." she trailed off.

"It is OK . . ."

Chau turned his attention away from the older couple. What he'd hoped would be a small respite became a debacle he'd just as soon forget.

A short distance away, he could see Vinh's stunned wife, her arms wrapped protectively around her daughters. It was clear to Chau that she had seen the whole thing.

April 26th, 1975
TAN SON NHUT AIR BASE
5:00PM

Vinh had been certain that the distant artillery thumps had been picking up earlier in the day, but things had quieted. There was a sense of imminent trouble that hung heavily over the nose dock, and the gloomy state that Chau had been displaying on-and-off had his co-pilot nervous. His wife and daughters secure and fed, Vinh decided he had to get out of the building and had gone to get a small bite to eat for himself and Quan.

With his dinner mission complete, he drove toward the hangar in Chau's Jeep through sporadic traffic and the odd group of people making their way on foot towards the ramps where American airlifters were loading. He'd only found a single lonely staff member in the small mess facility along with two very young base security personnel who couldn't have been much older than eighteen or nineteen. All three looked frightened. With South Vietnamese military desertions reaching a critical state, few troops were around to guard the installation, much less fight if it were attacked. It worried Vinh — he hadn't been out of the hangar much, but every time he left, it seemed as if fewer and fewer people were around to staff the base's work areas. He'd also been completely out of contact with any other pilots or aircrews, and had little idea how many were even still around. It didn't matter.

The lonely kitchen staff member could only provide a few

bowls of noodles, and Vinh couldn't help but notice the small cooking area was nearly barren of food. Before leaving, he told all three young men that he and Chau would be leaving in short order and that they should get on board with them. Besides, Vinh thought, it would be a good idea to have a couple security personnel present after hearing about Chau's brief altercation with the old man with the gun. Things wouldn't get much better—there'd be no telling who the most dangerous people were in the hangar. Vinh figured an unsupervised cook and two soldiers could get away with parking themselves there and not be missed. At the suggestion they join Vinh and Chau on Monday, they only nodded nervously and gave him their thanks. Maybe they'd show up and maybe they wouldn't.

The Jeep sputtered as the hangar came into view, its large doors rolled slightly apart in the growing twilight of the day, creating a tall black space between them, which allowed some of the dwindling light into the interior. He swore he could see the tail end of a dark green fuel truck and felt a deep sense of relief. He knew obtaining fuel might be sketchy—like in most other places across the base, airfield refueling personnel might be scarce at best, and he was afraid the installation's fuel inventory itself could be nearly drained, especially with all the American airlift activity. The seasoned major could only hope there would be a couple individuals who could operate the controls on the refueling vehicles to ensure the necessary levels of JP-4 could fill their tanks. If no trucks could be found, they might be stuck getting gas from 'war reserve' drums, which even with the right equipment could take forever to pump into the aircraft.

He got closer and readied to come to a stop and park.

It was definitely a fuel truck. Braking at the hangar opening, the silver-colored aluminum ladder on the rear end of its dark green tank removed all doubt, as did the thick black hoses that appeared to be attached to the plane's port-side hose coupling. Vinh blew one quick blast of the reedy horn and waited as two young men in civilian clothes came to pull the large right door open wide enough for him to sneak in past the large tanker. He pulled in and took in a scene that surprised him. He'd only been gone for an hour or so, yet the small crowd of people had increased to what had to be at least two hundred, maybe more. A large and dusty two-and-a-half ton, American-made troop carrier sitting parked in the corner was one of the likely means of transportation for many of the additional bodies.

It was both gratifying and scary—on one hand, they'd be able to get some more people on board and out of the country, but it also meant things could be getting more desperate outside the base gate. Nobody in their right mind would fill a military vehicle to the brim with civilians and hope not to be noticed—but it had clearly happened, meaning the populace was probably making their way to whatever transportation remained without a care of how they got there.

Vinh halted his vehicle as the doors closed behind him, slightly darkening the hangar once again. As his tired eyes adjusted in the dim light, he grabbed the three half-spilled bowls of noodles from the front passenger seat and did his best to egress without spilling more. Figuring it best to go up the ramp and put the food inside the cockpit where it wouldn't be stolen, he noticed another sight that gave him immense relief. Not only was there one fuel truck, but there were *three*—the remaining two parked tightly on the port side of the aircraft and out of the way. The plane was a C-130 "B" model from the late 1950s, which was equipped with fuel capacity in the wings and additional storage in large, gray-green wing-mounted tank pods. Assuming each truck was full, they'd have about 15,000 gallons on hand—a lot more gas than they needed. That was good news, although they'd be heavy on takeoff, which could require increased runway space to get airborne. Vinh figured it was a small price to pay.

Chau's loyal co-pilot bounded up the pocked cargo ramp, slightly dented in places from the years of cargo loads and placed the three bowls of noodles on a small seat near the missing door. Detecting voices outside, he hopped back out to the hangar floor and found Chau and Quan engaged in conversation with a young man who was detaching a hose from the airplane. Vinh could barely contain his elation and sprinted toward them.

"Quan!"

Quan and Chau quickly looked up. Vinh was beaming from ear to ear as his feet skidded to a stop in front of his crew.

"*Three* fuel trucks?" he asked excitedly.

Quan looked sideways at Chau, who remained expressionless, then cracked a half-grin back at Vinh.

"Yes, sir," Quan answered a little smugly. "The last three that would still run."

"How did you get three?" Vinh asked. "I thought we would be using barrels!"

"I have friends in low places, Major."

"Low places?"

"Quan's friend was one of the last of the fuel personnel," Chau explained, turning back to Vinh. "They filled the trucks, found a third driver, and came straight here."

Vinh could not contain himself.

"You came through, Quan!" he exclaimed, placing his hand on the young man's shoulder. "Great job!"

"My friend Duc here and I have been friends for a long time. He will join us on the flight out."

"That's great," Vinh responded. "Well, I brought some food and it is in the bay. It is not much, but good enough for what is available."

At that moment, a car horn sounded outside the front of the hangar, getting the attention of the four men.

"Quan, go and see what it is," Chau ordered.

The crew's youngest member dutifully responded and trotted over to the large, still partly-open hangar door, followed by Vinh and Chau at a slightly slower pace.

As they approached, Vinh could see the short hood and weathered grill of a white Ford van. Shifting themselves through the door, he and Chau emerged into the muggy dusk and took note of the license plate indicating the van was a US Embassy vehicle…and there were two Americans in the front seat.

"Is that Chuck's men?" Vinh curiously.

"Let them in!" Chau said loudly through the opening before waving at the driver, who sported a set of mirrored, teardrop-shaped sunglasses resting on top of his head amid a tangle of wavy, red hair.

Two sets of hands could be seen opening the facility's massive doors, then Quan stepped into the opening to marshal them inside. The van heaved forward with a lurch and drove through the opening. As it passed, Chau and Vinh could see that it was packed with a contingent of passengers.

"Do you think there are any old men with guns inside?" Vinh chided.

Chau ignored him and followed the van through.

The driver's side door swung open and Rusty McClay

stepped out, his red hair and pale skin a stark contrast to the darker features of the Asian men that surrounded him.

"Hello, Chau."

Chau bowed slightly toward Rusty.

"Got a load here for you guys," he said.

On the other side of the van, Jesse Flounders was assisting passengers, and Chau immediately recognized Mr. and Mrs. Tham from the bakery.

"Mai did it!" he muttered to Vinh.

"Did what?"

"Mr. Tham!" Chau called.

The Thams broke into relieved smiles as Chau approached them with Vinh on his heels.

"Hello Chau," Mr. Tham responded with a slight bow, a small dual-handled brown leather bag at his side.

"It is good to see you," he said, "I trust you have spoken with my wife?"

"Yes," he responded with a nod. "We are glad to join you, but it is a sad time."

"Yes, it is. But we are very lucky to have a way out. *Thank you.*"

Mr. Tham bowed respectfully.

"Indeed."

Chau paused.

"Mr. Tham, I know things must be changing fast outside the air base. What can you tell us about what is happening right now?"

"The streets are dangerous. Just now in a few places we saw looting, and it looks like some of it is being driven by police and soldiers."

It was disappointing, but it didn't surprise Vinh to hear it.

Obviously, law and order were breaking down in a hurry, even since he was last off the installation early that morning. Although the shelling was far off, people must have been moving more and more quickly into survival mode.

"On the way to the airfield we saw uniforms piled in some places along the sidewalks and streets—next to black boots and helmets."

Vinh knew what that meant.

"Soldiers are deserting in greater numbers, Chau."

"Have you heard the shelling?" Chau asked Mr. Tham.

"Yes," Mr. Tham answered, "but in the last several hours it has slowed."

"We noticed that too."

"When will we leave, Chau?" Mrs. Tham interrupted.

"We want to try and depart by Monday morning," Chau explained. "We need more passengers first. The aircraft must be full."

"Of course," Mr. Tham replied.

"The accommodations in the hangar are not comfortable, but it is all we have."

"We will survive," Mr. Tham said. "Where are Mai and your children?"

No doubt Tham was worried, having seen what was happening in the city. Before Chau could answer, his conversation was interrupted by Rusty and Jesse.

"Hey Chau," Rusty said, "we're gonna get some food, maybe bring you a few more people, then bed down here for the night."

"How many more will you bring?"

"As many as we can get," Jesse cut in. "If we can get two or three runs completed, it could mean thirty to forty more people."

Chau nodded. Vinh knew hangar space would be limited, but they'd find room.

"Chau," Rusty said, "the streets are bad. We've been to the port and the other side of the airport. Lots of crowds."

"Mr. Tham told me."

"If you're gonna get your family out," Rusty continued, "you better do it real damn soon. We won't be making many more runs with your countrymen."

An aircraft could be heard taking off from the airfield and the three men stopped talking. As the engine noise dissipated, three unmistakable impacts could be heard.

Artillery.

…and this time, they were closer than before.

11

April 27th, 1975

CIA OFFICES AT THE NGUYEN HOME

7:30AM

Jesse and Rusty pulled up to the alley next to the Nguyens' home to the sight of a large stake-bed truck that had been partially-filled with CIA office furniture, the smashed remains of what was once their KY-3 phone, and pieces of the roof antenna array. In front of the truck, the rear fender of their battered Citroen could be seen.

Must have been Bob Frailey.

"What's all this?" Jesse asked.

"Looks like someone's emptying out all our shit," Rusty responded, "Bet Frailey slept here last night."

Rusty parked their van and as the two men emerged from it, the distinct aroma of a fire could be detected coming from the direction of the house's courtyard.

"Smell that?"

Rusty opened the small metal gate leading to the tiled enclosure with a slight metallic screech, Jesse at his heels. Near Hong's queen flower tree was a thin pillar of brown smoke and ash emanating from a metal drum being filled by none other than Hong himself. He looked up curiously at the two men as he threw in a stack of loose papers and a few yellow legal pads, then nodded before reaching to the ground to add more to the orange flames that licked up the barrel's inner surfaces. Rusty looked at Jesse before nodding to Hong in response, then turned to go back through the gate.

"I suppose Mr. Nguyen doesn't want anyone to know Americans were here."

Jesse followed him the short distance to the door that led into Chuck's recently-vacated residence and the CIA offices on the upper floors. There were sounds of knocking and thumping from above the small vestibule area, and Bob Frailey emerged from the stairwell with a gray-cushioned desk chair.

"Good morning, guys," he said as he passed, nearly taking the smaller-framed Jesse out in the process, "You're just in time to help. Chau's upstairs."

"Great," Rusty exclaimed with faux-excitement. "I love moving!"

The distinctive drone of a C-130 resonated overhead as the two men ascended the stairs and upon entering the office discovered Chau, looking as disheveled as he ever had—hair a sweaty mess, his flight suit soiled, and his black boots scraped and worn. The large room was mostly emptied of furniture, save for a couple desks and a table that held their percolator.

Jesse rushed over to Chau to help him slide a desk across the linoleum floor.

"Good morning, Chau," he grunted slightly as he helped pull it. "How long have you been at this?"

"Since five this morning."

Rusty shook the coffee urn in hopes that Bob Frailey had

at least thought to make some, but the dull aluminum pot only rattled emptily.

"No coffee?"

It was seven thirty in the morning…for Pete's sake.

Chau and Jesse had managed to turn the large heavy desk on its side and had slid it to the top of the staircase, where they stopped before taking it down.

"Five AM, huh?" Jesse asked. "You must really want this stuff out of here."

"Hong is taking it out," Chau explained. "If he does not make it out of Saigon, he does not want the communists to know you were here."

"Is Hong coming with you?" Rusty asked.

"I do not know," Chau answered as a bead of sweat dripped down his forehead. "Sometimes he says he will come, and other times that he will stay."

"What're you gonna do?"

"I am leaving with Mai, even if her father will stay in Vietnam. My family will go to the hangar with me tomorrow."

There was no sense talking about it anymore. All of them wanted Hong to leave with his wife and children, especially Chau, but Rusty knew it had been discussed to death. There was no sense beating a horse that was already dead, bloated, and stinking.

"OK, well," Jesse said, "let's move this thing, then we'll get the rest."

Jesse and Chau shifted the large desk to line it up with the stairs.

"What the hell are you guys doing up there?" came a call from below.

It was Bob Frailey.

"Looking for some damn coffee!" Rusty replied.

"You guys are early," he called back up the steps.

Jesse got on the lower end of the bulky steel desk as Chau lifted the top end to tip it down the steps. Several drawers slid open as a silver-colored hasp rattled on one of them, spilling several writing instruments, a few paper clips, and bits of yellow paper. Rusty followed Chau down the steps as the desktop came to rest on the floor of the vestibule area.

"Where we taking this stuff, Bob?" Jesse asked.

Rusty figured it made sense that Hong would want all the American property out of his home, but it still had to be hauled off somewhere that wasn't too obvious so it couldn't be connected to his family.

"We'll drag it to the base and park it somewhere," he answered. "Let the commies have it."

Chau and Jesse slid the furniture out the door and into the alley, then leaned it upright against the opened rear of the truck. Rusty climbed the lift gate and into the bed.

"You guys ready to lift?"

Chau and Jesse nodded, placing their hands on each corner.

"One, two," Jesse started, "THREE!"

Up it went, on to the splintered wood surface of the stake bed. The smell of burning American office supplies wafted through the alleyway, and it was already getting hot and humid.

"Could've at least made us some *coffee*, Bob," Rusty groused.

Frailey's brow was sweating.

"How about if I hold your head underwater?" Frailey shot back.

It didn't faze Rusty, who turned to follow his boss' boss back up the steps.

"Any changes to our plan?" he asked.

"There's not much left here—we're gonna get this stuff out-ta here and–"

"Please don't tell me we're moving more people."

"No," Frailey answered. "We're outta time. We need to get to a safer place."

"Something happen?"

Frailey paused and began to speak under his breath.

"Still got forces getting closer on all sides of us. Past Bien Hoa and past Can Tho and that was almost twelve hours ago."

"Shit."

"I suppose you saw on your way in here that things are de-teriorating more."

"Saw a fire or two and some piled-up uniforms. Maybe a few people here and there digging around some storefronts, but—"

"We got thirty thousand ARVN inside the city and there's basically nobody in charge. Most of their brass is gone," Frailey explained. "We gotta get to the Embassy. If the airport gets hit, they won't be getting much more traffic out and we're gonna have to engage the rotary plan."

Rusty scooted up close to Frailey.

"What about Chau and his family?" he whispered, hoping not to be heard.

"We're about at the point where it becomes their problem and we go our separate ways," Frailey replied quietly. "He's gon-na have to pull the trigger on his plan by himself and we need to let it go."

Chau thumped upstairs. Jesse, who'd just joined the other two Americans, had a freshly-lit cigarette hanging from his lips.

"Oh, hey Jess," Rusty began, "Know what? We're surround-ed!"

"How much time we got?"

"Maybe a day," Frailey answered. "Maybe two. I don't know."

"Well, I guess we oughta quit screwing around, huh?"

Chau began to move more furniture. There wasn't much time to waste.

April 27th, 1975
ROAD TO TAN SOHN NHUT
9:00AM

"Hate to leave that classy French beetle behind," Rusty joked referring to their weathered Citroen.

Frailey sat in the passenger seat of the stake bed truck as Rusty made his way toward the base. Ahead of them, Jesse was in the empty van that had no passengers for the first time in days.

"Lookin' a little spooky out here," Frailey said. "Thought I'd see a lot more people on the street by this time of morning."

A scooter buzzed past, precariously imbalanced with an oversized load of luggage. Several bicycles circulated on the sides of the road around abandoned vehicles and past a number of store fronts, some with their shattered windows and doors hanging open, most of the lights inside powered off.

"See the uniforms over there?"

Rusty pointed ahead of them on the left side.

"That's what you get when shit's about to hit the fan," Frailey commented. "Nobody wants to be in the army anymore."

The twin golf ball-shaped radar domes on Tan Son Nhut came into view, with the unmistakable pagoda that stood near the main gate to the right.

"I think I'll feel better when we get on this base," Rusty quietly commented as they approached.

"Well, we still gotta get back through town. Things are teetering on the edge — let's just hope they stay that way until we can get back to the compound."

A fair-sized gathering of would-be refugees had gathered near the guard shack, skirted by several abandoned cars and small trucks. The entrance wasn't blocked, but it would be tricky getting their long-bodied stake bed vehicle around them. The crowd wasn't out of hand, but there was an extreme tension and it made Rusty nervous.

"Get up there, Jess," he muttered as they slowed to a crawl, knowing Jesse wouldn't hear.

The guards, replete with flak vests and helmets, slid the fenced chain linked gate open and Rusty slowly snaked his way around the serpentine security obstacles. Angry voices were suddenly heard outside and out of nowhere, a tomato hit Rusty's windscreen.

"Damn!"

A guard motioned to him, as if to say 'quickly!' but he couldn't get around the concrete obstructions as fast as Jesse. Frailey's shoulder blades were off the seat back and his eyes glued on the horizon ahead of him.

"Get on through and hope nobody has guns!" he called.

"That scared the shit out of me!"

The two men felt a slight sideways jerk from the rear of the truck. Rusty looked in his rear-view mirror and saw several young men had climbed into the bed.

"Hell, some guys just jumped on the back!"

Rusty instinctively put his hand on his pistol as Frailey uneasily looked through the back window to see what was happening.

"Keep going! Don't stop."

"Don't stop?"

"No!" Frailey answered. "Looks like it's only a few and I don't see any guns."

"Yeah, you don't see any, but any one of those assholes could have something in his pocket!"

"Keep moving. Just consider this your last passenger run."

Ahead of them, Jesse picked up speed and made his way through the base's pot-holed streets that as of that morning had been mostly deserted, but now seemed to have some people on them—all slowly making their way in the direction of the airfield. As they passed an old wood-framed barracks, three elderly men looked curiously at their vehicle, piled high with American office furniture and a few young refugees. It must have looked quite strange indeed.

"What're those guys doing? I can't see 'em!"

Frailey turned and looked through the back window again.

"I think it's fine. Just a bunch of teenaged kids. Don't worry about 'em."

"OK, but—"

"Just follow Jesse. We're gonna find a place to park."

Leading the way in the van, Jesse made his way to the edge of a long row of buildings that overlooked the runway. Across the ramp on the civilian side of the airport, a small white jet could be seen taxiing, but it only looked like a few civil tails remained at the terminal. Jesse pulled up between two massive hangars and came to a stop.

"All right, Rusty," Frailey said with uncertainty. "Here's where we leave this truck. I'm not sure what these yahoos on the back are gonna do, so when you're out, get away where you can see 'em."

Rusty slowed as Frailey looked through the back window.

"Better get that pistol ready, just in case."

Reaching back down to his right hip he quickly switched the safety off as he came to a full stop and exited. His hand was still on the weapon as he and Frailey got out. Rusty made his way over to Jesse and the van as their boss walked around the back of the bed where three males, who couldn't have been older than sixteen, jumped off and began to run.

"Dừng lại!" Frailey called after them.

Stop!

The skittish young men slowed and looked back, but kept their distance as Frailey approached, calling out to them in a fluent stream of Vietnamese.

"What the hell?" Rusty mumbled under his breath with bewilderment.

"He knows Vietnamese?"

"Evidently he does," Jesse replied.

"Three years in Saigon with this guy and I've never heard him say a word."

Frailey continued approaching, talking to the youths, then lowered his tone somewhat and got them to come to a full stop. In a matter of a few seconds, he was shaking hands with them, and as he turned toward Jesse's van, they followed him.

"I'll be damned," Jesse muttered. "Guess you won't need that pistol, Russ."

"Let's get these guys over to Chau's hangar," Frailey said as he walked past his agents and opened the side door for their three new passengers.

"What the hell was that, Bob?" Rusty asked. "What did you say to them?"

"I asked them where they were from, if they had any weapons, and if they'd like a ride the hell outta here."

"When in the hell did you learn Vietnamese?"

"There's a lot you guys don't know about me."

April 27th, 1975
EN ROUTE TO THE US EMBASSY
10:30AM

The streets were pulsating with cars, trucks, and bicycles, most of the vehicles packed with as many people as could fit inside. Rusty maneuvered the van on to one of Saigon's wide main streets and the traffic slowed to a crawl. Besides the direction the cars were pointed, there was no real feel for which direction people were traveling in — it made sense that the majority would still be moving towards the port or the airport, but things were impossibly choked on both sides of the road.

Rusty, Jesse, and Bob Frailey were slowly passing through an enormous traffic circle with a large dry fountain in the middle, flanked by ornately-decorated eight and ten story buildings on either side, originally constructed in the French style in the early twentieth century. If not for the lush, tropical vegetation, palms, and cyclos, it could almost have passed for Paris. In some places, more abandoned uniforms were visible and along the sidewalks there were a few people pushing small furniture items or carrying stereo equipment. One bare-chested, mid-twenties Vietnamese man wearing a pair of army fatigues and a helmet raced past the van pushing a wheelbarrow full of vinyl records and fruit.

"Yeah, I'd say it's about time we holed up in the Embassy," Jesse muttered from the first rear passenger seat.

"No shit?" Rusty quipped.

Whether it was because of the active South Vietnamese underground communication network or the ever-encroaching artillery impacts, it was clear that most people had lost whatever confidence they had left in local authority.

"Let's see if we can get around some of this and on to the next block."

"I don't think you're gonna get around much of it," Frailey commented doubtfully. "Hell, we'd be better off on bikes."

"Been doing this for a few days now, Bob," Rusty answered. "I'll get us there."

Upon reaching a cross-street, they took a right and passed a young soldier sitting on the sidewalk, frantically taking off his boots.

"Maybe."

Rusty was able to get on to a short stretch that wasn't as crowded, leading to another wide avenue.

"You're gonna have to muscle your way out there."

Rusty put his hard-earned aggressive driving skills to work and began nosing out into the slow-moving traffic. The next street was long, and extended quite a way, the tops of the buildings in the distance shorter and blockier than the last thoroughfare and partly obscured by trees and haze.

"At this rate, it may be a little bit before we—"

Out of nowhere, a thunderous explosion suddenly rocked a building several blocks ahead of them and the horrified cries of those on the street responded in kind.

"What the hell was that!" Jesse bellowed.

In an instant, a very fast whizzing sound could be heard, followed by another earsplitting blast erupting from a building about a block away, forcing Rusty to jam on his brakes to avoid hitting the vehicle in front of him.

"Rockets!" Frailey called out. *"Get us out of here!"*

People on either side of the road began to run, desperately trying to move away from the blasts.

"I'm workin' on it!"

Another whizzing sound cracked right over the van, followed by a deep detonation, and a building to their left gushed smoke and debris all over their hood and windshield. A chunk about the size of a softball hit the glass, shattering it and peppering Rusty and Frailey with small pieces of auto glass.

"Not working!" Frailey thundered. *"Get out!"*

The three men quickly exited as another rocket shrieked overhead, finding its target somewhere off to their right.

"What?" Jesse called out above the chaos as he instinctively threw his arms in front of his face to block any fragments coming his way. "We're going *on foot?*"

"You got a better idea?" Frailey called over the noise. "The Embassy's only a couple blocks away and we're not gonna get there quick if we stay in that damned van!"

They feverishly made their way through a mob of people toward a small alley as a fourth rocket tore low through the sky behind them. The deafening impact sent a hard shock wave through their chests, pounding their bodies like a bass drum.

Frailey, a big man but still fairly nimble for his age, cut into the small alley with the two younger agents close behind. Farther away, another rocket ripped into an unseen building, the explosion sending a furious thump through the thick air and rattling windows on the structure above them.

"We don't have far to go!" he called backward as he ducked between dumpsters, piled trash, and low branches protruding over a cinder block wall to their right.

Yet another missile hurtled over them as they quickly navigated through frightened people, smacking into a building to their rear and splitting their eardrums upon impact.

"Son of a bitch!" Jesse called.

Jesse's mind shot into a fog. His immediate reality mixed incomprehensibly with images of mortar rounds impacting near him and his Marines in the Hue of 1968. Smoke, bits of dust and stone, and grit landed all around him. He instinctively reached for his helmet to make sure it didn't come off in the mad dash to somewhere even a little safer.

Helmet? Wait, where's my rifle?

The sounds of horrified civilians filled the street behind them as Frailey emerged onto a wider boulevard and cut left between cars and people. On the side of the street, smoke and flame poured from a façade that had lost a large portion of its second story. People were running frantically as a hysterical young woman carried a young boy in her arms, his eyes dazed, body limp, and his shirt dusty and blood-soaked.

"Come on!" Frailey cried.

As the men dodged past people and other obstacles, another rocket careened into a street behind them, the explosion shaking the cracked asphalt under their feet.

"Shit!" Rusty cried out to his rear. "Jess, let's go! *Move your ass!*"

And they kept coming.

Another smashed into a building in a block to their right and they had a hard time keeping up with Frailey, who was already fifty feet ahead of them. Jesse briefly lost him in a cloud of dust, then saw his salt and pepper hair being hit by a beam of sunlight as he crossed a street ahead. A Vietnamese man passed in front of Jesse and Rusty, causing Rusty to run headlong into him before tumbling to the sidewalk. The middle-aged man's face and hair were covered in dust and his skin was gray and ashy. In his right hand he held his severed left arm, wristwatch still attached, as its stump hemorrhaged blood.

"Aw, *God!*" Rusty uttered, horrified by the human gore, as the man jabbered numbly in a language he didn't understand.

It spurted blood on the front of Rusty's pants. Jesse caught up and his eyes grew wide. He grabbed Rusty's upper arm, "We gotta go, Russ...let's go..."

They'd lost Frailey again but knew where the Embassy was and continued forward with purpose in its general direction. In the distance, farther off this time, two more rockets could be heard slamming into the city.

"Where's Frailey?" Rusty called over his shoulder. "Can you see him?"

Jesse dodged a tree and three small children following their frenetic mother.

"No!"

His ears rang. Another rocket impact hit, farther off this time as they weaved through a small surging crowd, struggling to get between two newly-planted decorative trees and a parked motor scooter.

"Get up to the next block!"

They came to a cross street and made their way through another small group of people to quickly emerge on the shabby pedestrian sidewalk of the next block. The street ahead curved and the sidewalk faded from view, making it hard to see if they were any closer to Frailey. Another rocket whizzed overhead, causing both men and everyone around them to simultaneously wince, duck, and look above them, but rather than hit anything on the street they were on, it landed somewhere a block or two to their left.

"Where in the hell is Frailey!" Jesse called out. "Did he get behind us?"

"I don't know!"

Weaving past storefronts and a hotel entrance, they ended up in a sunny spot and stopped, panting heavily.

"Do you see him?"

All the vehicles on the street were stopped, most of them empty—people had instinctively exited their cars where they had come to rest in a desperate search for cover.

"Hey!"

It was Frailey—peeking around the side of a building from a small alleyway through a crowd of panicking citizens.

"Come on," he yelled. "We're cutting down here!"

Frailey slowed the pace, in part to navigate the narrow throughway as another missile could be heard sailing through the air above the city farther away, followed by the deep thud of an impact only God knew where.

"Might be safer with the high walls on both sides!"

"I'm not so sure about that!" Jesse called in response.

Frailey got to the bottom of the alley and stopped at the ready. As Rusty and Jesse arrived on his flanks, there was another impact—this time even farther away than the one before. Frailey turned left on to a larger avenue, choked with stopped traffic and motorbikes, then began to meander up the sidewalk, not quite at a run, but definitely at a jog. While the street was busy, the sidewalk didn't seem as bad.

"I think this is OK," he stated breathlessly, making a 'slow-down' motion with his right hand as he began to move at an even slower pace. "It may be OK..."

"How do you know?" Rusty asked uncertainly.

"Yeah...I think—"

Out of nowhere, a *whiz* sound preceded an intense blast be-fore any of the men could react...and everything turned black.

April 27th, 1975
US EMBASSY, SAIGON
12:00PM

"Wha...?"

Jesse Flounders woke in a spartan, white-walled room with two fluorescent lights hanging from the ceiling—one of them powered on, the other switched off. His ears whined and rang like a television left on too long, and tiny gnomes with giant sledge-hammers pounded the inside of his forehead. Realizing he was lying flat on his back on a small bed, he lifted his hand to rub his eyes to find them caked in grit. As his fingers ran down his face, he discovered that the same sandiness that encrusted his eyes also covered his cheeks and the stubble on his chin. There was some kind of rough spot on the lower left of his face right next to his mouth that felt like a horrendous chunk of dry skin. Jesse brushed his nail across it to try and scrape it off, but it wouldn't come loose.

"Hey Bob," someone called quietly in the hall, "Jess is com-ing around."

Footfalls echoed in a nearby hallway.

"You alive, Jesse?"

The sound of Bob Frailey's low, but authoritative voice reached Jesse's seemingly cotton-stuffed ears. It felt similar to being exposed to hours of some ostentatious clamor...not un-like what he remembered after seeing a Creedence Clearwater Revival show in downtown D.C. after he'd gotten home from Vietnam six years before.

"What is this?" he asked, scratching the dry patch on his face. "Where's Rusty?"

"Right here, brother."

Jesse felt dizzy as he tried to prop himself up.

"Hang on there, cowboy," Frailey moved towards the gurney. "You took a pretty good lump. Here, sit up slow."

Jesse felt a pillow being placed behind his head to prop him up.

"I feel like I drank a whole bottle of Jack."

"Doc says you're gonna be OK. Ya kinda gave us a scare, though."

He remembered the rocket attack like it was a forgotten dream.

"What the hell was with the rockets?"

"First major attack on Saigon in about four years and we got to be a part of it," Rusty commented. "Kinda makes me feel like we were a part of something special."

Jesse propped himself up on his elbow and took in the scene, squinting in the low light and rubbing his head.

"Oh, yeah. I feel real damn special."

"Blast likely gave you a concussion, Jess," Frailey explained. "Take it easy. You're gonna be a little dizzy."

"What time is it?"

"About noon. You've been out a little while."

In the half-dimness, Jesse observed Rusty sitting on a metal folding chair in the corner and Frailey leaning up against the door with his arms crossed. The small room in the Embassy compound's infirmary was cold and stark. Rusty's face was greasy and dirty, his shirt disheveled and bloody from the man who'd lost his arm right in front of them. Frailey wasn't much better, his normally perfect hair looking more frazzled than normal. They looked terrible, and Jesse could only imagine what *he* looked like.

"One of those rockets smacked right into the first floor of a building we were next to," Frailey explained. "Blew the crap out of it."

Seeing the shooting near the airport was enough, but then it was the Nguyen boys' firecracker-gunshots, and now rockets. He'd yearned to get out of Vietnam without having to go through anything resembling his time in Hue, but that hope was quickly evaporating.

"What's on my face?" he asked, running his fingers across the dry spot he'd found earlier.

"Don't mess with it," Rusty answered. "Stitches — flying glass. Nice bloodstain on your collar too. Damn good thing it didn't hit higher up your face and hit your eye."

"Are you guys OK?" Jesse asked.

"Well," Rusty explained, "the blast knocked us all off our feet. You were closest — Bob and I were a little farther away. Put us all flat on our asses."

"You guys walked away?"

"Not exactly," Frailey went on. "We were part of all the debris on the street and a couple teenage kids found us. Dragged Rusty and I through all the people and abandoned vehicles half-conscious, then came back and got you. We were lucky — a couple good-sized chunks of concrete landed right near us and one of 'em could easily have taken someone's head off."

"Man," Jesse said, "my ears are ringing."

His temples throbbed.

"The kids that pulled us away flagged down a guy on a cyclo," Frailey continued. "Somehow, the driver got us through the crowd and to the gate. Marines helped us into the compound. I was a little out of it."

Jesse looked confused.

"Crowd?"

Frailey and Rusty looked at each other.

"A lot more people at the gate now, Jess," Rusty said.

"Yeah, it's grown pretty big," Frailey explained. "People want in. There are folks already turning up missing. A good number are flashing photos of family members trying to find out if they've been seen. The rockets were the tipping point and now the city's in full panic-mode."

The sound of rubber-soled footsteps could be heard coming down the hall and moments later, Mosey Copenhaver darkened the doorway.

"Wow, consciousness!" he said, trying to sound light. "How you doing, Jesse?"

Still leaning up on his elbow, Jesse's eyes were starting to open up a little more as he adjusted to the subdued light.

"Got a hell of a headache, stitches in my face, and it feels like someone stuffed a corncob in each of my ears. Other than that, I guess I'm fine."

"These guys fill you in on what's going on?"

"I'm a little groggy."

Jesse laid his head back down.

"Heard there's a bunch of pissed off people at the gate," he said as he closed his eyes again.

"Yeah, the Marines have their hands full right now."

"I bet."

"We got bad guys are all around us. No ARVN to be found. The looting was bad before, but ever since the rockets hit, it's really kicked into high gear. It's bad."

"Sounds great. So, when we gettin' outta here?"

It was the question of the day.

"Ambassador Martin's still in la-la land," Copenhaver said.

Jesse lifted his hands to his face in exasperation.

"That guy…"

"Yeah, I know. Some are still trying to make a few runs to the APOE and SPOE, but time's running out. The call was made an hour ago to cease all of the C-141 flights. The Air Force is going full C-130 ops since they're a lot more maneuverable."

"That's comforting," Jesse looked up at Mosey. "I'm surprised anyone's still doing PAX runs at all."

"Ain't gonna last much longer," Frailey said. "The 130's will be lucky to get ten or fifteen more missions out. The bad guys have hit the city — won't be long before they hit the airfield too. Once that happens, it's all-helo."

Rusty shook his head with annoyance, muttering a handful of unintelligible curses under his breath.

"We just need to take it easy for a little longer. We'll get out. I've seen the rotary plan. They've got plenty of assets and there are LZs all over. It'll happen because there's no other option."

Jesse's head thumped.

"How many Americans still in the city?"

"A few thousand, we think," Rusty answered.

"What about the high-risk locals?"

"Dunno," Rusty answered, "but probably also in the thousands."

It took Jesse a minute to absorb the information.

"Does Martin know we're moving people?" Jesse asked, hands still over his eyes.

"Maybe," Copenhaver answered tiredly. "We sure ain't gonna ask."

"He's got a lot of other stuff on his mind," Frailey said. "For now, the three of us aren't going anywhere."

"That's a relief."

"The Navy's processing refugees on Con San Island," Copenhaver added. "They've got their hands full. What's left of the South Vietnamese Navy is still moving people from the port, plus any other vessels in the area just like before. The ambassador has ordered as many of the Embassy staff as possible to stay off the streets. Thinks it'll negatively affect our morale."

Mosey Copenhaver huffed at his own words.

"We need to relax," Frailey said. "All three of us are a little unsteady on our feet right now and we don't need to be driving anybody anywhere."

Even though the airfield was a fair distance away, the low buzz of a C-130 could be heard in the midst of the quiet room as it took to the skies and headed over the city for unknown safe havens. Frailey was hoping Chau and his family would get out before the airfield fell. It was only a matter of time before it would be too late

April 27th, 1975
NGUYEN HOME, SAIGON
6:30PM

It had been hours since Mai, Hong, and Dat had heard the explosions. There had to be ten or twenty...or more. Waiting around at the house without knowing anything was agony. Mai and her mother had discussed it with alarm as it was happening. Hong stayed silent, perhaps in an attempt to keep from making the situation worse. First it had been the dull thuds of artillery in the far distance and the faint pillar of smoke that Mai had seen from the roof, and now it was blasts coming from downtown. She'd gone back to the top of the house to see if she could see anything, and sure as the sun would rise, there was smoke on the skyline—lots of it. It filled the low sky with several white and brown columns, leveling out into a flat haze as it hit the next layer of air high above the buildings. Nobody said anything, but Mai had been quietly thankful that it wasn't coming from the airfield—Chau was there, presumably still making final preparations.

She tried to busy herself and was in the kitchen putting things away following the family's evening meal. They were consumed with worry, wrestling the demons of the unknown, and nobody'd been hungry.

The phone rang, its loud bell tones piercing the silence of the small room, giving Mai's heart a jolt and causing her to jump.

"Á-lô?"

"Mai," came the staticky response from the other end. It was Chau.

"Chau! What is happening? We heard explosions."

"I know."

"What *were* they?"

"The city was attacked with rockets," Chau answered, his voice very composed.

"*Attacked?*"

"A passenger arrived here earlier, and he was in the middle of it."

"*Rockets?* My God, Chau!"

She paced the floor.

"It is OK, Mai, we knew—"

"It is *not* OK!" she interrupted. "It means they are *close* and –"

"We knew something like this could happen," he went on, talking over her, "they have been firing artillery for days."

Dat's short frame entered the arch of the kitchen's doorway. Her hands were on her head and she looked very upset.

"*Rockets?*" she whispered to Mai.

Mai covered the plastic mouthpiece of the clunky telephone receiver and looked at her mother.

"Chau said the city was attacked!" she whispered.

Dat slumped into one of the chairs around their small table.

"Mai," Chau said. "There are a lot of people here right now. Passengers who will leave with us."

"How many, Chau? When will we leave? Why—"

"*Listen!* I need you *not* to panic!"

She put her hand on her sternum, closed her eyes and exhaled slowly.

"There are more than one two hundred fifty people here," he explained. "I do not know if we can accommodate many more."

"Who are they? Do you know them all? Where did they come from?"

"They have come from all over the city. I do not know them all, but people have been arriving steadily. The Thams are here and Vinh and his family as well. We still plan to leave tomorrow."

"*When*, Chau?"

"I will leave the base and come to get you in the afternoon."

It was really happening. Mai, Chau, Trung and Truc, her brothers, her mother, and hopefully her father...would finally leave Vietnam for the last time. It was real. Tangible. She didn't know what to say.

"Mai?"

It was like her childhood nightmares where the fear was so

intense that it was impossible to enunciate words or even whisper. Except this wasn't a dream.

"Are you there, Mai?"

She took another deep breath, feeling like her lungs were stretching all the way to the tips of her toes.

"Yes."

Her mother wrung her hands at the kitchen table.

"What is he saying?" she asked.

Mai stiffy held her palm up towards her mother, as if to say STOP.

"Did you hear what I said?" Chau asked from the distant end. "We will leave tomorrow afternoon."

"Yes, I understand."

Her voice quivered, and a sob grew deep in her chest.

"Will you come home tonight?" she cracked.

"I will try to leave soon," he answered. "Vinh is here and will remain with his wife to make sure the plane and the hangar stay secure. There are also some military policemen who have joined us—in exchange for their presence I have offered them seats when we leave. I think that will be helpful."

"Please be careful."

"I will."

"Would it be smarter for you to stay there?"

"No. I am not far. It will not take me long to get to you."

The line cracked and popped.

"Mai," Chau said after what seemed like an eternity, "you must gather up our things tonight. The children, your brothers—make sure everything is together. Have the valuables in one place so we know where they are. Check and recheck all of it."

"I will."

"I love you, Mai."

He *had* to say that, didn't he? She couldn't hold back any longer and the emotional dam broke in a torrent of tears.

"We will be all right," he said calmly.

Mai closed her eyes and imagined her husband's kind, soothing eyes as he said it. She trusted him with her life.

"OK, Chau."

Mai took one last deep breath and did her best to regain control of her faculties.

"I love you too."

12

It was Monday the 28th—the date that had been pinned on the calendar for days marking the Nguyens' intended departure. Aircraft of every kind had been leaving Tan Son Nhut all hours of the day and night, even though it was unknown how large an enemy threat there was to airfield operations. Chau was tired and his nerves were shot. He didn't want to take any unnecessary chances, but he knew that any action he took would be risky. There were already more people on the ground than his hold could handle, and with all that humanity packed like sardines in a hot and smelly cargo bay he figured it best to try and get out under the cover of darkness without exterior lighting to make the airplane less of a target. The plan was to be wheels-up by about eleven o'clock to take full advantage of the night. Chau would leave the base to get Mai and the family around nine pm.

The plane itself was about as ready as it could be. It was gassed up, generators were in-place for pre-flight, and any possible maintenance that could be done (which amounted to very little) was complete. The night before, Quan and his buddy from the fuel farm had moved the three petro trucks and abandoned them, so the hangar space was much roomier than it had been previously. Chau and Vinh had spent the day trying to keep the growing crowd of passengers under control. By now, he estimated the numbers inside his nose dock were over three hundred, and more were arriving by the hour. All of them were sweaty, tired, and uncomfortable, and most had heard the rumors of the rocket attack in Saigon the day before. Figuring they couldn't fit any more than three hundred souls in their bay, it was becoming clear that some would have to be turned away. It wasn't an ideal situation, and he hoped no more would show up looking for a ride.

Chau and his crew had done their best to vet passengers by checking identification and disarming them of any weapons, but the effort was haphazard at best. Around noon, he had decided to direct the military policemen to conduct another sweep to make sure the hangar was free of small arms. Alarmingly, more than a few were found to possess semi-automatic pistols, revolvers, and one ten-year-old boy was discovered to have an eight-inch Bowie knife. Chau knew things might get worse before they could take off (especially once people realized not everyone was getting on), and there was no way they could allow anyone to have weapons in such a state of affairs. Desperate people might view the aircrew as 'the enemy' if they didn't perform to the standards or timeline that some armed passenger might demand.

For the moment, things had calmed a little. The late afternoon was hotter than normal, and the oppressive humidity inside the yawning facility stifled much of the tension felt by the passengers. Chau was on the flight deck in the right pilot seat, deducing that it was probably the best place to keep a wide eye on things from a high position. The plane couldn't be any more ready, and by now, Mai and her mother should have had their belongings together and ready to go. Before he left her that morning, he'd taken most of her expensive jewelry, their gold coins and small ingots, and Dat's sizeable stacks of American currency, dutifully stuffing them in any free zipper pocket on his flight suit that he could find. All their valuables—everything—was safely secured in Chau's unwashed, nasty, flame retardant uniform.

It had been fairly quiet for the last hour except for the American C-130s that had been taking off and landing throughout the day, and Chau was glad to be far from the loading ramps where Americans and refugees had been boarding American jets to fly to safety. He figured the geographical separation was still helping them remain somewhat inconspicuous. At least for a few minutes, kicking back on the flight deck proved to be a fleeting but nice moment alone, until his relative peace was interrupted by clunky footsteps climbing the steps to the cockpit. Vinh, foul and ripe, emerged from behind him with two handfuls of American MCI cans and a canteen of water on his hip.

"I brought you some food. Are you hungry?"

Chau had spent the previous night at home but hadn't a morsel to eat since right before he left Mai that morning.

"It depends on what you have," Chau answered without taking his eyes off the hangar floor.

"Turkey loaf and a hard tack biscuit."

The two men had tried about all the different MCI menus over the years. Originally formulated as a long shelf-life and high-calorie ration for soldiers in the field, it was not known for its culinary excellence. It did fill the stomach, though. Turkey loaf was among the most disgusting of the bunch—right up there with meat chunks and beans in tomato sauce and the worst one: tuna fish.

Whatever. Chau was hungry.

"Thank you."

"Smells like feet in here, Chau. Why don't you open a window?"

"The windows are already open, Vinh."

Chau pulled the tab and opened the small can of meat, immediately wafting a pungent field ration funk through the cabin.

"Now it smells like feet and shit," Vinh joked with a straight face.

"Uh-huh."

Chau threw the popped lid on to the floor by his feet.

"Did you get any?" he asked as he searched for a utensil.

"Chopped ham and eggs with a piece of fruit cake."

"Sounds good," Chau commented dryly. "Where did you find these? I did not know we had any."

"One of the MPs brought two cases."

"I hope nobody saw him."

"They are in the hold. I had to break them down and stow them in a few inconspicuous places."

Chau used the meal's chintzy fork to tear into the turkey. It was terrible.

"Chau, when are you going to get Mai?"

"Once there is less light in the sky I will go," he replied, his mouth concentrating more on chewing than talking. "I told her I would be there some time after nine o'clock."

"I wish you had gone sooner. It will be more dangerous after dark," he said. "You have heard about the looting and people armed with clubs and guns."

Chau swallowed.

"If I do it during the day, they see me. At night, they do not see me."

"Yes, but you do not see them either."

"I have a greater chance of getting home without trouble if visibility is low."

"Is your pistol loaded?"

Chau reached toward the floor to his side and held up a web belt and holster, complete with a pistol and two pouches with extra magazines.

"Can I come with you?"

"No," Chau answered flatly, returning his gun to the floor. "I need you here with Quan and the MPs to make sure things remain peaceful. We will have four hundred if people keep coming at this rate."

"It was a good idea to do another weapons sweep."

"Hmm," Chau chewed. "Yes."

It was quiet and hot. Chau glanced over his shoulder at the partially open hangar door. The light was starting to get dusky. He scraped the last bite from his turkey can and shoved it in his gaping maw.

"We are as ready as we are going to be," he said, putting his empty can on the center console near the throttles.

He grabbed his web belt and pistol, stood, and threw it over his shoulder.

"I want to go outside and get some air for a few minutes."

The two men descended the stairs into the cargo bay, then out to the hangar floor. As they stepped outside through the narrowly opened hangar doors, a slight breeze tousled Chau's grimy hair.

A Jeep was parked near the personnel door—the one he would take to go get his family, hopefully with Hong in tow.

"At least there is a breeze out here."

"Yes," Chau answered, pulling the belt around his waist and buckling its hook.

In the hazy dusk an American C-130 filled the sky with its distinctive buzz, and Chau could see its wheels go up. He didn't realize that it masked the sound of something else.

"Chau, do you see those? They are moving awfully fast."

Two dark dots, clearly small aircraft, appeared on the darkening horizon and were rapidly growing in size.

Chau squinted to see them.

"They look like A-37s."

Ordinarily, he wouldn't have thought twice about seeing the planes, which were sold to the South Vietnamese Air Force by the US at the height of the war, but their speed puzzled him. He hadn't seen any A-37s at the air base in more than a week. Yet, now here they were.

"Why aren't their wheels down?" Vinh asked. "…and no landing lights."

Two more dots appeared in the growing twilight, bringing the total to four. Then the first two peeled south and appeared to line up with the ramp the Americans were using about a thousand yards away. As they were not aligned with the main runway, it was clear that landing was not their intention.

Vinh became very alarmed, very quickly.

"Something is not right, Chau!"

Within seconds, the two lead jets went into a steep dive, their engines whining. One released something from its underbelly, then the sky over the American ramp was consumed by a deafening, brilliant flash before a punishing shock wave from the monstrous blast rippled their uniforms. Absent any real cover, Chau and Vinh instinctively hit the tarmac in a prone position, covered their heads, and closed their eyes tightly.

The crowd of South Vietnamese passenger-refugees inside the hangar erupted into screams and shouts.

Tan Son Nhut Air Base was under attack.

April 28th, 1975
TAN SON NHUT AIR BASE
5:57PM

Two more blasts slammed into Tan Son Nhut, presumably from the pair of aircraft that had followed the first two, jolting the ground like a nine-point-zero earthquake. Small bits of rubble and debris began to fall, even though the bomb impacts were a good distance away.

"We need to get inside!" Chau bellowed through the booming echo of the explosions and jet noise.

"*Inside?!* What if they hit the hangar!"

The A-37s whisked overhead at great speed, rapidly passing over their position.

"If any large pieces fall, they could kill us. I will take my chances in the hangar!"

He wasn't waiting for agreement from his co-pilot. Chau got up from his prone position as tiny pebbles rained down and dust blew past with Vinh dutifully following. They reached the narrow gap in the hangar doors in a full sprint and emerged inside to the terrified, scrambling crowd of passengers. MPs and a few of the middle-aged men were doing their best to keep everyone calm as they kept low on their knees or bellies, but their efforts were in vain.

Chau and Vinh did their best to hop over the scattered bodies and belongings of their passengers, ultimately diving into a section in the back of the hangar to find some thin cover where the rear wall met the expansive floor. Some people had struggled successfully to get underneath the C-130's belly and wings, others were lying, mothers were covering their children, and two old women rocked back and forth murmuring in a panic. Vinh overheard one of them say, *"Death, please come quick."* The reality was that if a bomb hit the hangar, the entire facility, airplane, and everything inside both would be blown to atoms. Despite being inside the seemingly safe hangar, the truth was they were horribly exposed on the vast airfield.

The sound of bits of debris hitting the angled steel roof was replaced by the heavy *bam-bam-bam* of friendly anti-aircraft fire in lengthy bursts of ten to fifteen rounds. A large gun was close by, and when it paused its continued stream of fire, other guns could be heard farther away. Chau could envision the sky filled with red and green tracers, but from his location, it was impossible to see. A small boy near Vinh plugged his ears as tears rolled down his face, his mother tightly gripping a hysterical younger sibling whose cries couldn't be heard over the deafening roar of the anti-aircraft artillery.

In the distance, another bomb pounded its target, sending a shock wave across the building that rattled the aging building like a rusty cage. Like many of the other American-built structures on the base, the nose dock facility they occupied had decayed significantly in the years since the Americans left, and there was no way to tell how much vibration it could handle.

JASON NULTON & EVA NGUYEN WHITFIELD

Another bomb—closer this time—slammed into the base, the resultant shake rolling toward the helpless passengers and crew at the speed of sound.

The entire facility shuddered forcefully and flickered the dim lights, rattling their housings to the point that one came loose and crashed to the floor, shattering in clatters of broken glass amongst those unfortunate enough to be underneath. Chau closed his eyes and held his hands on the back of his head as he laid prone, jerking with each successive burst of anti-aircraft fire. He couldn't see Vinh, had no idea where Quan was, and felt concern not just for his airplane, but everyone who would ride in it.

His thoughts whirled as everything around them erupted. Would a bomb find them? The communists didn't have A-37s, only the South Vietnamese Air Force. Why were they attacking their own base? Were these pilots defectors? How many bombs would they drop? What about Mai and his kids? Would he make it home to them? Would they be able to escape? Was it too late? It was only minutes into the attack, but it felt like hours. Rubble rained down on them—each bit that landed on their roof made a different sound, the larger chunks as loud as hammers hitting bare sheet metal in a closed room.

This is what it must have been like for the Army, he thought.

In the old days, Chau and Vinh had known an ARVN officer who had long since passed away. As his head swam in terror, he recalled the old man's war stories of fighting during the early stages of the war in the nineteen fifties. He'd endured countless artillery attacks, which were terrifying because it was impossible to tell where the next round was going to land. It was a hellish anticipation that often changed people forever.

Torrents of anti-aircraft filled the air, their bursts deafening the hapless humans inside the nose dock. A fast whine tore through the dimming skies overhead again as the large caliber rounds traced the noises' route—the A-37s had returned to make another pass. Within seconds the sound abated, only to be replaced moments later by more anti-aircraft fire. A series of deep secondary explosions emanated from the direction of the first bomb impacts when out of nowhere, garish cracks could be heard pummeling the outer skin of their nose dock extremely rapidly. Chau knew what this was—the fighters had likely dropped all the ordinance they could and were now strafing the airfield. Another gun burst from a second fighter filled the cavernous space and tore holes the size of basketballs in parts of the roof and hangar doors.

Please do not hit the airplane, Chau silently requested.

April 28th, 1975
NGUYEN HOME, SAIGON
6:05PM

"Mai! What is happening?" Dat called in horror.

Mai and her mother had been checking their baggage and documents in the downstairs bedroom area when the unmistakable thuds of explosions landed on their eardrums. Dat was terrified. The sounds of the attack could not be ignored—she and everyone in the Nguyens' home knew it had to be some sort of fighting, although from inside the house it was difficult to tell which direction the sounds were coming from. Mai ignored her mother and met her father in the lower level's small hall, then bounded up the steps towards the top of the house to see if they could find out what was going on. On their way through the home's second level, they encountered Son, who had emerged from a bedroom doorway.

"What is happening, Ba?" he asked.

"Stay in there!" Hong barked without looking at him.

Son went back into the bedroom where Trung and Truc were playing, probably ignorant of what was going on outside. Lights in the narrow stairwell flickered with the pounding outside, then went brown for a moment following a deep thud they could sense slightly in their chests. Whatever these explosions were seemed relatively close by.

Hong reached the base of the small staircase that led to the roof with Mai close on his heels and Dat not far behind. In seconds, they were topside. Mai had never seen her father move so fast. They could immediately see fires and palls of thick black smoke coming from the airfield, barely two miles distant. Hong put his hands on his hips and could only stare at the tracer rounds that filled the dusk of early evening. Utterly terrified, Mai's blood ran cold and she could barely keep her knees locked. Her mouth watered like she was about to vomit, and she stared in horror as two enormous orange and black blasts erupted from the air base.

"Oh..." Dat managed breathlessly as her hand covered her mouth in shock, "oh, no ... oh, no ... oh, no ..."

In the growing darkness, several aircraft could be seen flying low over the base as bits of flaming wreckage arced high into the air, falling downward then landing unseen behind the low roofs of the buildings in between. The ceaseless *pop-pop-pop* of the anti-aircraft batteries reached their ears as tiny silhouettes of the attacking jets swarmed.

Mai grabbed her father's shoulder and stifled the urge to

gag. All she could think about was Chau. For a brief moment, Hong took his eyes off the base and grabbed Mai around the waist as she finally gave into her wobbling knees and slid to the roof surface.

"Ba?"

Dzung and Tuan had emerged from the roof's portal hatch without being noticed.

"I told you to *stay inside!*" Hong growled angrily, unable to peel his eyes away from the devastation on the horizon.

It was as if they didn't even hear him. The boys approached their parents and older sister. Dzung stopped cold, frozen next to the roof's port once he saw the flames on the horizon, as Tuan timidly walked up and stood next to Dat, reaching for her hand.

"What is going on? What is on fire?" Tuan asked, sounding on the verge of tears. "Is Chau over there?"

Hand still over her mouth in a stunned silence, Dat couldn't answer.

Mai choked, unable to breathe as her father knelt next to her.

"Chau..." she rasped. "Chau..."

April 28th, 1975
TAN SON NHUT AIR BASE
6:10PM

The anti-aircraft batteries continued to pour round after round toward their targets in the sky, but in between the bursts, Chau could no longer hear the high-pitched wails of the A-37 attack jets. Dust fell around him. The hangar was filled with screams and the reverberations of alarmed humans, many plugging their ears.

"Chau!" Vinh called from only a few feet away over the clamor. *"Chau!"*

Lying prone, Chau looked over at his friend. Only a few feet from him, Vinh had his index fingers in his ears and his mouth open, calling something inaudible over the pounding anti-aircraft fire. His sopping wet hair was covered in whitish-gray dust.

"Can you still hear the planes?"

Chau cautiously lifted himself to his knees and did his best to listen over the yelps, cries, and screams of the over three hundred passengers laying across the hangar. The dangling ceiling lights still had power, though they only glared dimly from the high rafters.

He could only hear the frightened sounds of screaming civilians and crying children, punctuated by less and less frequent anti-aircraft firing. A few men and several MPs were already on their feet attempting to calm the masses. Holes peppered the walls and roof, revealing the scant light left in the darkening skies behind them. Several of the openings created by the strafing were as wide as dishwashers and Chau found it hard to tell whether they'd been created by flying debris or large-caliber shells.

"No planes," he responded loudly, turning an ear to the air as if trying to listen. "I do not think so."

He got to his feet and crouched low, followed by Vinh and several other civilians who had lain near them.

Suddenly, from the main runway the piercing thunder of fast-moving jet engines cut the air. Chau jerked as the noise grew in volume.

"Wait!" Vinh interjected, his attention strongly attuned to

the hangar doors and the palm of his hand turned downward towards Chau. "I believe they are ours!"

The sound shook the superstructure of the hangar as it grew, then peaked before finally dissipating as the planes left the ground. Within seconds, another pair of jets took to the air behind the first, the sound once again shaking the roof of the nose dock before dissolving into the skies.

Chau knew they were friendly F-5Es, scrambled as quickly as possible, he hoped, to pursue the attackers.

"What was all that?!" Vinh called out.

"They are here," Chau said.

"Do you think it is over?"

Chau ignored him. Instead of fear, he felt an angry resolve. He knew he had to lead. People were panicking and they had to know things were under control — the human fight-or-flight urge would be very strong, and it would have to be suppressed if things were to stay orderly in the crowded nose dock.

"Find Quan. Check the plane for damage."

Vinh launched into action, running to find their loadmaster amongst the large, distressed crowd.

Two loud gunshots rang out from inside the hangar, prompting screams from several women, and causing Chau to duck, followed by relative silence.

"Everyone must be calm!"

Chau couldn't see where the shots were coming from but suspecting that one of the MPs was trying to get a handle on the mass of people, he quickly jogged around to the rear cargo ramp of the aircraft to get a better look.

A helmet-clad soldier near the hangar opening held his M-16 rifle at a forty-five-degree angle above the crowd. It appeared it was an attempt to exercise crowd control, and the firing of a weapon was all that could be done to gain anyone's attention.

"*The attack is over!*"

The shots were a good idea, Chau thought.

"Is anyone hurt?" the MP called.

Incoherent voices responded, but they were not to the level of the frightened cries of only moments before.

The MP called out again, "Is anybody hurt!"

They quieted slightly to hear. There was no response from anyone until a middle-aged man spoke up.

"We need to leave here!"

"YES!" someone else called out. "*We need to get out of here right now!*"

The crowd erupted again. Chau was in charge — the captain of the ship. People were standing in protest of the MP's attempts to calm them and the panicked, angry voices continued to grow. As irritation rose, he felt duty-bound to speak and began fast-walking to the front of the dim and dust-filled hangar.

"We will be leaving soon!" the MP called out as Chau approached, but his response was drowned out by a crescendo of frustrated voices.

The furious demands for departure had reached a fever pitch by the time Chau reached the young MP.

"Colonel, I –"

The frustrated crowd surged aggressively at the two men, causing them both to take several steps backward. Chau glanced tensely at the soldier and then back at the mob.

"Give me your rifle."

Chau grabbed the M-16 from the young sentry and fired four rounds into the air. Before the echo of the weapon's reports faded, Chau spoke with commanding authority.

"EVERYONE WILL LISTEN TO ME!"

He was hyper-aware that he was taking a risk—but he would either get run over or take a chance on controlling the insanity and get run over anyway. He figured he didn't have much to lose.

"I am Lieutenant Colonel Chau Tan Nguyen!" he boomed. "I am a pilot in the South Vietnamese Air Force. *I am YOUR pilot!* You will only escape Vietnam through *ME!"*

Chau held the M-16 in his right hand, finger on the trigger and ready to fire, the muzzle pointed slightly upward. The crowd quieted to a murmur.

"Now," he continued calmly, but firmly. "I need to know if anyone is hurt."

The only response from the mass was continued mumbles and whispers, speckled with a cry or two from a few children. There was no definitive response that indicated anybody was anything but scared to death.

"If anyone has suffered an injury, please see one of my aircrew or a military policeman immediately."

Chau paused for effect and allowed the grumbling crowd to process his words. In his officer training and ensuing experience over the years, he had learned early on that much of leadership was simple theater. Even General George Patton believed it. Want to make people listen? Be dramatic.

"The attack has ended," he called loudly, not even sure if he was right. "We will depart soon, but until we know if the aircraft has been damaged, we cannot leave."

Another pause.

"This is our only way out and our plane must be as airworthy as possible for all of us to get to a safe location."

The crowd began to back down. He finally had them under

some measure of control. If there were more attacks though, he knew that control would disappear.

He gritted his teeth.

"This is *my* aircraft!" he stated emphatically, forcefully jabbing his finger in the direction of the C-130. *"I am its commander, and I am in charge of our flight!"*

It was an interesting comment, because Chau was basically only in charge of *stealing* the C-130 from the South Vietnamese Air Force—a self-appointed role—which essentially made him and his crew *pirates*. He was not functioning under orders of any kind from a higher military authority, and he had not been ordered to fly anybody anywhere. The truth of the matter was that in a normal environment, Chau could be imprisoned for such actions. However, with the South Vietnamese military establishment essentially collapsing all around them, he was doing what he had to do under his own volition, and a sense of duty to get his family and as many of his countrymen as possible to safety before the inevitable communist takeover.

He glared at his passengers. The muscles in his temples swelled as sweat poured down his cheeks.

"All of you are here because I have allowed it!" he yelled, thrusting his left index finger at the mob.

Theater...and it was working.

His M-16 was still trained above the sea of craniums, the pad of his index finger affixed to the trigger like super glue.

"I will keep you informed of our progress. But if any one of you threatens or behaves violently toward me, my crew, or any of these military policemen, *you will be shot."*

Chau paused again, never taking his eyes off the people in front of him.

"I hope this is very clear," he continued. "Until we can get this aircraft ready to depart, I expect full compliance."

Dust from the attack filled the air, creating a haze in the dimness that wasn't unlike the inside of a smoky barroom on a Saturday night. Chau lowered the rifle but kept his eyes pinned on his countrymen. Without looking away, he forcefully shoved the weapon back into the hands of the MP, then exited the stage toward his airplane. The crowd was stunned. Chau had been pushed over the edge and had said as much to those that needed desperately to hear it.

Within a few minutes of the conclusion of Chau's intense instructions to his passengers, he huddled in the spacious cargo bay of the C-130 with Vinh and Quan.

"Is the plane damaged?" he asked.

"We did not find anything significant," Vinh responded. "It is just dusty and has a few dents in the skin."

Chau absorbed his co-pilot's words.

"What do you want to do now?" Vinh asked.

Chau's heart was still racing.

"I want our sentries locked and loaded at all times," Chau began. "I want the three of us armed. Pistols will be holstered, each with a full magazine, a round chambered, and the safety switched off."

"Sir," Quan asked, "should we fire on passengers who become unruly?"

The young airman didn't seem so sure he was ready to shoot anyone.

"No," he responded coolly. "These are our fellow citizens, and they're scared for themselves and their families. Our objective is to *save* lives. Nobody gets shot unless a life is threatened or it is in self-defense. But nobody needs to know that."

Quan nodded.

"What time is it?" Chau asked.

"About twenty minutes before seven in the evening, sir," Quan responded after looking at his watch.

"We leave tonight. I want the two of you to re-check the plane for damage. Once you are finished, I want it checked a third time. Keep the hangar doors closed and all the outside lights turned off. I will go and get my family. Once I have returned, we will begin pre-flight and passenger loading. What are your questions?"

Chau paused and received no response.

"Is everyone clear on my direction?"

"Yes, sir," Vinh and Quan responded in concert.

"Execute."

Vinh and Quan took their leave from their commander and set about their orders, beginning with ensuring the MPs had their rifles fully loaded and ready. Alone in the cargo bay, Chau unsnapped his holster and removed his pistol. Pushing a button on the side with his right thumb, he ejected the magazine into his left hand and pressed down on the exposed, copper-tipped bullet at its crown. It gave very little, indicating the small, eight-round single-stacked clip was full. After pushing it back into its hilt inside the grip, he put his left hand over the charging slide and chambered a round. The oddly satisfying metallic *'clack'* when it slammed back into place gave a slight echo inside the C-130's large bay. He switched the safety off.

God help me if I have to kill a man tonight, he thought.

The smell of burning rubber penetrated his nose and irritated the back of his throat. It was hard to tell what was hit during the attack, but from the odors he was smelling, it clearly included aircraft…perhaps the airlifters the Americans had been loading. He hoped nobody had been killed, but in all likelihood, he'd never know—it wasn't like he was going to run out and take a look. He holstered his weapon, walked down the ramp, and made for one of the side offices attached to the hangar space.

Emerging through the worn-looking door, he switched on a bare light bulb that hung from the ceiling, bathing the filthy work area in brownish-gold light. It consisted of two old desks, their accompanying shabby desk chairs, and a plain four-drawer metal filing cabinet intended for use by maintenance personnel. The room was mottled with grease and dust on what few pieces of decaying furniture were present, as well as at chest and hand-level across the walls. It was hard to avoid noticing the fresh, large bullet hole that had penetrated through the outer wall. The desk in the back of the room had a grimy black phone and Chau went right to it to call his wife, who he knew must be frantic.

"A lô? Chau?"

Mai's voice shook with anticipation and terror.

"Mai, I am–"

"*CHAU!*" and she burst into tears on the other end of the line.

"I am all right," he consoled her.

"What happened?" she sobbed.

"I do not know what has been hit or if anyone was killed, but we are all fine here in the hangar."

"Oh, thank God," she whispered through her tears.

Chau imagined her with her hand holding fast to her chest as she leaned back against a wall or lowered herself into a chair.

"We saw the fire," she said. "As soon as we heard the bombs we went to the roof and could see it all."

"Mai," Chau started, "we need to move our departure time. I am coming to get you *now*. We must leave immediately."

The other end was silent.

"Mai?"

"Yes," she whispered after a short pause. "I just…. I am scared."

"We must leave before there is another attack. They could crater the airfield and make it impossible for any more planes to take off."

Chau noticed his hands trembling and suddenly felt weak in the knees. He sat in one of the chairs, its cushions torn and springs flying wildly out the sides.

"What must I do?" she asked.

"If you have anything left to pack, you must do it now."

"I understa—"

Suddenly a very high-speed 'whizzing' sound could be heard outside the hangar, followed by a sharp explosion somewhere nearby. The phone line went dead.

Rockets.

Several more *whoosh* noises were audible as fresh projectiles zipped through the air, each followed by a similar loud explosion. Chau dropped to the floor and went on his knees behind the desk as two massive impacts landed somewhere outside the nose dock.

The attack was not over.

April 28th, 1975
NGUYEN HOME, SAIGON
6:45PM

"Chau?" Mai called into the mouthpiece. *"CHAU?"*

Chau, PLEASE.

But there was no response. How much more of this could she take?

"Chết rồi!" she cried.

Dammit!

Mai slammed the phone into its cradle and made her way back to the roof stairs.

By the time she got there, her mother and father were already watching the terrible spectacle that once again lit the horizon a short distance away. She hadn't even gotten to the surface, but immediately upon reaching the outside air, she caught the unmistakable odor of burning plastics and rubber. Thuds of artillery cut through the darkened sky and the angry orange contrails of one rocket after another tore over the rooftops near the base, creating silvery-white bursts that reminded her of the large camera flashbulbs from old black and white movies. She didn't want to watch but found it impossible to take her eyes off of it.

"Dieu," she whispered quietly, her feet still inside the house as she leaned weakly on the frame of the hatch observing the silhouettes of her parents against the flames.

April 28th, 1975
NGUYEN HOME, SAIGON
9:45PM

Mai and her parents had been flitting between their roof and the front door for nearly three hours, Mai's heart aching with crushing worry and anxiousness. Chau still had not showed. Their bags were packed at the front door ready to go — including her father's. Nobody questioned him — would he leave with them after all? Everything was secured, but so much would be left behind. So much of what made the Nguyens "the Nguyens" would not go with them. All their worldly belongings, save for what little they had in their bags and Dat's lone, dingy yellow suitcase, would remain in Vietnam. She thought of the armoire in hers and Chau's bedroom. A simple piece of furniture she loved, yet would never see again.

And now, they waited. When Chau arrived, they would get into his Jeep and depart for the base, never to look back. Even though she'd be safe with him, their kids, and her family, it was a surreal and wretched feeling.

The shelling and rockets that began when she was on the phone with her husband had only lasted about fifteen minutes, but flames and smoke continued to rise into the sky. With his energy spent trying to keep his sons off the roof, Hong seemed to have given up on trying to make them stay inside, and Son was sitting next to Mai.

"Do you think Chau is all right, Mai?"

At thirteen, she knew he understood the seriousness of the situation better than his brothers.

"I do not know, Son," she replied in a pained whisper.

Once the shelling was over, flights resumed. It was hard to

tell what was taking off, but Mai knew it wasn't jets—the deep vibration of propellers was a far different sound, and she'd been around Chau's airplanes long enough to know it was probably the C-130s the Americans had been launching for days before the attack. They took to the black night sky without any lights and could only be heard in the darkness, but once airborne, the red glow of enemy tracers from guns far outside the base perimeter betrayed their positions in the air.

The absence of news was excruciating. The family had turned the radio on, but aside from the civil authorities' declaration of martial law in Saigon and that everyone should stay in their homes, it was the same old public information blackout they'd been used to. Hong had sent Dzung back into the house some time before, directing him to stay inside and listen for the phone in case Chau would call again. But it never rang.

Mai sat in despair next to Son on the family's rooftop, trying in vain to hide her tears from him. Was Chau alive? Was he dead? Would someone call? Would *he* call? At this point, she didn't care whether they stayed in Vietnam or left. She just wanted her husband back still breathing. What would she do if he was killed? How would she go on raising their children?

In the distance, an aircraft could be heard circling the far side of the airfield in the darkness, buzzing low like a slow-moving bumblebee, then moving away again, sporadically traced by anti-aircraft fire before turning about and coming closer. White sparks emanated from it, followed by staccato flashes of brilliant white-colored fire in impossibly straight lines aimed at the ground surrounding the base.

"Do you know what that is, Mai?" Son asked.

Mai realized in her numbness that she had barely uttered more than a few words to her younger brother in more than a month.

"Tell me."

"It is an AC-119 gunship."

"A...gunship?"

"Yes," he replied emotionlessly as it continued firing. "It has a large cannon coming out its side and fires at the ground."

It could be heard flying gracelessly off to the southwest before the sound faded.

"How do you know this?" she asked.

"Chau told me about them."

The two siblings stared numbly at the flames coming from the airfield, mesmerized as if it was some giant, crazy campfire.

Within minutes, the sound of the gunship in the distance quickly grew louder—as if the craft was heading toward their house. They looked to their left as the volume increased but saw nothing until the massive cannon began opening fire at targets right below the horizon, it's *"BRRRT"* sound audible over its engines. The plane passed loudly overhead as dazzling and terrifying bursts of white lit the rooftop and filled the air with a deafening noise. It prompted Hong to take nervous action.

"Everyone under the water tower!"

The family quickly complied. As the aircraft passed, an odd noise came from the other side of the flat-top roof—like a fistful of oversized jingle bells clinking together. In the low light, Mai shot a confused glance at Son, but he didn't look back.

"Shells!" he exclaimed with excitement.

Even in the middle of a war, Son could still get excited about boy things. Before Hong could stop him, he jumped out from under the water tower and ran to the other side of the roof as the aircraft flew into the distance, still belching its brutal gun-fire.

"*Son!*" Mai and her father yelled after him simultaneously, but he didn't listen.

Quickly reaching the far side of the roof Son picked up something, but Mai couldn't see it.

"Look, Ba!" he called.

"*Get back over here!*"

Mai felt her father's anger.

"Look!" he exclaimed as he jogged back to them. "Shells from the gun! Whew! They are hot!"

In the distance, Mai thought she heard helicopters...then the booming thuds of artillery, and this time it was not coming from the direction of the base.

April 28th, 1975
US EMBASSY, SAIGON
11:30PM

Bob Frailey walked into the cigarette-smoke-filled SCIF in the middle of a conversation between Rusty, Jesse, and Mosey Co-penhaver and shut the heavy vault door behind him.

"So, Martin was pretty pissed off, I guess?"

Jesse was responding to Mosey as Frailey took a seat in an empty desk chair at the end of the narrow, long room.

"Yeah, pretty pissed. Guess I'm out of a job."

He had been discovered, outed by who knew who. But Graham Martin was now fully aware that the underground high-risk-Vietnamese-personnel-evac operation wasn't just about some isolated flight to Clark Air Base a few days ago.

"He asked me who else was involved and I said everyone was already gone. Before he could say much else, Tan Son Nhut started getting shot up again."

"Oh, great!" Rusty commented. "So, we can keep doing it! Thanks for not ratting us out, Mosey."

"Shut up, Rusty," Frailey chimed in. "He asked me about it too—just now."

"What did you tell him?"

"Said I didn't know shit about it. Anyway, don't worry about it. We got some changes coming."

"Yeah?" Jesse said, his head still pounding from the rocket attack as he tugged on a Camel. "Someone's making good decisions tonight?"

His face bandage had come off earlier in the day, revealing a gnarly inch-long eight-stitch wound that oozed blood in one or two small places.

"Hasn't happened yet, but I think Tan Son Nhut's gonna be abandoned as an APOE," Frailey said. "We'll see what Martin does, but most of us agree it's getting too damn dangerous now to get any fixed-wing airplanes in or out."

"'Bout time."

"And now hear this: Martin caved. He just gave authority to start getting people out without any immigration paperwork," Frailey continued. "Maybe too little too late, but this is the beginning of the end. Won't be long before he caves on other stuff."

"Does that mean it's an official 'full' evacuation now?" Copenhaver asked.

"Not exactly."

"What the hell does 'not exactly' mean?" Rusty asked.

"He stopped short of calling it an 'official' evacuation, and there's still no approved plan to get the remaining high-risk

South Vietnamese out. We got a lot of them, but many are still here."

"Many are gonna stay here, because they're gonna be dead."

"There was no way we were gonna get 'em all to begin with, Rusty," Frailey answered. "We got through a lot of Mosey's list, as well as all the names we added individually. There's a ton of 'em still on it, and those are the ones we *know* about. You and I are both aware there are some that won't make it out. We simply don't know everyone and our time's about up anyway. If we hadn't done what we did, most of 'em would still be sitting here or be caught up in the rioting crowds at the port and airport. Or surrounding the Embassy. It's every man for himself out there right now if you're local. Even though Mosey's off the job now, there's still work to do."

"Happy to pay the bill for you guys."

"You won't be paying long, Mosey," Frailey said. "You think you'll never get a job again in the agency? Come on. There are rules, and then there's right and wrong. There's not a senior leader outside Vietnam who's gonna blame you for any of that. Your 'firing' is gonna get swept under the rug like it never happened."

"How many have we moved?" Jesse asked.

"You mean in total?" Frailey replied. "Thousands since the second week of April out of Tan Son Nhut alone."

"You really think Martin will give up Tan Son Nhut?"

Mosey Copenhaver was clearly doubtful.

"Well, whether he does or not, does it really matter? In the Air Force, aircraft commanders are gods. They fly sovereign ships in the earth's seas of air and even the president can't tell 'em to land or not land. It is solely the AC's call, and the hotter of an LZ that Tan Son Nhut becomes, the more likely there's not a pilot in the service that'll land there to be a sitting duck for an hour to load up two hundred people a hack. We still got burning planes on the ground right now."

"So what difference does it make, right?" Rusty muttered.

"Exactly. *Who cares?*" Frailey responded. "I guess he's got some idea that he can still pull off keeping the airfield open with the hope the NVA will stop shelling it, but everyone knows it's not realistic. I don't know how he thinks it'll happen."

All three knew Tan Son Nhut was lost whether Graham Martin liked it or not.

"You become pretty invested in a place when it's tied to the loss of your kid. Maybe it's idealism, I don't know. But to some extent, I get it."

"You're defending this guy?" Rusty asked. "He's gotten people killed, Bob!"

"I'm not defending him. I'm just saying I understand him."

"So, we're still moving the high-risk guys or what?" Jesse asked.

"Some are still trying to move passengers, yes," Copenhaver answered. "But only to the port, which is getting dicier by the hour."

"OK, Bob," Rusty began, "so the base is gone, and the port is dicey. When do the choppers start flying?"

"Soon. That's how we will go."

"From here? You think we'll be able to keep the crowds out? There're thousands of pissed off civilians and not a lot of Marines. If the mob grows much bigger, the compound's gonna be overrun. We're not leaving this place. Not now—not in a vehicle."

"No, we're not. The guys that are still out there driving folks to the port will get on a helo someplace else. The rest of us? We're in the compound until the bitter end and we'll helo out from right here. We got the pad on the roof and if we have to, we can double up and land 'em in the main parking lot."

"Seems to me there's a big ass tree out there that might interfere with rotors," Jesse pointed out.

He was referring to a massive tamarind tree that grew near the main entrance to the Embassy's primary office facility—it was old and large, and he'd personally heard Graham Martin say that it symbolized the American commitment to Vietnam—deep roots, and strong in its stature…able to hold up through the worst of storms.

"Then we'll cut the sonofabitch down."

"Huh," Rusty blustered. "I wonder if Martin would agree to that."

"Reality will hit him and he's not gonna care about a damn tree."

Jesse thought it was pretty profound that Martin's tamarind would probably be cut. The ambassador was right—it was indeed symbolic of the American commitment to South Vietnam.

"How much time do you think we have?" he asked.

Frailey exhaled slowly, as if he didn't like what he was about to say.

"I think we'll be lucky if we have twenty-four hours."

"Shit."

"When's the first helo come, Bob?" Rusty asked.

"My money's on tomorrow…early," Frailey finally admitted, unable to look his agents in the eye, but it gave Rusty and Jesse a small sense of relief. "Martin just has to give up on this notion of South Vietnamese independence. We had the rocket attack in town and the base is about done. Won't be long before the rest of the South Vietnamese Air Force starts getting the hell outta here, and I'm betting that'll happen tomorrow too, if they can even take off. If the real world hasn't hit Martin yet, it's about to. Once that happens, helo ops are gonna get going quickly. Right now, the best thing to do is for us all to get some rest. No telling what's gonna go down tonight, and tomorrow will be a busy day."

"Is there a name for all this?"

"Operation Frequent Wind."

13

"Guys!"

Jesse, Rusty, and Mosey had appropriated a few bunks in one of the compound's small, no-frills temporary billeting facilities apart from the main Embassy building in an attempt to get a little rest. Frailey was shaking Jesse's foot.

"Get up, guys."

His head foggy from a lack of sleep coupled with the concussion, Jesse raised his head and looked bleary-eyed at his surroundings, momentarily forgetting where he was. Rusty sat up on a separate bunk and rubbed his eyes as Frailey banged his hand on the metal frame of Mosey's bed.

"What time is it?"

It was dark out.

"Four thirty," Frailey answered. "Come on, we got stuff to do."

Frailey switched on the light, temporarily blinding everyone.

"Something happen?" Rusty mumbled.

"We lost some Americans."

Mosey, slow to rise, was now fully upright. Frailey had gotten his attention.

"Shit! Who?" he asked.

"Two Marine guards over at the DAO," Frailey answered. "Been kinda concerned about that place for a while now—pretty close to the airfield, Alamo, and with all the shooting over there, they took a stray rocket."

"Anyone we know?"

"Their names were McMahon and Judge."

"I don't remember them," Rusty murmured.

"McMahon had only been in-country for a week."

It was sobering. Jesse figured people were gonna get killed, but he'd always thought they'd be Vietnamese. These were Americans—and Marines, just like he used to be. It was hard not to feel some anger towards Ambassador Martin. After all, if the man would have made the call to evacuate, McMahon and Judge might not have been killed. In fact, McMahon may never have set foot in Vietnam.

"There's more," Frailey continued. "One of our 130s got blown up during PAX loading about half an hour ago."

"Holy *shit*," Rusty said. "Any KIA?"

"A couple civilians got hurt, but nobody killed. We're trying to get the aircrew here. They'll have to go out on the helos with us or something."

"What's Martin doing?"

"Not much."

"Well, what are *you* gonna do?" Jesse asked.

Bob Frailey sighed and scratched the back of his head.

"Crowds around the perimeter are still growing and nobody's done much to destroy our classified. Security here seems more or less set with protective measures and weapons, at least for now, but ..."

"...but what?"

"Time's ticking. I need you guys to find some drums and start burning what's in the SCIF. Paperwork, documents, crypto, everything. There's no telling what'll happen next—could be a mob scene at the gates, could be a rocket attack, who knows?"

"What's our projected timeline for the start of helo ops?" Mosey asked.

"Still don't know, but we're expecting an execution order from the Navy real soon to kick things off."

"Finally," Rusty quipped.

"Yeah, finally. It'll force Martin's hand. He's not all too happy about it."

"You mean to tell me he's pissed off at the Navy while Marines are getting blown up and American airplanes are in pieces on the ramp?"

"It's not a pretty picture, Rusty."

"Has Martin ordered the destruction of classified?" Jesse asked.

"No. I'm ordering it. At least the stuff we're responsible for."

"What do you want us to say if someone sees us doing it?"

"Tell him I directed it," Frailey said. "I don't really care, and it doesn't matter anyway. Take a look out the window."

The three men moved toward the window of the small open bay, which looked a lot like the Marine Corps barracks Jesse had spent so much time in during his military service. Outside and not far from their location were what appeared to be two fifty-five-gallon drums, each with flames leaping out the tops. Surrounding each one was one or two people throwing papers into them.

"Maybe they'll let you use *their* drums."

April 29th, 1975
NGUYEN HOME, SAIGON
7:00AM

The echoes and thumps of the brutal enemy onslaught at the base that was still underway had kept them up all night, terrified of the ramifications for Chau, who was still somewhere over there and hopefully alive. There had been no phone calls, and the agonizing wait for news had been difficult to endure. Mai was exhausted, unsure if her husband would be able to get to the family at all. There was no way to escape the reality of what was unfolding around them. How long would it be before North Vietnamese soldiers were in the alleys and streets of Saigon, taking over everything? If the family didn't get out, it would be only the beginning of their misery.

Son, Dzung, and Tuan hadn't slept much either and although Mai didn't believe they completely grasped what a North Vietnamese takeover might mean for them, based on the family's grim mindset for the last month she was sure they knew it wasn't good. Dzung in particular was directly affected, having experienced North Vietnamese brutality first-hand with his father only weeks before. His bruises faded, yet the emotional wounds were still quite raw. Tuan was worried sick and had been in and out of the bathroom with a nervous stomach since about five o'clock in the morning. Dat offered him something to drink, but all he could do was sip at it. Eventually all three boys made their way to the roof once there was enough light in the sky to see clearly. Hong didn't stop them.

There was nothing that could be said. Against her better judgement, Mai decided to join her brothers. She reached the roof and was hit with the early morning humidity. The boys were near the water tower, each sitting on the tarred surface staring hypnotically at the smoke and fire gushing from Tan Son Nhut, now garishly visible in the morning light.

It turned Mai's guts into a knots.

A few military aircraft had taken to the skies, most disappearing into the distance after being harassed by anti-aircraft fire, and Mai wondered if they were launching for defensive missions or fleeing. She suspected the latter. A handful of others remained in the vicinity, and she could see a gunship like the one she'd seen the night before, firing at the ground as it circled. The bright white-hot fire emanating from the gunner's door was so bright, it left images in her eyes that she could still see when she looked away. As she made her way towards her brothers, it flew away from a large concentration of tracer fire and banked over the city south of the air base at a low level.

"Look!" Dzung cried out, pointing at the aircraft. "Smoke!"

Although the air was hazy and dense, it was clear the port tail section of the fuselage had been hit and a trace of brown smoke trailed from its rear. Son, Dzung, and Tuan arose to their feet.

"Will he land?" Tuan asked.

The aircraft circled slow and wide over the city before making another approach to the base, its smoke circling behind it. As it passed near their home, a small flame on the tail became more pronounced and the airframe decelerated further, its engines beginning to cough and turn audibly slower.

"I do not know," Son replied.

Off to their right, an ear-piercing hiss filled their ears. In a flash, a long, thin, and cylindrical missile sped from behind the buildings to their right at a blinding clip, headed directly for the gunship, its tail bright with dazzling thrust. In less than a second, it met the wounded aircraft with a crunching blast, blowing it to mere fragments in a massive orange and yellow fireball. The heat wave could be immediately felt on the roof by the three terrified brothers.

"WHAAA!!!" Dzung cried out.

Burning bits of airplane and floundering crewmen could be seen plummeting helplessly through the air as the largest flaming chunks of the destroyed plane fell spectacularly toward the ground, ultimately crashing in an explosion into buildings and structures just out of sight. Mai was horrified at the spectacle of the flailing, burning, and still living people that tumbled from the sky toward certain death when they met the ground.

Breathless, she fell to her knees.

Chau, where are you?

April 29th, 1975
US EMBASSY, SAIGON
10:00AM

"What the hell does a guy have to do to get a cup of coffee around here?" Rusty asked, slamming the door behind him as two helicopters thundered overhead moving eastward.

"Is that our ride?" he opined.

They stopped briefly to listen and see if the engines got closer, but they dissipated in the distance.

"Don't think so," Jesse said. "Going too fast."

The tumult of the expanding mob of Vietnamese civilians outside the ramparts of the Embassy compound could be heard through the open windows of their stark, eight-bunk billeting facility. Jesse had overheard some of the Marine guards late the evening before stating that they estimated it to be in the neighborhood of ten thousand souls.

Jesse chain smoked and paced the floor nervously as Mosey sat on his mattress trying to ignore the noise. Every now and again, he picked up an old, tattered copy of US News and World Report and flipped the pages, but it didn't look like he was paying much attention. Rusty just wanted coffee. In the six hours since Bob Frailey had woken them, they'd managed to burn what little was left in their safes, and Jesse swore there couldn't be one single morsel of classified information left inside the SCIF. The last thing they did was destroy two KY-3 phones.

Now, they waited.

"Sure would be nice if one of those choppers landed here," Jesse said. "Dunno about you guys, but I'm ready to get out of here."

He'd checked and re-checked what few belongings he hadn't left in the van when they got caught up in the rocket attack downtown. It only amounted to his wallet and a small ruck he'd gotten from one of the mission's Marine guards that he'd filled with a few items still left in the Embassy's small shop — two T-shirts, a pair of shorts, and a small toothbrush kit with toothpaste and floss.

"Why're you worried about coffee right now, anyway, Russ?" Mosey asked.

"You still here? I thought you got fired?" he jabbed. "What're we gonna do? Go to the roof and watch for choppers? Man a position on the parapet with the Marines? This is a waiting game, and I want a damn cup of coffee. The cafeteria is closed and there isn't even an urn around."

"Rusty?"

"Yeah?"

"You stink."

Rusty smelled his armpit.

"I sweat when I'm nervous."

Two fighters passed overhead, roaring to the east. It wasn't something Jesse expected to hear, and visions of the presidential palace bombing from a few weeks before invaded his thoughts. More defectors? Were they being flown by escaping South Vietnamese pilots? Or were they en-route to attack enemy positions around the perimeter of the city? There was no way to tell.

"Didn't figure we'd be hearing much fighter traffic today," he said, stopping mid-pace to listen.

The stitched wound on his cheek had begun to scab over with an angry red ring skirting its edges, and he lamented the slight dizziness and pain that remained from his jolt by the rocket. The station doctor had told him the vertigo could take a couple of weeks to go away, but he knew he was lucky his proximity to the explosion didn't cause a more severe injury.

The knob on the main door to their room jiggled open and Bob Frailey burst in with a folder full of papers and a transistor radio.

"Gentlemen, we are evacuating. Just got done with Martin and his staff. Much like us, most of 'em haven't had much sleep."

"Thank you, Lord," Rusty said to nobody and everybody, his hands together as if in prayer, and his eyes sarcastically looking towards heaven.

"When's it start?" Jesse asked.

"It's already underway."

Frailey placed the transistor radio on a small nightstand and switched it on. American radio was playing *'Why Can't We Be Friends'* by the band War. Jesse thought it a darkly funny song title sung by a band that had a darkly funny name, given their current situation.

"We got seventy-some helos on fifty-some ships just off-shore. Some are already airborne, and blades are turning on the rest. Tan Son Nhut's still under attack, and it's going on the twelfth straight hour."

"Shit."

"A lot of what we've got is still unconfirmed, but there's reports of shelling in some of the outer neighborhoods of the city, tanks overrunning police checkpoints, and the DAO estimates their compound has been hit with some forty rockets and artillery rounds since the two guards got hit."

"Wonder how long it'll take the bad guys to get here?" Rusty asked.

"The ambassador was told early this morning that flying ops at the airport were over. No way there was anything that would get in or outta there."

"That's funny, because it sounds like the VNAF just got two fighters out."

"They were lucky to get airborne. Anyway, Martin didn't wanna hear it and opted to go out there himself to see it first-hand, even though rounds were still coming in. Took his damn limo right to the gate."

"Well, the guy doesn't lack backbone, I'll give him that," Jesse said.

"Nope."

Frailey sat down on an open bottom bunk, his tired eyes dim with pronounced purplish bags hanging underneath them.

"What's the status of the VNAF?" Rusty asked.

"Leaving if they can get off the ground," Frailey responded. "Some of 'em probably escaping, maybe others going to shoot bad guys or defect. Their chief of staff showed up at the DAO with some of his minions a couple hours ago and said he'd completely lost control of his air force. Wanted asylum and evacuation."

"Wow."

"What about the Hueys that went over earlier? Part of the evac?" Jesse asked.

"If I had to guess, they're probably South Vietnamese and full of people heading out to sea to find any ship they can land on. It's who you know, remember?"

"I wonder if the Nguyens got out?" Rusty asked.

"Chau could have been flying any of the 130s that we've seen and heard moving in the last day or so," Jesse cut in.

"My guess is if he hasn't gotten out yet, he won't," Frailey added.

"So who in the bloody hell goes on the helos? Just Americans? High-risk Vietnamese?" Rusty asked. "What about the people outside the gate?"

Frailey reached into a folder, pulled out a few paper-clipped sheets and threw them on a vacant bunk.

"Read it for yourself."

///DTG 290130ZAPR75///

SUBJECT: EXECUTION ORDER FOR OPERATION FREQUENT WIND, SAIGON, VIETNAM
SECSTATE
SECDEF

AMPOTUS
AMVPOTUS
CJCS
NAVCHIEF
ARCHIEF
AFCHIEF
AMEMBASSY SAIGON
USDAO SAIGON
COMPACFLEET
US ARMY CINCPAC SUPPORT GROUP
COMPACAF
21 SOS
40 AEROSPACE RESCUE AND RECOVERY SQ
56 SOW
16 SOS
388 TFW
307 SW
1BN 9TH MARINES
SUBJECT: OPERATION FREQUENT WIND
1. INSTRUCTIONS
1.A THE PRESIDENT DIRECTS THE EXECUTION OF OPERATION FREQUENT WIND BEGINNING IMMEDIATELY UPON RECEIPT OF THIS MESSAGE.
1.A.1 THE UNITED STATES MISSION IN VIETNAM IS OFFICIALLY CLOSED AS OF 0130Z 29 APRIL 1975. ALL UNITED STATES GOVERNMENT PERSONNEL ARE ORDERED TO EVACUATE AT ONCE USING PRE-IDENTIFIED ASSEMBLY POINTS AT LOCATIONS THROUGHOUT SAIGON AND DEFENSE ATTACHÉ FACILITIES UNDER PLAN ALAMO.
1.A.2. IN THE INTEREST OF MAXIMIZING LIMITED

SPACE, ACCOMPANIED BAGGAGE IS LIMITED TO ONE SMALL BAG OR SUITCASE PER PERSON.

1.B. DUE TO HOSTILE ENEMY ACTION, TAN SON NHUT AIRPORT AND TAN SON NHUT AIR BASE FACILITIES ARE NOT TO BE UTILIZED UNLESS ABSOLUTELY NECESSARY AND PRACTICAL. SEAPORT FACILITIES WILL ONLY BE USED IF PRACTICAL.

1.C. COMPACFLEET IS ORDERED AND AUTHORIZED TO EXERCISE COMMAND AND CONTROL FROM FLAG SHIP USS BLUE RIDGE UNDER TASK FORCE 76.

1.C.1. US MARINE CORPS AND US NAVY ROTARY ASSETS ARE DIRECTED AS PRIMARY MEANS OF TRANSPORTATION. TASKED VESSELS AND UNITS:

1.C.1.1. TASK FORCE 76.4 (MOVEMENT TRANSPORT GROUP ALPHA)

1.C.1.1.1. USS OKINAWA

1.C.1.1.2. USS VANCOUVER

1.C.1.1.3. USS THOMASTON

1.C.1.1.4. USS PEORIA

1.C.1.2. TASK FORCE 76.5 (MOVEMENT TRANSPORT GROUP BRAVO)

1.C.1.2.1. USS DUBUQUE

1.C.1.2.2. USS DURHAM

1.C.1.2.3. USS FREDERICK

1.C.1.3. TASK FORCE 76.9 (MOVEMENT TRANSPORT GROUP CHARLIE)

1.C.1.3.1. USS ANCHORAGE

1.C.1.3.2. USS DENVER

1.C.1.3.3. USS DULUTH

1.C.1.3.4. USS MOBILE

1.C.2. OTHER TASKED VESSELS

1.C.2.4. AMPHIBIOUS SUPPORT

1.C.2.4.1. USS MOUNT VERNON

1.C.2.4.2. USS BARBOUR COUNTY

1.C.2.4.3. USS TUSCALOOSA

1.C.2.5. MISSILE DEFENSE SUPPORT

1.C.2.5.1. USS WORDEN

1.C.2.6. INDIRECT FIRE, ESCORT, AND AREA DE-FENSE SUPPORT

1.C.2.6.1. USS RICHARD B. ANDERSON

1.C.2.6.2. USS COCHRANE

1.C.2.6.3. USS KIRK

1.C.2.6.4. USS GURKE

1.C.2.6.5. USS ROWAN

1.C.2.6.6. USS COOK

1.C.2.6.7. USS BAUSELL

1.C.2.7. AIR SUPPORT (TASK FORCE 77)

1.C.2.7.1. USS ENTERPRISE ATTACK GROUP

1.C.2.7.2. USS CORAL SEA ATTACK GROUP

1.C.2.7.3. 56 SPECIAL OPERATIONS WING

1.C.2.7.3.1. 16 SPECIAL OPERATIONS SQUADRON

1.C.2.7.4. 388 TACTICAL FIGHTER WING

1.C.2.7.5. 307 STRATEGIC WING

1.C.3. OTHER UNITS

1.C.3.1. 21 SPECIAL OPERATIONS SQUADRON

1.C.3.2. 40 AEROSPACE RESCUE AND RECOVERY SQUADRON

1.C.3.3. 9TH MARINE AMPHIBIOUS BRIGADE (TASK GROUP 79.1)

1.C.4. MILITARY SEALIFT COMMAND VESSELS

1.C.4.1. ASIATIC STAMINA

1.C.4.2. CHITOSE MARU

1.C.4.3. HARUMA

1.C.4.4. OSCEOLA

1.C.4.5. SHIBAURA MARU

1.C.4.6. SS AMERICAN CHALLENGER

1.C.4.7. SS BOO HEUNG PIONEER

1.C.4.8. SS GREEN FOREST

1.C.4.9. SS GREEN PORT

1.C.4.10. USNS GREENVILLE VICTORY

1.C.4.11. SS PIONEER CONTENDER

1.C.4.12. SS PIONEER COMMANDER

1.C.4.13. USNS SGT TRUMAN KIMBRO

1.C.4.14. USNS SGT ANDREW MILLER

2. SAFE BOOKLETS

2.A. SAFE BOOKLETS PREVIOUSLY DISTRIBUTED BY STATE DEPARTMENT WARDENS WILL BE USED TO FACILITATE ORDERLY DEPARTURE OF PERSONNEL.

3. SOUTH VIETNAMESE PERSONNEL

3.A. SPECIAL ATTENTION WILL BE PAID TO HIGH-RANKING SOUTH VIETNAMESE GOVERNMENT AND MILITARY PERSONNEL, INCLUDING LOCAL NATIONAL PERSONNEL WHO HAVE SERVED IN ANY SIGNIFICANT CAPACITY FOR THE UNITED STATES IN VIETNAM SINCE 1958.

3.A.1. WHERE PRUDENT AND WHEN LOCATION OF PERSONNEL IS KNOWN, WARDENS AND US GOVERNMENT PERSONNEL WILL ENSURE THESE INDIVIDUALS AND THEIR FAMILIES RECEIVE PRIORITY ON DEPARTING AIRCRAFT.

4.A. CLASSIFIED MATERIEL

4.A.1. ALL CLASSIFIED MATERIAL WILL BE DE-

STROYED IMMEDIATELY IN ACCORDANCE WITH ES-
TABLISHED GUIDELINES.
5. ENGAGEMENT WITH ENEMY
5.A. SHOULD ENGAGEMENT WITH ANY NORTH VIET-
NAMESE ENEMY FORCES BECOME NECESSARY, IT
MUST BE DEFENSIVE IN NATURE ONLY. NO OFFEN-
SIVE OPERATIONS WILL BE CONDUCTED AGAINST
ANY KNOWN NORTH VIETNAMESE FORCES WITH-
OUT PRIOR AUTHORIZATION BY COMPACFLEET.
6. ACKNOWLEDGE RECEIPT IMMEDIATELY TO
COMPACFLEET N3.

///END///

"Plenty in here about Americans and important South Viet-namese folks," Copenhaver commented. "What about the ten thousand muldoons outside the gate looking for a ride?"

"No instructions—just high-ranking officials," Frailey re-sponded, examining the message further. "But I can tell you this: as orderly as it all looks on paper, things'll be getting more chaotic throughout the day, and it won't be too hard to get a few on our helos."

"What's Martin doing?" Jesse asked.

"He's going along with all this. This is a military order for a military evacuation operation. State will fall in line, and I don't think Martin's got a vote anymore."

Bob Frailey's transistor radio cracked and popped in the background.

"…and a quick look at our weather in Saigon today. It's a hundred and five degrees and sunny. Here's a little Bing Crosby for you."

"I'm dreaming of a White Christmas…"
"How about that? It's Christmas in April."

April 29th, 1975
TAN SON NHUT AIR BASE
10:30AM

The incoming artillery and mortar rounds had subsided slightly, and Chau stood looking out from the hangar door wondering if it was time for him to go get his family. Behind him, almost four hundred noisy, and very nervous people filled the hangar. Several aircraft had been getting out during brief lulls in the attack, but North Vietnamese anti-aircraft fire had still chased them into the sky, and Chau was intimately aware that an AC-119 gunship had been shot out of the sky with an SA-7—Quan had seen it with his own eyes, its wreckage nosediving into a cluster of buildings right outside the base fence and touching off a series of fires. Their slow-moving C-130 would lumber at about the same sluggish speed as the gunships did, and he certainly didn't want to be the next casualty, along with his crew, his family, and hundreds of his closest friends. Had he waited too long to leave? All he could do was pace and shudder.

While the hangar had sustained some additional damage throughout the night, his C-130 appeared to remain relatively unscathed, save for dust and a few dents in the outer skin from falling debris created by the violence of the last twelve hours. The bigger issue was maintaining control of the ever-growing and increasingly frightened crowd of people. At this point, Chau knew he couldn't stay on top of them much longer, and he was getting worried he wouldn't be able to fit everyone on board.

What remained of the installation's fire crews raced between buildings and destroyed airplanes, their trucks moving without their emergency lights or sirens activated. Jeeps and small vehicles buzzed across the ramp in a few places, and he could actually see a number of people running about between vehicles and wrecked buildings and hangars. Friendly M-60 machine gun fire could be heard in the distance, along with other small arms. The passengers, tired and exhausted from being awake all night and enduring attack after attack, were intermittently subdued and then hysterical. It was like a sine wave of destructive behavior which had threatened at multiple points to bubble over.

Mortars impacted near the base perimeter. They were close. Nobody had seen the runway itself to tell whether it was even suitable for a takeoff, but Chau had no option. He'd do his best to get airborne or die trying. If there was a long enough stretch of tarmac to get some air under his wings they'd be OK, but with a big fuel load they'd be heavy. Still, people weighed less than vehicles or other heavy cargo when they were in the hold, so maybe they'd be OK. His mind could barely process anything. He was tired and hungry, covered in dust and gritty sweat, and was emitting an odor that might have been the worst thing he'd ever smelled.

Across the airfield, a helicopter of some kind could be detected, its rotors spinning, waiting for the opportunity to get airborne. In another direction, a jet engine could be heard whining, most likely waiting for the same thing. Artillery could be heard firing in the distance, the thuds noticeable in the depths of his torso.

"Chau," Vinh called from behind him, clad in a flak vest and grimy helmet as the nervous din of the shattered passengers filled the cavernous hangar behind them. "Things have calmed some. You must get Mai."

Chau nodded and placed his helmet on his head, buckling the chin strap.

"I know."

"It may not get any better than this," Vinh continued, "and it will not be long before it is far worse."

Without a word, Chau made for the Jeep. Abandoned cars, an American-made two-and-a-half-ton truck, a motorcycle, and several Vespa-style scooters from a handful of passengers that had arrived in between the shellings the night before rested to the front and sides of the hangar, silent witness to the mayhem that had occurred since their arrival.

"Get these vehicles moved," he ordered, shouting over his shoulder. "We will not be able to get out of the hangar with them here."

Vinh nodded in acknowledgement, his unfastened helmet bobbing on his head.

In an instant, a massive shell destroyed what had been a small white Citroën, shaking the ground violently and throwing fire and large chunks of the vehicle into the air.

"*CHAU!*" Vinh called, barely audible to Chau.

The explosion couldn't have been more than two hundred feet from them, and it knocked him over. His ears rang loudly.

Another howitzer round impacted near the first, shaking the ground and the hangar. Debris began to fall all around him, and he reached up to hold his helmet on his head, hoping a large piece of something wouldn't fall on him. He belly-crawled as fast as he could towards the Jeep, thinking its engine block and wheels would offer some cover.

BOOM!

Another shell. Fire. Smoke. Dust. Falling rubble rattling his steel helmet and bruising his back and buttocks. Deafening noise echoing and ringing in his head. He was alone outside the hangar, exposed, and terrified of where the next one would land.

BOOM!

And another. It felt as if the molars in the back of his mouth would shake out of their sockets if he didn't bite down hard enough to keep them in place.

His ears rang. The sound was so intense that it was as if they'd shut down completely, drowning out all sound. Bits of rock and mud forcefully bounced and rolled past him as he low-crawled, finally reaching the Jeep and crouching low next to it. Chau thought the noise was enough to make a man crazy if he was exposed to it for too long of a time. The rumble of the impacts echoed across the flat surface of the airfield and its low, largely destroyed buildings, dissipating slowly as Chau peered carefully around the front bumper of the vehicle, taking stock of his surroundings.

He looked back at the hangar. Still intact, but no movement, and his ears were so rattled that he couldn't hear if there were any cries from the inside. He turned back around to look back in front of him and the air abruptly reverberated with one final, horrible *WHOOSH.*

Chau didn't hear the impact.

The next thing he remembered was being dragged across the tarmac.

April 29th, 1975
US EMBASSY, SAIGON
12:00PM

Bob Frailey had disappeared to who-knew-where in the midst of the full rotary evacuation that was underway at the Embassy compound. Jesse, Rusty, and Mosey Copenhaver had gotten sucked into assisting with the processing of evacuees on the ground, within the main building, and on the roof. Copenhaver, recently jobless, figured nobody would turn away an extra set of hands, even though he'd been fired by the ambassador, and he stationed himself on the roof.

Rusty had been placed in charge of a few people who were trying to get as many refugees as possible through the facility and up to the top. Jesse was on the ground outside the building, parked near the main entrance next to a long line of people waiting to get inside. Despite the chaos that reigned outside the gate, he was amazed how orderly people were behaving inside the compound. Perhaps, he thought, they finally felt safe on the 'American soil' that was securely under their soles inside the gates.

Even though the incoming Sikorsky CH-53 Sea Stallion was landing six stories above his head on the Embassy roof, the gale force winds it generated under its rotors tossed the compound's large tamarind tree like a hurricane. Jesse found it necessary to cover his eyes to avoid the blowing dust. It was about the fifth or sixth helicopter to land in the compound since *White Christmas* was blasted over the airwaves about two hours earlier. The Embassy site and its surroundings in this part of the city had become a confused gaggle. Refugees hoping for a flight to freedom had begun climbing the perimeter walls in some places—throwing clothing, towels, or blankets over the spiraled razor wire to avoid being injured. In many cases, the overwhelmed Marine guards forced the crowds back, but there was just too much humanity for them to maintain any serious control.

What had to be over ten thousand people surrounded the Embassy like it was under siege—mostly South Vietnamese citizens, but also a large number of the several-thousand Americans and other westerners that were still present in Saigon—and crowds were stacked at least three hundred feet deep in most areas. On the interior, thousands of people had gotten through the loosely controlled fence line, and more had continued to stream in. Jesse was baffled—not everyone could be making it over the razor wire, so the only thing that made sense to him was that guards and possibly other Embassy employees were helping them get in, or at least looking the other way as they vaulted the walls.

Families, students, luggage, and trash were gathered haphazardly around the mission's large swimming pool, which Jesse had noticed earlier had a number of pistols and knives thrown into it, abandoned at the bottom. Thousands of pages of classified documents still burned in several drums, which filled the area with smoke.

Jesse's Marine Corps math told him that the current rate of six helicopters every ninety minutes amounted to about one airframe every fifteen—at that rate, even with thirty to forty passengers per flight, there was no way they'd get everyone out that had to get out unless the communists somehow slowed their approach, or the ambassador agreed to chop down the tamarind. Jesse held out hope that people would still have opportunities to get away from the other identified locations within the city.

As far as the Embassy was concerned, it was an unspoken truth that once all the Americans were out, the Department of State, the Navy, and their handlers in Hawaii and Washington would halt the evacuation. Graham Martin and his staff, including Bob Frailey, knew this—so the subtle guidance was to pack the helicopters with as many Vietnamese citizens as possible. For Jesse's part, he did what he could to vet family after family, citizen after citizen, and let the guys on the roof sort it out.

He squinted upward at the helicopter, its rotors visible as they idled over the edge of the roof. Within a few moments, it throttled up and lifted off the helipad, headed for the sea. In the brief calm that followed, several Marines wearing civilian clothes emerged from between two small buildings nearby with axes and chain saws. Was the tamarind about to come down like Bob Frailey had predicted?

With a forceful yank on the starter handles, the men revved their small machines to full power and began cutting into the massive tree. Jesse knew it would be imperative that they get it down as fast as possible to ensure more than one helicopter could be on station at the same time, doubling the opportunity to increase their evacuation numbers.

He turned his gaze skyward again and detected one or two more aircraft headed in their direction over the treetops, stacked like airliners at Chicago-O'Hare International waiting for their turn to land. The line of people moved slow. He placed himself nearer to the door and began searching bags and frisking people for weapons of any kind—everyone. There hadn't been any violence in the compound that he was aware of, but of the few hundred people he'd already checked, he was able to find a handful of weapons, which was slightly unnerving. His pistol was strapped to his waist in order to immediately respond if he had to.

The noise of a new set or rotors filled the air and a brutal wind gusted trash and debris from the work on the tamarind tree into the air. Jesse shielded his eyes again and did the best he could to continue checking people before letting them in the door.

"You a Marine?" came a loud voice from the long line over the whup-whup of rotor blades.

It was perfect American English coming from a mid-fifties heavy-set American with a younger Vietnamese woman at his side. His wild and graying hair, in desperate need of a cut, tangled and wafted in the wind. Jesse hadn't seen him in the lengthy queue until the man was next to him.

"Yes, sir. Used to be. Are you armed?"

"Negative," he called out over the wind and engine noises. "Left my guns behind. We just wanna get ourselves outta here. Waited as long as we could."

Jesse leaned in close to be able to hear the man's answers over the engine noise.

"Where are you from?"

Jesse thought the man was amazingly calm amid the frantic activity around them.

"Washington, D.C. area. You?"

"Originally from Winchester, Virginia," he answered loudly, extending his hand to shake Jesse's. "Name's Howard Sloat."

"Jesse Flounders. Nice to meet you, sir."

Jesse didn't feel like there was a lot of time to talk and was interested in getting the guy inside so he could check the next group of people.

"Been working for Lockheed for the last ten years — C-130

maintenance for the South Vietnamese. Gotta admit we haven't been that busy for the last few years."

Jesse nodded.

"Can you extend your arms out please, sir?"

The man complied, and Jesse frisked him.

"Let me check your bag."

Jesse unzipped the tattered leather duffel and ran his hand quickly through it. Shirts, socks, underwear, and a shabby hard-back copy of Ray Bradbury's *Fahrenheit 451.*

"Yeah, seen it all," he shouted. "Now it's time to go."

"Arms out, please ma'am," he loudly called to the Vietnamese woman with Howard Sloat, gently frisking her. "Are you guys heading home?"

"Not sure where the company's gonna put me yet. For now, we're gonna try to make our way to Hawaii or something."

"I completely understand," Jesse boomed back before turning again to the woman he presumed to be Sloat's wife. "Let me see your bag please, ma'am."

A handful of beauty products and a few changes of clothes. Nothing alarming.

"Thank you," he said over the rotors and wind as he turned back to Sloat. "There'll be people inside who will guide you to the roof and a guy at the top will take your names. We're trying to keep track of the Americans that're cycling out."

"Thanks," he called. "Don't wait too long to get out yourself."

"Roger that, sir. Not sure when I'll be outta here, but I'm betting it'll be sometime today or tonight."

"Good luck."

Sloat and his wife disappeared through the Embassy's main entrance and into the rest of their lives. Soon after, the helicopter above increased its RPMs and Jesse could hear it lift off. The conversation with this random American reminded him that he wasn't even sure when he was leaving. The last several hours had been so busy and fluid that it was hard to tell how much time they had or what chopper they'd get on. The North could be on their doorstep within an hour, or it could be a day or two, depending on a lot of factors. He and Rusty hadn't discussed it with Bob Frailey, but parts of Jesse hated leaving. It was like admitting defeat.

While the engines spun above him, he began frisking again.

Not far in front of him, men worked on the tamarind tree. Before long, it would be gone, opening up another landing zone to get more people out.

…and the refugees kept coming.

April 29th, 1975
TAN SON NHUT AIR BASE
1:45PM

Chau had awoken with Vinh at his side on the floor of the C-130 cargo bay amongst several families who'd set up small encampments near the forward bulkhead. It was just before eleven o'clock in the morning and he had a pounding headache. Certainly, he didn't want to be knocked on his hind quarters again by anything that exploded. By the time he was up and moving, he had to relocate again to find some thin cover for yet another barrage of shelling and mortars, which surged outside once more. He knew it wouldn't be long before the North Vietnamese penetrated the base perimeter, and he had to get to Mai as soon as he could.

He did his best to ignore the headache and had been trying

to help Vinh, Quan, and the base sentries keep the crowd of refugees calm in between mortar and shell blasts. They were in the middle of another break in the attacks, and this one had lasted over thirty minutes so far—one of the longest yet, and the absence of explosions around them was a welcome respite.

On the other hand, when rounds weren't incoming, passengers got upset and demanded they be flown to safety. There were a number of occasions where the military policemen had to fire their weapons and he and Vinh had to scuffle with a few people to try keep a lid on things. Chau felt his speech the evening before was a masterful soliloquy of intimidating prose and it had worked for a while, but the more shells that came in and the more people became scared for their own welfare, the less effect it still carried. They just wanted to be gone, and the longer they were forced to wait, the angrier they became.

The simple fact was that Chau wasn't going anywhere without Mai and the family, and with all the hostile action around him, it had been near impossible to leave the confines of the air base. His passengers were no longer resting on the uncomfortable hard floor with their belongings and when they weren't on the verge of rioting, most had given way to nervous pacing and worried conversation. All of them were terribly shaken from the relentless bombardments and, like Chau and his crew, few had slept.

Chau and Vinh were spent, tired of fighting passengers, and deathly sick of the shelling, which threatened to kill them all with no warning. Waiting around any longer was pressing their luck. The two men met at the bottom of the stairless crew door on the port side of the aircraft, trying to keep their conversation quiet as the crowd's murmur remained at a dull roar.

"Vinh, I am going."

"Good idea."

"We cannot keep this crowd calm much longer, and the sentries will soon get low on ammunition if they keep having to fire into the air for crowd control. I do not like it."

Chau had even considered leaving to get Mai and the family if the base was under active hostile fire. Enough was enough.

"The firing has relented, and this may be my last chance. I am going to try the phone again and then I will leave."

"Can you drive?"

"I have some dizziness, but I should be fine."

Vinh nodded as Chau took his leave and quickly walked to the dingy side office, the heavy flak vest causing his sweat-soaked flight suit to stick to his back as he moved. He silently hoped for a dial tone as he picked up the hand set…

…and there it was.

A beautiful, solid tone waiting for a number to be called. He dialed.

"*Chau?*" came the barely-controlled answer.

His wife's voice cracked on the other end.

"It has to be now, Mai."

14

April 29th, 1975

TAN SON NHUT AIR BASE

3:15PM

They'd seen the pickup truck from a good distance away—abandoned and sitting on the right side of the taxiway—and hoped they might be able to get around it. As they got closer though, Vinh felt Chau starting to hesitate.

"I do not think we can get past it, Vinh."

There was no time to waste, and they had to get by. With several rockets having impacted uncomfortably close within the last few minutes, they were quite obviously a target and he knew there'd be more. Furthermore, Quan had communicated through the radio that people were chasing the airplane in a final, frantic bid to get on. There simply hadn't been room enough for everyone in the bay and some had to be turned away during boarding, nearly causing a riot amongst those that were left behind. As it was, the tiny flight deck was unusually packed with people—Vinh thought there must have been at least ten or twelve, uncomfortably sharing space with him and Chau. It wasn't exactly safe, but they taxied onward.

He had heard that when Da Nang fell, people ran after taxiing aircraft and in some cases, were literally kicked, punched, and thrown off by aircrews as they gained airspeed for takeoff. He didn't want to get into such a situation here. Their taxi speed ensured they were away from most of the mob that remained, but some had arrived days before with scooters and even small motorcycles, as well as one or two cars. It would be easy for them to catch up if they didn't keep going...

...but then Chau brought the aircraft *to a stop.*

"What are you doing?" Vinh asked incredulously?

"I must get out there and move it," Chau commented through his headset.

"Go around it, Chau! There is no time!"

He was itching to leave. They were *so close.*

"No!" Chau snapped. "The propellers could hit it! If that happens, they will be damaged, and we will be unable to take off!"

"Chau! *We must go NOW!*"

"I am going outside, Vinh," he answered stubbornly, then ripped off his headset and unlatched his shoulder harnesses.

Chau parted the tightly-packed crowd of standing passengers crammed onto the flight deck, then exited as fast as he could. In moments, he was in front of the idling airplane. Vinh watched with intense frustration from behind the large windscreen as the engines buzzed loudly, anxiously awaiting flight. His boss, friend, and brother-in-arms jogged toward the truck.

But two men raced toward him from the other side of it on a motorcycle, rapidly dismounting and throwing it down in the high tan grass next to the concrete. Vinh recognized one of them from the hangar—an individual that had been there for several days. They must have gotten on the bike as the plane pulled away from the nose dock, then followed closely behind it to make a last-ditch attempt to get on board.

There appeared to be a brief argument.

...and that's when Vinh saw the gun.

Oh no, no, no...

The man he didn't recognize—paunchy, middle-aged, and agitated—raised what looked like a snub-nosed revolver to Chau's chest and fired a shot at point-blank range.

"NO!"

Chau collapsed and laid motionless on the tarmac, his black hair blowing in the breeze as his head came to rest on its side.

He didn't move. Completely, deathly...*still.*

Major Vinh Do was so stunned that he sat momentarily frozen until the man leveled his weapon at the cockpit. Instinctively, he throttled the engines forward. The plane lurched rudely, and the man shot wildly twice more before scattering out of the way with his counterpart.

My God.

Oh...NO...No...no...

Vinh cleared the truck and soon reached the runway, then hastily turned the aircraft to line it up with the center. There was almost no time to process what he'd just witnessed. Out of the cockpit it looked like a hundred people were coming at him from the space he'd just left, using any means they had available—wheels or feet.

He needed to get airborne.

...please...

Sad and angry tears of anguish filled his eyes. The pilot seat was strikingly empty, and Vinh had never felt so alone.

Lieutenant Colonel Chau Tan Nguyen…pilot, patriot, combat veteran, military officer, father, brother, husband, and friend…was gone.

Just gone.

Forever.

And he wasn't coming back.

My God, my God…

Seconds later, a rocket tore past Vinh's position and landed in the grass ahead of him and to his right, exploding harmlessly. They were targeted again.

We have to go RIGHT NOW.

The runway was pocked with craters in a few places, but it was either risk a rough takeoff or stay behind and die.

Chau…oh, Chau.

I am sorry…my brother.

It was now or never. He jammed the throttle levers forward as far as they would go when another rocket raced overhead, missing him by a mile.

Focus.

The C-130 heaved, shaking violently as it picked up speed over shallow holes, rubble, and broken concrete. The damage wasn't severe enough to keep him from taking off…was it?

Focus!

Tears poured bitterly down his cheeks.

You can do this.

The plane accelerated…faster…faster…the wings and fuselage shaking and shuddering as he gained speed.

GO.

He closed his eyes and pulled back on the yoke. The nose pitched upward….

…and he was airborne.

April 29th, 1975
US EMBASSY, SAIGON
6:00PM

Choppers had been arriving nearly every ten minutes since about three o'clock that afternoon and Operation Frequent Wind was in full swing. Graham Martin's tamarind tree—his self-proclaimed symbol of the deep-rooted and steadfast American support for the South Vietnamese—had been swiftly cut down. In its abrupt death, its limbs and branches lay crudely tossed to the sides of the large parking lot it once grew in the center of. The only thing that was still protruding from the ground was a low stump that Embassy Marines had done their best to eliminate completely, but without a grinder they settled for abandoning what was left at a few inches above the surface.

At the request of Ambassador Martin's staff, the Navy had sent in a unit of Marines dressed in full combat gear during the mid-afternoon to augment Embassy security, manning posts around the walls to help maintain control of the perimeter. Crowds had grown significantly throughout the day—partially a result of the sound of helicopter after helicopter landing on the compound, which had carried the exact message Graham Martin had originally hoped to avoid in the first place: *"the Americans are leaving."* With their last, most staunch international advocates quickly disappearing, thousands more of Saigon's citizens were drawn to the American Embassy complex in attempts to take flight from the inevitable hostile takeover that would follow.

Rusty McClay could see everything from the roof, even though the sun was disappearing. The mission's grounds below were packed with people, many of them clustered around the pool near a row of buildings, their lines extending around and to the bottom of the main facility. The entire situation tugged at his conscience—there was no way everyone would get out, and as Americans, it was difficult not to feel a deep sense of culpability. After all, it was Rusty's countrymen that came here starting in the late 1950s and engaged in a war that ultimately killed hundreds of thousands of people. Yet here they were, fruitlessly abandoning it all. Cutting their losses, leaving what was left of the desperate humans they'd tried to help save from communism in the hands of communists. How many had they moved? How many had gotten out? He was cruelly aware that it would be impossible to evacuate a city of millions on-board seventy-plus helicopters with time rapidly running out.

A CH-46 US Marine Corps "Sea Knight" was loading passengers over the former site of the tamarind tree, its lights and strobes blinking and lighting up the side of the building on the other side of the parking lot. The sound of the dual-rotored aircraft was distinct, and much louder than its counterparts. A Naval CH-53 that Rusty had helped load with passengers was airborne, having just taken off from the roof with only a few Embassy personnel aboard as the pilot left the confines of the small helipad. The rest were Vietnamese, in equal parts frightened to death and relieved to have scored an escape to freedom for themselves and their families.

Over the course of the last several hours, Rusty had swapped jobs with Mosey Copenhaver, who was now huffing and puffing up the steps leading anyone he could to the top in order to get them out. It was a welcome break because he'd become exhausted and sweat-soaked, offending everyone within ten feet with his inhuman body odor. He figured the best place for him was the roof where nobody would have to smell him.

In the dimming daylight, another CH-53 drew closer and approached the six-story building's crown, its engine noise growing louder and wind increasing as it descended. Rusty worried that their lights would turn any helicopter landing in the area into a huge target but with no other option he went with the flow, content that if a North Vietnamese shell or rocket took out the rooftop evac effort, it might just be his time to meet the maker. His only regret would be that he wouldn't be able to say any last words to Jesse, who over the course of their time in Saigon had become a true friend. There was no telling where he was right now—likely somewhere on the ground.

The wind from the Sea Stallion was like a tornado and the *whup-whup* of rotors cutting the air was deafening; each blade's pass through it hit Rusty in the torso like an oversized bass drum. Like a hundred times before, he turned his eyes away and held tight to his clipboard. In addition to helping civilians shuffle on board choppers, he'd been doing his best to account for each American who got on if there were any. As the craft came in to touch down, an Embassy employee used both of his hands to marshal the pilot safely into place. On the other side of the roof, a plainclothes Marine stood in front of about twenty civilians who had just exited from the small rooftop door, facing them with his arms outstretched as if he thought he could hold them all back. Each flight was usually able to lift forty to fifty people, depending on the number of baggage articles and children present.

The torrent of sound was some of the loudest Rusty had ever been exposed to, and he knew when he left, he'd have tinnitus for days. The aft wheels touched the roof as the nose came down and the rear ramp slowly dropped. Inside, a crewman in a flight suit and clean white helmet emerged and motioned to him to begin bringing people over to board. The Marine who'd been standing by the door turned and walked in a crouching position toward the extended ramp, a line of passengers closely on his heels. He placed himself at its bottom corner while Rusty came into position on the opposite side with his paperwork. On the clipboard a tablet of tattered, yellow legal paper secured at the bottom with a rubber band had large letters in black marker across the top that read, "PRINT YOUR NAME LEGIBLY." It was too loud to ask any boarding American 'what's your name?' or 'can you spell that for me?' so he figured the best solution was for people to print their own names. With most of the passengers of Vietnamese persuasion, they had only recorded about a hundred and fifty names on the tablet so far.

In the unremitting noise, the crewman in the rear of the helicopter motioned everyone on as he walked backwards into the large passenger space. Uncomfortable-looking seats designed for military personnel and their gear lined the sides, and the hold was diffusely lit. The first twenty people slowly made their way on board as the Marine who'd been helping them went back toward the door, counting heads on his way. As more appeared, he stopped counting at about forty-five and spread out his arms again, forcing the next group backwards to await the next lift. Rusty held his clipboard in his right hand and motioned with his left for people to get on quickly, alternatively looking at the crew chief inside the passenger compartment and the line of people. The last one to get on was a thirties-ish, small-framed American and his wife with three young kids who all had their ears plugged with their fingers.

"Write your name here!" Rusty yelled inaudibly, pointing to the paper with his pen, his ginger hair whipping wildly in the strong rotor wash.

The man understood when he saw other names listed. He grabbed Rusty's pen.

John D. Porter, Shell Oil Corp.
Linda Davis Porter, spouse
Agnes Porter, daughter
Laura Porter, daughter
John D. Porter, Jr., son

Finished, the man nodded to Rusty, being as careful as he could to hold tight to everything in the fast-moving air.

"Thanks!" Rusty called. He couldn't even hear himself.

The crew chief returned to the top of the ramp right before Rusty moved away and gave him a thumbs-up.

All aboard safely.

Rusty returned the signal and the ramp retracted. Crouching low, he left the helipad as the large gray aircraft lifted gently off the surface, its strobes flashing brightly.

As Rusty readied himself for the next landing, he looked back toward the next load of refugees. Standing stoically in the dissolving wind was Bob Frailey. The helicopter lumbered into the sky above, its engine noise giving way to rotor sounds from the ground—another was on the parking lot with its engines spinning.

"Haven't seen you in a while, Bob," he yelled.

"Come inside, Rusty. Someone wants to talk to you."

"Me?"

Who would want to talk to him now? They were in the middle of an evacuation. He followed Frailey through the crowded door and handed his clipboard to the Marine who'd been marshalling passengers.

"I'll be right back."

The two men shoved and pushed their way past the tightly-packed crowd occupying the narrow stairwell. It smelled like a swampy locker room and had to be a hundred degrees inside. Reaching the floor below, they emerged into a long hallway with only a handful of people inside.

"Who in the hell wants to talk to *me?*"

Frailey didn't answer. He walked about half way down the hall and opened the door to a dimly-lit work area. There were several desks visible, two of them with their lamps lit, casting a yellowish glow across the small room. Inside stood Jesse, Mosey Copenhaver, and a number of CIA agents who had participated in the underground mutiny to move high-risk Vietnamese — Ben Frederick, Harry Moran, and Conrad Spurgeon included. The men were completely silent, each wearing a morose expression as Rusty and his boss walked in to the small room. Behind them at another small desk, sat the man himself. The man each of them had grumbled a fool for weeks.

US Ambassador to South Vietnam, Graham Martin.

The tall and aging diplomat had his elbows on the desk surface with his hands folded, covering his mouth. His silver, slicked back hair appeared slightly ruffled and his eyes tired but determined, and he wore a scruffy button-up short-sleeve shirt and a silver Timex watch. The ambassador didn't look up as Rusty and Frailey came into the room, only stared off in weighty silence like he was waiting to say something. Behind him, the CIA station chief, Tom Glenn, stood expressionless with his hands behind his back.

Aw, hell.

Rusty knew what was coming. It was a firing. In the midst of a hostile enemy takeover, enemy tanks at the doorstep, and with refugees leaving from the compound in droves, Rusty McClay, his boss, and his cohorts were about to lose their careers.

Martin unfolded his hands and got up slowly from behind his desk without looking anyone in the eye.

"Is everyone here?" he asked calmly to Tom Glenn.

"Yes sir."

Martin nodded affirmatively and kept his gaze from anyone standing before him.

"Gentlemen," he began in his soft-spoken North Carolina drawl, "I know what you've been doing."

He finally raised his eyes, and it occurred to Rusty that even Bob Frailey might not have known what the man was about to say.

"Each of you participated in an unauthorized evacuation of South Vietnamese citizens over the course of the last several days in direct disobedience of my guidance."

Here it comes, Rusty thought.

He walked from behind the desk and stood right in front of Conrad Spurgeon.

"...and I want to *thank* each and every one of you for your great service to the United States and to the people of South Vietnam."

What?

He took Spurgeon's hand and shook it before moving to Jesse Flounders to do the same. Without a word, he shook the hands of each of the other speechless agents successively until Rusty, ever the big mouth, couldn't keep quiet any longer.

"Mr. Ambassador," Rusty asked as Martin shook his hand, "we aren't fired?"

"You're McClay, right?" Martin asked.

"Yes, sir."

"No," he answered unemotionally before releasing Rusty's hand and walking away. "On the contrary, I am very proud of what you did. It was risky on a number of levels, but in the middle of all this turmoil, it was the right thing to do. Frankly, you saved lives in the process."

The men were utterly stunned.

Martin stood in front of them and took a deep breath before continuing.

"I am sure many of you know my son was killed in in this country about ten years ago," he continued quietly. "I made the decision to delay evacuation from Saigon as long as I could for Glen. My son gave his life for human freedom and it was in his honor that I refused to let go easily."

If it weren't for the rumble of rotor blades above and below them, a pin could have dropped, and it would have been deafening.

"Glen was a servant until the day he died in that helicopter in Chu Lai," Martin said. "He stopped the enemy, and sacrificed himself to save a great many of his comrades on the ground that day."

Martin, a father clearly feeling the painful absence of his son, took a deep breath in an effort to maintain his composure.

"I am proud of Glen. Proud of his Marines," he said before nodding to himself. "Although he died, his life made a difference."

The ambassador hesitated for a second time, reaching to touch his nose with his fingers as if to scratch an itch before pacing to another spot on the cramped floor.

"My wife, Dorothy—also has a servant heart," he continued. "Earlier tonight, I watched as she boarded a helicopter. When she saw a young South Vietnamese father being left behind because the aircraft was full, she threw her suitcase off to make room and motioned him on-board in defiance of the crew chief's direction."

Everyone stared at him, hanging on his every word.

"It was then that I realized that this 'black' operation you participated in would ensure that families would stay together and survive. Had my wife not done that, what would have become of that father? Sure, he might have made it to a ship, but how long until he would be reunited with his wife and children?

"That's when it hit me that two things are natural for Americans. The first is service, and the second: defiance. Throughout our history, going against the grain has been the rule and not the exception, especially for those of us who serve our fellow human beings. It is what makes us great and distinguishes us from other nations.

"Each of you violated my orders as the president's ambassador to this nation. My wife disobeyed a Marine aircrewman, responsible for the safety and security of his passengers. It was all in the name of serving, just like my son did a decade ago. In each of these cases, lives were spared. In your case, many were saved from certain death at the hands of communist forces. It isn't a secret to me that many of the high-ranking South Vietnamese that you helped to escape would have otherwise been placed in camps or prison, or worse. We saw it happen in Da Nang and Hue a month ago."

Rotors of two helicopters on the property shook the building slightly in the relative silence. Martin looked away momentarily and paced to the window. After a brief glance outside, he returned, looking into the faces of each man. Rusty, a harsh critic of Martin in the previous days and weeks, couldn't help but feel ashamed. This was a man with a heavy burden—an

American, like him. He was a father with a painful past, and a public servant who was only trying to do what he thought best under the most difficult of circumstances. Would Rusty have done things any differently?

"No. You are not being fired. Far from it. I want to thank you for your resolute and brave service in very challenging conditions."

Martin turned his eyes to the floor, then walked to the back of the gaggle where Bob Frailey stood.

"Bob, none of us will remain here long. My final orders to you are thus: continue with the safe evacuation for as many as you are able, same as you've been doing all day."

The ambassador turned to everyone else.

"Some of you know North Vietnamese forces are about to penetrate the city. They could be here at any time, so don't wait too long to leave."

"Sir," Frailey said, "When will *you* leave?"

"Soon," he answered. "When the time is right. Gentlemen, I—"

He stopped.

"I wish things had turned out differently. I offer you no excuses, but there is still time to save some. Go forward and do it with my blessing."

April 30th, 1975
US EMBASSY, SAIGON
4:45AM

Just prior to three o'clock in the morning, it was announced that North Vietnamese tanks had decisively broken through barriers and checkpoints in northern and western portions of the city and were making their way in the direction of the Presidential Palace nearly unopposed.

Time was short.

It had only been about forty minutes since Bob Frailey had seen the message that had come across the wire from Washington which gave them their final, crystal clear instruction: wrap it up and *GET OUT*. In addition, from this point forward, only Americans would be allowed on board departing aircraft. No more refugees. Not even an hour before, Frailey himself had told a gaggle of Vietnamese families on the ground that *nobody* would be left behind—that all the citizens inside the Embassy perimeter would make it safely out of Saigon.

He *promised* them.

But there were more than a thousand people inside and now that he'd heard about the tanks and seen Washington's most recent message, he knew what he'd told the families simply wasn't true. In fact, he felt it was a bald-faced lie, even though he hadn't known it when he said it.

Frailey watched as a Sea Stallion came into the roof's helipad, carefully shepherded through the late morning darkness by an exhausted Marine wearing a Hawaiian button-up shirt, khaki pants, and sandals. His shirt rippled violently in the wind. Before the back wheels even touched down on hard surface, the ship's crew chief jumped out and made his way for the rooftop door in the direction of Bob Frailey. The sound of the engines and the spinning rotors was like an incessant and unbroken roll of thunder.

"*Sir!*" the crew chief called barely audibly at Frailey, "We need Ambassador Martin *ASAP!*"

"He's inside!" Frailey shouted back.

"He needs to get up here *now*, sir! It's time for him to go!"

"Well good luck with that! He ain't going until the last chopper leaves!"

"This *IS* the last chopper! We have direction from the president himself, sir! Ambassador Martin is ordered to be on this helo, and we cannot leave without him!"

"There are still Americans down there!" Frailey angrily bellowed back, pointing at the large space inside the Embassy's perimeter. "You ain't gonna get 'em all on!"

"Sir, please understand me! I need Ambassador Martin!"

Frailey wasn't going to argue and he nodded in acknowledgement of the solid, unequivocal order. It was time. He opened the door to the roof and shouted down at the next landing below.

"Jesse!" Frailey called out down the stairwell as Jesse Flounders was trying to organize people with Rusty for the flight. "Need you up here!"

Jesse vaulted the stairs.

"Gerry Ford wants Martin on *this* chopper!" he roared. "Go find him — *FAST!*"

"Saw him downstairs about fifteen minutes ago!" Jesse bellowed. "I'll get 'im!"

"Jess!" Frailey called out after him, the wind and sound a vicious maelstrom of stress and disorder.

Jesse sprinted back up the steps.

"Get Rusty and bring up as many Americans as you can find! This is the last helo — *no refugees!*"

"But there are still people outside!"

"Not my call! Get it done!"

With that, a frustrated Jesse Flounders bounded down the stairs. As a precaution and because things were getting desperate, the Marines on the roof had been keeping subsequent loads of Vietnamese passengers inside the building in the sixth-floor hallway in preparation for loading. The rooftop door had been closed for some time, and only opened when the next lift was ready to begin loading. Frailey jogged over to a waiting Embassy employee who stood on the helipad, apparently waiting for instructions—everyone was in limbo anticipating the emergence of refugees out the door as the craft's engines turned and lights blinked repeatedly in the morning darkness.

"Go stand by that door!" he yelled out, pointing toward the roof's lone port. "Don't let anyone through unless they're American!"

The Marine complied and Frailey raced back over to the crew chief.

"Give me your radio!"

"What?"

"I said give me your damned radio! I wanna talk to the pilot."

Under any other circumstance, an aircrewman would have told Bob Frailey to go pound sand. But today, it was Cowboys and Indians. He removed his helmet and gave it to Bob Frailey, revealing a fresh, young face and sweaty crew cut. The senior CIA agent slipped it on his head—it was a tight fit and smelled like halitosis.

"PILOT!" he shouted into the mike. "*PILOT!* This is Agent Robert Frailey! Acknowledge!"

"Sir, please return the radio to my crewman," came the terse response.

"This is Agent Robert Frailey! Ambassador Martin is en route!" he boomed. "Please confirm this is the last helicopter out of the Embassy!"

"Confirmed, sir. Please ensure the ambassador is aboard.

There will be no other flights into Saigon. The American mission is closed by order of the President of the United States."

"Well, you tell the president there are still Americans in the damned compound!"

Frailey angrily removed the helmet and jammed it back into the hands of the helicopter's crew chief and cursed.

"DAMMIT!"

He turned to the door as Jesse and Rusty emerged. Graham Martin and a large group of his staff followed with their bags, their hair and clothing blowing wildly in the turbulence. The ambassador looked haggard and worn, yet resolute. Despite their previous judgments, Frailey and his agents discovered a new-found respect for the man after the fairly one-sided discussion he'd organized with them the last evening. This had been a long month for Martin, and it was finally coming to an end, at least the part that ended in Vietnam. Bob Frailey figured there'd be a lot for him to answer for when he got back to the States. He jogged up to him and put his hand on Martin's shoulder.

"Sir!" he shouted. "We're told this is the last helo, but we still have Americans on the ground!"

"Well, let's get 'em up here!" Martin boomed back in frustration.

"There won't be room and there isn't time. This helo is a sitting duck the longer it sits here burning gas!" Frailey thundered. "You need to get yourself on and tell them to send us one or two more! I'll get whoever's left to the top! You GO!"

A highly agitated Graham Martin stood firm and uttered an inaudible expletive.

"I've got this, Bob!" he yelled, unusually angry. "You go! Take your agents!"

"*Negative, sir!* This crew has orders from the president to take *you!* I'll stay and get the rest—just make damned sure you send us back a couple more flights!"

Martin stood by brooding in the tumult, furious as his staff and a number of other Americans climbed aboard the awaiting helicopter.

"I am not leaving without the flag, Bob!" he demanded angrily, referring to the American flag that was still flying proudly outside the main entrance of the building.

Rusty appeared out of the darkness.

"What's the word, Bob!" Rusty shouted loudly at Frailey with his ruck on his back. "We going? Or what!"

"Rusty! Go get the flag for the ambassador!"

"How do you think I'm gonna do that and not get mauled by a bunch of Vietnamese guys! Don't you think they're gonna know it's the end if they see me?!"

"Dammit, I don't care! Grab Jesse or someone and do it. *Fast!*"

Rusty nodded wordlessly, clearly frustrated at his task. What would the citizenry who saw him removing the American standard think when they watched him take it down? He'd have to act fast. He made for the door and left the roof.

"Bob, once I'm gone, get yourself below and gather up who's left before daylight," Graham Martin uncharacteristically boomed. "Play it cool, get them to the roof, then lock the door!"

"Roger that, sir!"

Several agonizing minutes went by and the Marine loadmaster at the rear of the helicopter yelled imperceptibly at Frailey, who knew what he was saying: '*hurry up,*' or words to that effect. He ignored him as he stood with the ambassador, waiting for the delivery of the flag.

Within five minutes, Jesse and Rusty appeared on the roof out of breath carrying the flag, folded haphazardly into a square shape, then handed it unceremoniously to Graham Martin without a word. There was no time for pomp and circumstance. Martin nodded, then looked back at Bob Frailey.

"I don't like leaving you here!" he shouted over the rotor noise.

"You aren't leaving me, sir! I'm here to mop up!" Frailey hollered back. "Now, *GO*—find your wife and get us some more lift! We'll be fine!"

Martin wordlessly extended his hand toward Frailey as he held the flag to his chest with the other. He shook it briefly, then swung around toward the Marine crew chief waiting at the bottom of the ramp.

"Your agents better be right behind me!" he ordered loudly over his shoulder.

"OK," Frailey nodded numbly as the ambassador turned toward the ramp.

The senior diplomat stopped short in front of the ramp and stood next to the crew chief at the bottom, refusing to set foot on the aircraft without Bob Frailey's agents. Rusty, planted solidly next to Jesse on the helipad called out to his boss over the noise.

"We're staying with you, Bob! Gonna help you finish!"

"The *hell* you are!" Frailey countered irritably. "You get your asses on that helo and get outta here!"

"*No! You need us here!*" Jesse roared into the tempestuous wind, unable to hide his indignance at Frailey's order to climb aboard and get to the Navy.

"*You are not going to tell me NO, Agent Flounders!* This is MY decision! Not yours!" Frailey called out. "This order is non-negotiable, and I'm telling you the two of you WILL get on that helo right now!"

Jesse and Rusty could only stare helplessly, with their mouths twisted into grotesque scowls at Frailey's stubborn direction, but there was no argument. Bob Frailey was staying. His agents were going.

"I'll see you when I get to the fleet!"

They stood firm. Behind them, Mosey Copenhaver materialized at the roof door and ran up to Frailey.

"Heard this was the last helo! Am I late?"

"*YES!*" Frailey answered. "It's about to take off, so get yourself on it!"

Nobody had to ask Mosey Copenhaver twice. He turned toward the ramp and quickly climbed in.

Let's go! the crew chief mouthed, holding his hands out as if to say, '*what the hell is taking you so long?*'

Frailey grabbed Jesse's and Rusty's shirt sleeves and literally drug them in the direction of the aircraft.

"I said GO, *dammit!*"

"OK, OK," Rusty said nearly inaudibly before coming to a halt and turning around, then extended his large paw towards his boss.

Frailey shook it hard, feeling a very atypical lump in his throat before Rusty swung around and boarded without a word.

"You watch your ass here, Bob!" Jesse, short-statured but scrappy as hell, uttered the last words he'd say in Vietnam before shaking Frailey's hand one final time.

"I'll be right behind you."

He didn't yell it. The words went unheard as he nodded his head.

Rusty yelled something, pointing at Frailey from inside as

Jesse climbed in. The engines throttled up and the raging rotor wash increased as the deep drumbeat of the blades ripped holes into the sticky darkness. The aircraft was off the surface before the ramp was completely closed. As it lofted skyward into the blackness, its strobes flashed brightly and alighted the large "H" on the landing zone like flashbulbs, then the sound died slowly off as it aimed for the flotilla about twenty miles out at sea.

There were no other aircraft stacked in the sky waiting to land as the *whup-whup* faded quickly into the distance.

Bob Frailey was alone in hostile country with only a handful of Americans, praying there'd be more helicopters to retrieve the few who were left.

April 30th, 1975
US EMBASSY, DOWNTOWN SAIGON
7:40AM

"Tôi sẽ trở lại ngay."
I'll be right back.

It was the second lie Bob Frailey had told in the last few hours — this time to a group of young Vietnamese students on the ground at about five o'clock in the morning before he went inside the Embassy for the last time. Before making his way to the roof, he instructed the Marines near the door to keep things nonchalant on the ground — in other words, *don't all come inside at the same time.* If the refugees that remained — each one of them doomed to be left behind in Saigon for the Marxist takeover — saw every remaining American leave simultaneously, there'd be a panic.

Every lower-level door in the building was locked tightly

415

and permanently secured before the final push to the roof. Once everyone arrived topside, the roof hatch was blocked with abandoned wall lockers and large-wheeled halon fire extinguishers to keep refugees still in the building from getting through it.

Americans only. Ford's orders. Frailey could hear the direction echo through his skull, and it ate away at his conscience like stomach acid.

The small head-level window in the door was the most heartbreaking sight. On its other side, would-be refugees pounded continuously and screamed obscenities in Vietnamese and English, their faces twisted into irate expressions of shock and abandonment.

Frailey thought how wrong it all was. He had *promised* that everyone would get out, and now he was reneging. It tugged on him so hard that he even considered remaining in Saigon, but then thought better of it. What if communist forces started targeting helicopters? No ... this war was over. The Americans that lingered — that he was in de facto "charge" of — needed him, and he wouldn't make any foolish decisions.

On the horizon, several pillars of brownish smoke could be seen rising from the ground only blocks away from them. The pops and booms of shells, mortars, and small arms fire punctuated by frightened shouts of citizens, echoed through the shallow canyons created by Saigon's squat buildings, easily detectable from the roof. The skies, by very stark contrast, were as quiet as the dead. At about an hour before — around six-thirty — a CH-46 had carried out about forty Marines destined for the fleet. Frailey, eight Marines, and two Embassy staff were all that were left, impatiently waiting for what they hoped would truly be the last helicopter out of Saigon.

On the compound's grounds below, several hundred refugees still milled around aimlessly. Most of them had freely come over the walls with no American personnel to stop them, however the size of the once immense mass of people had dwindled with their hopes that they'd get a ride out of town courtesy of the Navy and Marine Corps. Most gave up and scattered to the winds to hunker down and wait for the communists.

Frailey watched the scene over the roof's chest-high wall, standing next to a sergeant who throughout the night had been manning positions along the perimeter.

"You think they forgot about us, sir?" he asked over the odd pounding, knocking, or cursing of a few refugees behind the blocked roof door.

"Nah," Frailey responded as another mortar shell exploded in the distance. "They're coming."

Just the same, he thought to himself, *maybe we ought to call the fleet again.*

"Give another radio call to the Navy," Frailey instructed a radioman. "Your sergeant over here is makin' me nervous."

"Roger that, sir."

"If you don't get a response, give it a second and do it again."

The young corporal raised the receiver and flipped a few switches on its panel.

"US Navy, US Navy," he called into the mike, "US Embassy Saigon requests immediate extraction. Over."

The sergeant standing next to Frailey watched the smoke on the horizon and scanned for enemy. From the roof, it was easy to see straight down one of Saigon's wide avenues. Movement on the long thoroughfare hadn't let up very much throughout the day and evening before, having been clogged with mobs of people and vehicles of every kind. But since dawn, things had thinned considerably.

JASON NULTON & EVA NGUYEN WHITFIELD

"Wait a minute," the Marine sergeant said, his eyes glued westward on the low skyline.

"What?" Frailey answered nervously. "You see something?"

The Marine produced a set of small binoculars lying next to a nearby rucksack.

"*REPEAT.* US Navy, US Navy," the radioman called again, "US Embassy Saigon requests immediate extraction. Over."

"I'm not sure."

"US Embassy Saigon," came a crackling response over the radio, "be advised, bird is en route to your location. Standby for extraction."

"US Navy. We copy. Can you advise ETA? Over."

There was no response. Only static.

"What do you see?" Frailey asked again anxiously as the NCO stared intently into the distance through his binoculars.

"Oh, *shhhhIT!*" he said under his breath. "They're here."

Frailey ripped the binoculars from the man's hand and looked for himself. Only eight or ten blocks away, a column of North Vietnamese tanks could be easily seen moving toward the Embassy at a slow speed, unchallenged. Many of them were covered in camouflage vegetation, soldiers riding on their tops, with red and yellow flags fluttering in the breeze.

"*LOOK!*" came a shout on the other side of the helipad, causing everyone to turn and glare into the far distance.

On the horizon, a tiny black dot had become barely visible, but it was growing bigger and bigger. The cavalry was inbound.

"Thank God," the radioman muttered.

"Just in time," Bob Frailey said to himself.

"They better hurry their asses up," the Marine sergeant commented. "What's to keep those commie ass holes from lobbing a shell up here?"

"Hell if I know," Frailey answered, his eyes transfixed on the growing silhouette of the helicopter coming their direction.

Within minutes, its rotors became visible and shortly after, the CH-46 was descending on to the helipad, filling the air with the most beautiful vortex of wind and sound any of the men had ever heard. It wasn't a moment too soon. Frailey looked down on the street below and could see the large, green North Vietnamese tanks, flanked by motor scooters and bicycles, without the aid of binoculars. There had to be seven or eight of them in a line.

Over the deafening noise, the ramp opened as the rear wheels landed and the remaining eleven American personnel climbed quickly aboard. Bob Frailey was the last in, and he wasn't even sure the nose gear touched the surface of the roof before the pilot closed the back and throttled forward, taking immediately to the sky. After finding an uncomfortable seat, he stared out the window at the ground—people were alternatively scattering from and hailing the arrival of the communist People's Army of Vietnam.

It was the most overwhelming sense of guilt he'd ever felt.

April 30th, 1975
US EMBASSY, SAIGON
7:58AM

Hong Nguyen watched from the street with a devastating sentiment of hopelessness as the helicopter lifted off the roof of the now-abandoned United States Embassy. He knew it was probably the last one. As a South Vietnamese man who aided

Americans for years, it was risky for him to be downtown near a place that would be such a large target to the communists, but he just couldn't stomach being inside his home anymore without his wife and children. Had he made the right decision to stay behind? His heart wrenched, and tears filled his eyes. Standing in the debris and trash-filled street, absent any organized traffic of any kind, he mourned Dat's conspicuous absence...and his children...and his children's children.

The large facility's unguarded front gate lay open, and people were looting anything they could carry on foot, in cars, and on motor scooters and cyclos. Couch cushions, telephones, a large television, desk chairs, and other items were being removed from the American Embassy at a terrific clip.

A tear streamed down his face and he couldn't hold in his emotion anymore. His face melted into a twisted expression of bitter agony. The country he loved had crumbled on full display as North Vietnamese tanks entered the scene from behind him, ramming into the gate and outer walls of the former US Mission to plant the flag of occupation at what was once the largest beacon of freedom in the sprawling city.

The Americans were gone. The communists had taken over.

Hong Nguyen's family—his blood, and the loves of his life...had left. Would he see them again? Where were they? When would he hear from them?

Worse, what had his countrymen fought for to begin with? Why did the Americans even come to Vietnam over twenty-five years before? So many had died...is this what they had to show for their sacrifices? To allow the communists to take over in the end anyway? What was the point of it all?

As the walls of the failed US Mission in Vietnam crumbled

under the tracks of North Vietnam's Soviet-made tanks, Hong ruefully began working his way home.

It was over.

Finally … it was over.

Epilogue

May 10th, 1975
FORT CHAFFEE, ARKANSAS
1:00PM

The long line of buses turned left and began heading down a lengthy, straight stretch of road over the hot, flat Arkansas asphalt. Fields of newly-planted crops, the seedlings barely poking through the surface of the soil, extended across the hazy horizon as far as the eye could see. At only three years old, Truc Nguyen sat next to her mother, having no idea where they were, or where they were going. All she knew was that she was hungry and tired.

"Where are we going, Má?"

"To our new home," Mai answered forlornly, trying to put on an optimistic face for her little girl.

For Mai, it had been a week unlike any other in all her life.

She had learned the frantic flight that brought her and her family and hundreds of others out of Saigon was the last to depart Tan Son Nhut before northern forces breached the perimeter. It brought them to Thailand. From there, it was on to Guam, then Hawaii, then San Diego, and finally…Arkansas.

Fort Chaffee, which housed one of four American refugee centers run by the US Department of State, would be their home until they were able to begin putting down more permanent roots. She'd never seen so much paperwork, felt so much confusion, or endured so much debilitating bewilderment in her entire twenty-four years. They were refugees...immigrants...stateless people without a home or even a valid passport.

Everything she knew lay behind her, and in front of her lay the menacing unknown. She knew she might never be back to Vietnam, and Chau, her beloved husband and father of her children, was gone. Hong Nguyen, her father and her first love, was still immersed in the chaos that was Saigon, facing who knew what. Would they ever be reunited with him? There were so many unanswered questions, so much pain, and so much to recover from.

Nobody had been able to give her a straight answer about exactly what had happened to Chau...for now, she only knew he was dead, and whatever money they had planned to use to restart their lives in the United States was still zipped up in his flight suit somewhere in Vietnam. Quite literally, she and her mother had nothing but each other, their children, and precious few belongings. She didn't know how she'd pull off this new life in such an unfamiliar place, but she did her best to hide her apprehension.

She barely even knew any English.

"Where is our new home?"

"America."

As the bus carrying the Nguyens rounded a long, gradual turn, she became very surprised to see something she never expected.

All along the road on both sides stretched long lines of

Americans. Men, women, children…people of all ages, stood in the shoulders for what looked like miles as the buses approached the main gate.

They all waved small American flags and held signs that said *Welcome.*

The pain of loss that clung to Mai's heart like vise grips loosened ever so slightly, and it was replaced by something she hadn't felt in what seemed like years…

…hope.

Afterword

THE NGUYENS

The fall of South Vietnam ended a dark chapter in the history of the United States and Vietnam; however it wasn't the end of the story. This book is based on the Nguyen family's escape, but there were countless other families who endured similar gut-wrenching circumstances. This story dramatizes true events that the Nguyens really did experience. They were some of the fortunate ones who escaped a horrible situation and have managed to survive and flourish in the United States into the present day.

The Nguyens left Fort Chaffee after only a week, then relocated to northern Virginia. With the help of the congregation at Falls Church Presbyterian Church and a number of non-profit refugee assistance organizations, they were able to perfect their English and find meaningful work. By the 1980s, the family became naturalized American citizens. A strong mother figure, Dat insisted that her children take advantage of every opportunity to receive a good education, and all of them did — as a result, each became very successful in later years and recovered and prospered.

Chau Tan Nguyen died that day in Vietnam. His death was dramatized in this volume, but in reality, even today the Nguyens are not sure who killed him or if he even died immediately. When the family reached a refugee processing center in Thailand late in the day on April 29th, they only knew he wasn't there, and it would be several days before they were aware that he had been killed. Chau gave his life for his country, the cause of human freedom, and most importantly, his family.

Hong Van Nguyen stayed in Vietnam to try and salvage his once-lucrative rubber plantation and business, but by 1976 it had been completely seized by the government. He was able to avoid being discovered as a collaborator with Americans and fortunately never had to enter a re-education camp, but he still lost everything. Missing his family and having nothing left, he made a desperate attempt to escape Vietnam and was one of the first "boat people," who aimed for asylum in Malaysia, the Philippines, and other destinations hundreds of miles away. After several days at sea, he washed up on the shores of Brunei and was eventually reunited with his family in 1977. Hong Nguyen died in 1990.

Dat Thi Dang remained the respected matriarch of the family after leaving the refugee center at Fort Chaffee. She led Mai and her children, as well as Son, Dzung, and Tuan to northern Virginia where the children all entered school, learned English, and integrated into American life with the help of the church, a few sponsor families, and non-profit refugee assistance groups. It was through these gracious and plentiful resources that she was able to set her family up for their future successes. Dat lived a long life and died in 2023 at age 96.

Nga Nguyen completed her study abroad program in the Melbourne area, with a degree in Dietetics, after Saigon fell, though she was hysterical after losing complete contact with her family. She had no idea whether or not they escaped. It would be several months before she'd have any communication with her father, who at long last told her that the family, except Chau, had safely made it to the United States. After reestablishing a connection with her mother and Mai, Nga reunited with them in 1978 in Virginia. She received a master's degree from Virginia Tech, then did clinical nutrition research at Johns Hopkins University for more than two decades. She now lives in Maryland.

Mai Nguyen went to work for the World Bank a year after she arrived in the US and spent more than 25 years there before retiring. Focusing on her family and embracing the large Vietnamese community in the Washington, DC area, she found prosperity, but recovery from the devastating loss of her husband was slow. Indeed, she had several offers to write a book about her experiences, but it wasn't until 2015—forty years later—that she was ready to do it. She still lives in Northern Virginia where she visits regularly with her family and grandchildren.

Son (Sonny) Nguyen adapted well to American life, becoming a high achiever in school, and eventually studied engineering at Virginia Tech. This was followed by his achieving a master's degree in computer engineering from George Mason University. Today, Sonny lives in Northern Virginia with his family and works with the Federal Government.

Dzung (Eric) Nguyen also became successful in the United

States. He earned an associate degree in mechanical engineering from the University of Maryland and now lives in Houston, Texas with his family. He regularly visits Vietnam and is married to a wonderful woman he met there on one of his return trips.

Tuan Nguyen completed his bachelor's degree in Computer Information Systems from Radford University. He later earned a Master of Business Administration from the University of Phoenix. In the early 1990s, he attended Officer Candidate School at Quantico, Virginia and became a Communications Officer in the United States Marine Corps. Today, he lives with his wife, Martha and two daughters, Elizabeth and Julia in Maryland and works for the Department of Defense.

Truc (Eva) Nguyen Whitfield was very young when she left Vietnam. Her most vivid memory is traveling in the cargo bay of her father's C-130 with her mother, recollecting the "sea of black-haired heads," the heat and darkness, and the deafening noise of passengers and engines. She studied at Virginia Tech, graduating in 1994 from the Pamplin College of Business with a bachelor's degree in finance and marketing. She is happily married today and lives in Northern Virginia with her husband, Scott and sons, Jake and Chase.

Trung Nguyen was only eighteen months old when his family brought him out of Saigon, and as a result he remembers very little. Trung finished his bachelor's degree in management information systems from Radford University. He now works in cybersecurity and lives in Northern Virginia with his daughter, Sofie and son, Devin.

From left to right (standing): Trung held by Chau, Truc (Eva) held by Mai.
From left to right (seated): Hong and one of Chau's brothers-in-law.

Mai as a young woman before she left Saigon

*Nga as part of the wedding party, with her sister, Mai
and brother-in-law, Chau on their wedding day.*

Hong and Dat at her younger sister's house in Saigon

Dat Thi Dang as a young woman

Hong Van Nguyen as a young man

From left to right: Tuan, Dzung and Son as young boys
in their home in Saigon. They were inseparable.

Truc's (Eva's) original refugee ID card

From top left to right: Chau & Mai, From bottom
left to right: Truc (Eva) & Trung

FICTIONAL/COMPOSITE CHARACTERS

These characters were based on real people, were composites of several real people, or were created in the story where gaps existed. For example few people in the family remember in great detail who Chau worked with at Tan Son Nhut, but there was most certainly a chain of command he operated within, and aircrew members who filled roles within the military and airlift structures that existed at the time.

In addition, the Nguyens really did rent their unused home space out to Americans for years. They were never sure, but it has always been assumed by the family that the men who occupied the residence and offices next door were CIA agents working within the scope of the US Embassy mission in Saigon. One of those agents really did make efforts to help the family evacuate before he himself left the country.

The post-scripts below are fictional but provided as context to illustrate how the real people the story's characters are based upon might have fared after the war.

Vinh Do, much like Chau, was a hero who was singularly responsible for evacuating his family, the Nguyens, and many others out of Saigon. He reached the United States and possibly Canada after the evacuation, but the Nguyens lost contact with him by the late 1970s.

Quan Lac and his family emigrated to Australia after arriving in Thailand. While most of his extended family remained in Vietnam, Quan went to work in Australia's manufacturing industry. His three oldest brothers were arrested and sent to Communist "re-education camps," where two of them died. The third was released after four years and lives in Vietnam today. Quan struggled with alcoholism for years and finally recovered in the mid-1980s. He's been sober for nearly thirty-five years and still works in Australia.

Robert "Bob" Frailey made it to the U.S.S. Kirk on the final helicopter flight out of Saigon. A middle-aged man who swore he would never marry, he met the love of his life after he returned to the United States and went to work at CIA Headquarters at Langley, Virginia. While he never had any children, his wife Barbara never left his side. He retired from public service in 1985 and died in his sleep at the age of ninety-five in 2015.

Charles "Chuck" Sterrett ended up assigned with his family to Beijing in late 1975. Over the years, his career brought him to Seoul, Singapore, and Islamabad. He left the CIA in the mid 1980s and went to work for Ford Motor Company in Michigan, but missing his home state of West Virginia, returned in 2010—in his early seventies—to try and capitalize on the oil and gas fracking boom. Now in his eighties, he's retired and living in Marietta, Ohio with Lien. They regularly visit their grandchildren in Morgantown, West Virginia.

Michael "Rusty" McClay reached Hawaii after the evacuation and was reassigned to Moscow. He stayed there for years, learned Russian, and was present at the height of the Cold War years in the mid-1980s. When Iraq invaded Kuwait in 1990, Rusty worked with American Special Forces units to gather intelligence that contributed to the quick end of the conflict. He never married but retired from the CIA after thirty-five years of service in the 1990s, and now lives in the Dallas-Fort

Worth area where he's active in the lives of his nephews and grand-nephews.

Jesse Flounders was reassigned to a black CIA site in Egypt after leaving Vietnam and little is known about his activities there. In subsequent years, he operated under deep cover until the Cold War ended in 1990. He retired from the CIA in 1995 but was recalled to active service after the terrorist attacks of 9/11/01, although was never able to talk about his job. He died of lung cancer in 2003 and is buried in Arlington National Cemetery.

Mosey Copenhaver left the CIA in 1976 and settled in Moore, Oklahoma to open a small Ford dealership. He married a local farm girl in 1985 whom he had a daughter with a few years later. Mosey struggled for years to earn a living, but in the early 2000s, his dealership became one of the largest and most successful in the state. In 2013, the devastating F-5 tornado that hit the town destroyed his business. He took some of his insurance money and moved with his wife to Miami, where they remain today.

THE VIETNAM WAR

Following liberation from the Japanese at the end of World War II, Vietnam was plunged into conflict. It began with the French (and a brief occupation of South Vietnam by the British) through the end of 1954, then with an ever-escalating involvement of the United States beginning in 1955. The scale of the impact can scarcely be measured, but the staggering numbers are perhaps the most telling indicator of what was endured by millions over thirty years of violence—not just by the Vietnamese, but Westerners as well:

- 1.5 million Vietnamese killed—soldiers and civilians alike
- 3 million Vietnamese wounded
- 300,000 Vietnamese still unaccounted for into the present day
- 2 million killed in Laos and Cambodia
- 1.5 million refugees, the majority of which fled Vietnam by sea, often as "boat people." Many didn't make it, and others faced capture by pirates. Others were sold into slavery. At least 800,000 ended up in Australia, the United States, and Europe.
- More than 58,000 American military members killed
- Over 300,000 Americans wounded and more than 2,200 missing in action—most still unaccounted for into the present day
- More than 30,000 French soldiers killed
- 25 million acres of cropland destroyed
- 12 million acres of forest destroyed or rendered useless by Agent Orange
- $168 billion spent by the United States by 1973—this is roughly equal to nearly $900 billion in 2023 dollars (source: http://stats.areppim.com/index.html)
- Unexploded ordinance from years of war still kills people in Vietnam today

The Vietnamese economy was utterly devastated as a result of three decades of fighting. The country's infrastructure was in tatters, and civilians left destitute moved to new slums in urban centers. Over one million war widows and almost 900,000 orphans struggled to survive, nearly 200,000 of them resorting to prostitution and other illicit activities in order to subsist. When the communists took over in 1975, more than 60,000 people that had worked with or supported American war efforts over the years were executed, and hundreds of thousands were sent to "re-education" camps for months or even years.

In the United States, the war had political, economic, and cultural repercussions that are still felt strongly today. Healing was slow in the 1960s and 1970s, but collective American guilt over the unwelcome treatment of returning veterans began to take hold in the early 1980s, allowing societal healing to begin. Many former military members who suffered from post-traumatic stress disorder didn't receive treatment until concerted efforts were undertaken under President Ronald Reagan. In 1995, diplomatic relations were restored with Hanoi by President Bill Clinton.

OPERATION FREQUENT WIND

After the fall of Hue and Da Nang, tens of thousands of South Vietnamese fled their country between April 2nd and April 30th, 1975 using the Port of Saigon, Tan Son Nhut International Airport, and other locations. Augmentation by American fixed-wing military airlift ensured over fifty thousand more escaped to freedom through locations in Thailand, the Philippines, Guam, and elsewhere. Once initiated in the waning days of April, Operation Frequent Wind guaranteed nearly seven thousand more souls were evacuated via helicopter to American ships in the South China Sea.

In total, American-led operations transported more than seventy thousand people to ports across the South Pacific. During the final hours of the mass exodus, many South Vietnamese military aviation personnel used their own aircraft (like Chau did) and seagoing vessels to leave on their own. Many of the helicopter pilots filled their aircraft past safe capacities and made for the US fleet. Upon reaching it, nearly all of them were forced to abandon them or ditch over the sea, as deck space on Naval vessels was very limited. When it was all said and done, Frequent Wind, combined with other transportation efforts throughout the month, moved more than 138,000 refugees out of South Vietnam.

About the Authors

JASON NULTON

Jason Nulton is a retired Lieutenant Colonel and logistics officer who served 20 years in the U.S. Air Force. During his career, he completed nine active duty assignments, held numerous leadership positions (including as commander of two large units), and completed tours of duty on four continents. He served in deployed locations in the Balkans, Africa, the Persian Gulf, Levant, and Afghanistan, and retired in July 2015 from the Pentagon.

After retirement, Jason brought his experience to the classroom, and now teaches principles of management, leadership, and business ethics to undergraduates at Marietta College. He also currently teaches Leadership and Command to mid-level military officers as part of the Air Force's online Professional Military Education (PME), program, and has served as a facilitator for Marshall University's "Testament" veteran program. In addition, he collaborated on and published *"To War with the Fourth,"* a documentary book chronicling the 4th Infantry Division's history from World War I to the Global War on Terror, which was a finalist for the 2016 Army Historical Society Distinguished Writing Award.

EVA NGUYEN WHITFIELD

Eva Nguyen Whitfield was very young when she left Vietnam, and her most vivid memory is traveling in the cargo bay of her father's C-130 with her mother, recollecting the "sea of black-haired heads," the heat and darkness, and the deafening noise of passengers and engines. She studied at Virginia Tech, graduating in 1994 from the Pamplin College of Business with a bachelor's degree in finance and marketing. She is happily married today and lives in Northern Virginia with her husband, Scott, and sons, Jake and Chase.

Sources

Burke, William. (2015). Ghost of the Silver Run Tunnel. [online] Available at: https://vimeo.com/132744386.

Business Insider. (2018). The US Army is 243 years old — here's what its soldiers have worn into battle in every war since the American Revolution. [online] Available at: https://www.businessinsider.com/heres-what-uniforms-soldiers-have-worn-into-us-wars-2018-3#the-vietnam-war-24.

Catalog.archives.gov. (1999). [online] Available at: https://catalog.archives.gov/id/7367441.

Cbsnews.com. (2015). Fall of Saigon 40th anniversary. [online] Available at: https://www.cbsnews.com/pictures/fall-of-saigon-vietnam-anniversary/.

Cia.gov. (2015). The Last Days in Saigon — Central Intelligence Agency. [online] Available at: https://www.cia.gov/news-information/featured-story-archive/2015-featured-story-archive/the-last-days-in-saigon.html.

Cia.gov. (2015). [online] Available at: https://www.cia.gov/library/center-for-the-study-of-intelligence/csi-publications/csi-studies/studies/vol-59-no-4/pdfs/Glenn-Remembering-Saigon.pdf [Accessed 2 Aug. 2018].

Crypto Museum. (2018). KY-3 TROILUS Wide-band voice encryption system. [online] Available at: http://www.crypto-museum.com/crypto/usa/ky3/index.htm.

Elite Dresses. (1999). Vietnamese Wedding Traditions and Customs. [online] Available at: http://www.elitedresses.com/Vietnamese_Wedding_Customs_s/17.htm.

Everything.explained.today. (2018). Operation Frequent Wind Explained. [online] Available at: http://everything.explained.today/Operation_Frequent_Wind/.

Gerald R. Ford Foundation. (2015). Gerald R. Ford Timeline - Gerald R. Ford Foundation. [online] Available at: https://geraldrfordfoundation.org/gerald-r-ford-timeline/.

HISTORIC VIETNAM. (2015). Old Saigon Building of the Week – Former Grall Hospital, Late 1870s - HISTORIC VIETNAM. [online] Available at: http://www.historicvietnam.com/the-former-grall-hospital/.

HistoryNet. (2010). Final Fiasco - The Fall of Saigon | HistoryNet. [online] Available at: http://www.historynet.com/final-fiasco-the-fall-of-saigon.htm.

Historyplace.com. (1999). The History Place - Vietnam War

1969-1975. [online] Available at: http://www.historyplace.com/unitedstates/vietnam/index-1969.html.

Justgola (2018). Former U.S. Embassy in Ho Chi Minh - Attraction in Ho Chi Minh, Vietnam - Justgola. [online] Justgola. Available at: https://www.justgola.com/a/former-u-s-embassy-1978047772.

Kennedy, Rory, director. American Experience: Last Days in Vietnam. Moxie Firecracker Films, 2014.

Military Wiki. (2000). Operation Frequent Wind. [online] Available at: http://military.wikia.com/wiki/Operation_Frequent_Wind.

Ncdcr.gov. (2004). The Fall of Saigon and Ambassador Graham Martin | NC DNCR. [online] Available at: https://www.ncdcr.gov/blog/2017/01/19/fall-saigon-and-ambassador-graham-martin.

People.duke.edu. (2011). Propaganda Leaflets: North Vietnam to U.S. [online] Available at: https://people.duke.edu/~ng46/collections/propaganda/vietnam-to-us/.

The Web Pages of Jerry Proc. (2016). KY-3 (TROILUS) Wideband Voice Encryption. [online] Available at: http://www.jproc.ca/crypto/ky3.html.

ThoughtCo. (2018). Vietnam War: Fall of Saigon. [online] Available at: https://www.thoughtco.com/vietnam-war-fall-of-saigon-2361341.

Time and Date.com (2018). Available at: http://www.timeand-date.com.

Vietnam Charms. (2014). Traditional Vietnamese Wedding

Important Ceremony In Our Culture. [online] Available at: http://www.vietnamcharms.com/traditional-vietnamese-wedding.html.

Wiest, Andrew, and Chris McNab. The Illustrated History of the Vietnam War. Metro Books, 2015.

Printed in the USA
CPSIA information can be obtained
at www.ICGtesting.com
CBHW072051291223
3026CB00003B/12